T0287267

Volume III

Hierarchies:
the emergence of diversity

Chemistry
Condensed matter
Molecular
Atomic
Volume III:
Hierarchies:
the emergence of diversity
Quantum Physics
Volume II:
Quantessence:
how quantum
theory works
Nuclear
Elementary
Particles
Volume I:
The journey: from
classical to quantum worlds

Contents

II Quantessence: how quantum theory works

III Hierarchies: the emergence of diversity

Chapter III.1

The structural hierarchy of matter

Collective behavior and the emergence of complexity

> The behavior of large and complex aggregates of elementary particles, it turns out, is not to be understood in terms of simple extrapolation of the properties of a few particles. Instead, at each level of complexity entirely new properties appear and the understanding of the new behaviors requires research, I think, as fundamental in its nature as any other.
>
> P.W. Anderson in *More is different* (1972)

If we start from a large number of simple constituent particles which have simple interactions with each other, the collective of such particles may well exhibit a rich structural diversity and complexity. If we manage to identify the relevant collective degrees of freedom in the macroscopic system, then another simplicity may be regained, however. And relevance is what counts. This approach may reveal a hidden order and allow for an effective description of the apparent chaos and complexity in a limited number of variables.

Lost individuality. Let us start with a human analogy. Think of a couple, if they never talk to each other or seem to communicate, you'll treat them as separate individuals. You think of their 'relation' as a minor perturbation on their existence as individuals. However, if they are close and their relationship is a kind of symbiotic, you will treat the pair as a single entity: *they* are nice or crazy, or stupid. Their individuality is neither visible nor relevant it seems, what becomes relevant are the properties of the couple and these may be totally different from those of the individual.

Constituents and their interactions. The two cases represent two different regimes, which you might call *weakly* or *strongly* coupled. In the strongly coupled regime the next question is how the couples interact with each other, because that will have decisive implications for the collective behavior of a large crowd of people. To understand collective behavior one has to have some insight in the different aggregation levels below, in what the relevant agents at various levels are and how they interact. Are they individuals, couples, families or communities?

The differences in social organization between bees, ants, dolphins and humans can only be partially traced back to the difference in their specific species-linked features (for example the way their genetic information is passed over to the next generation) but to a large extent the social hierarchies they form depend on the nature of their interactions.

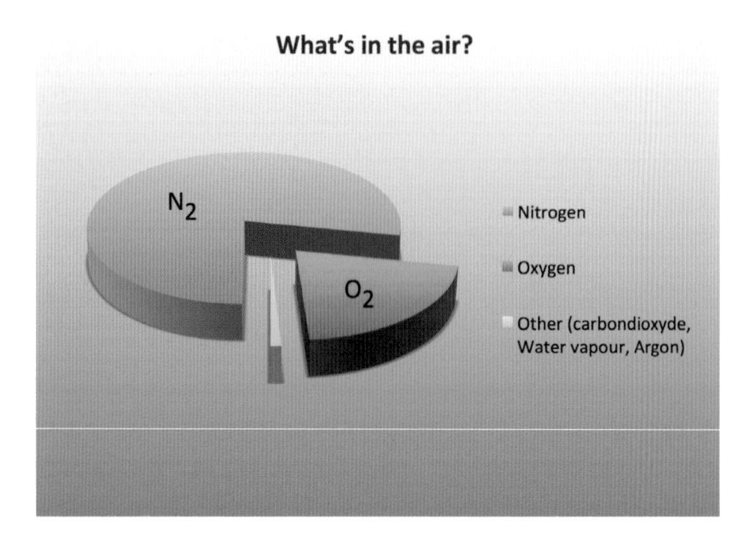

Figure III.1.2: *What's up in the air?* Air is a mixture of chemicals, and note that the nitrogen and oxygen components consist of the diatomic molecules N_2 and O_2. These atoms – like people – prefer to pair up somehow.

External parameters. Yet, there are still other important factors that play a role. Given the properties of the relevant constituents and their interactions, there may be different ways society becomes organized. In general it will also depend on external 'environmental' factors and dynamics. Revolutions may take place where a society reorganizes itself rather drastically. Depending on the external parameters it may go through 'tipping points.' A society may choose to adopt a new constitution, thereby redefining the basic set of behavioral rules. As external observer you usually don't directly observe the constitution, rather what happens as a consequence of it. What you may see is that the collective behavior changes drastically. And you may wonder whether they changed the constitution or whether the reason was a financial crisis for example.

What 's (up) in the air? Similar questions arise in physics if one wants to understand the binding of atoms into molecules or into macroscopic media like solids, liquids or gases. An everyday example is ordinary air: it is predominantly made up of the simple elements nitrogen and oxygen, and minor fractions of carbon, hydrogen and argon. But, in fact air is a mixture of chemical composites, since the nitrogen and oxygen have paired up (but for example not tripled up) while the others appear in composites like water vapor and carbon dioxide. Argon is the only element in the mixture perfectly happy on its own, an ideal *Einzelgänger* precisely because its electrons fill an entire shell of orbits, and this makes the atom inert, literally like a closed quantum shell.

From physics to chemistry to biology to... Here we enter the vast domain of chemistry, and condensed forms of matter in general, including the modern material sciences, biochemistry and molecular biology. These fields of science concern mesoscopic or macroscopic systems, which are characterized by a specific hierarchy of aggregation levels. The actual structural outcome may drastically change depending on external factors like density, temperature and pressure. The system may go through a so-called *phase transition*, where it reconstitutes itself in a tumultuous way before ending up in a new stable lowest energy ground state that may be drastically different from the state it started out from. We all know that water molecules can manifest themselves collectively in many radically different guises such as vapor, liquid and ice, but also in alternative structures like raindrops, hail and a huge morphological variety of snowflakes.

Emergent behavior. You can compare the ground state of a medium with what the constitution is for a human society. You do not observe it directly, only through the emergent behavior of the collective excitations it supports. The constitution is manifest in the way the society functions, or dysfunctions for that matter. It is the great variety in ways that matter has organized itself, which made it very hard to figure out what the constituents were in the first place. In this quest for ever more fundamental building blocks unrestrained reductionism reigned as we witnessed in Chapter I.4. To provide a broader context for the main subject of this book we will in the remainder of this chapter highlight some representative examples of *structural hierarchies* of ever increasing complexity. And these emergent hierarchies are in some way or another the collective expression of the underlying quantum principles.

The ascent of matter

Cosmic evolution. The hierarchy of structures found in nature is quite universal. If we think bottom up, we start with the stable constituent particles of the Standard Model as depicted in Figure I.4.35, in particular the up and down quarks, and the electron. From a history of science perspective, working bottom up is anti-historical in the sense that the most basic constituents are the ones that have been discovered most recently, while many of the chemical compounds have been known for thousands of years.

The reason to nevertheless work bottom up is because we know that that is the way matter has systematically built up in the early stages of our universe. Starting from the basic constituents that stepwise aggregate into complex structures on large scales turns out to be the true historical account after all. The universe cooled down in the course of its expansion. This means that thermal collisions between constituents became less and less violent, so that ever weaker and more subtle binding mechanisms could become effective in forming increasingly complex stable structures. These structures emerged as a result of the the four basic interactions and because the external conditions like temperature and density kept changing. Let us go through some of the very early stages guided by the events marked in Figure III.1.3.

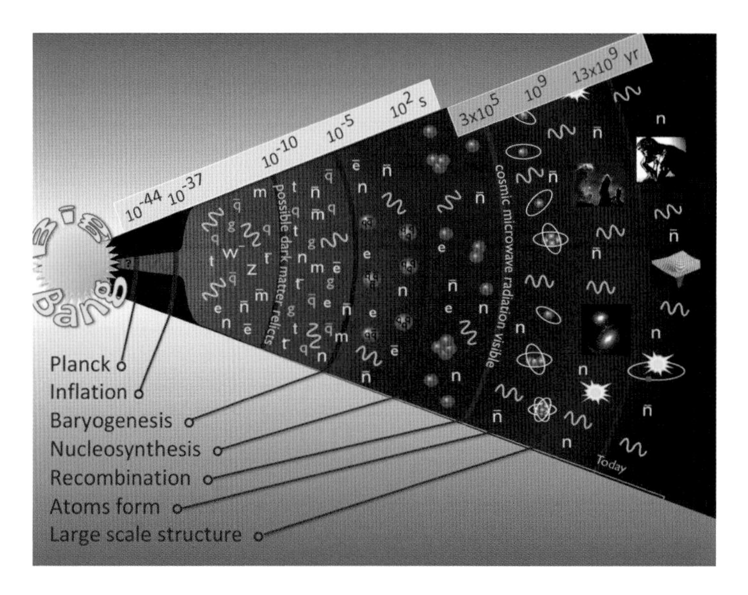

Figure III.1.3: *Cosmic evolution.* The figure shows the subsequent phases of the early universe, exhibiting matter organizing itself in ever more complex structures.

The Planck and inflationary era. We discussed the very early stages of the universe in the section on Big Bang cosmology on page 66 of Chapter I.2. The true origin of our universe is hidden behind the curtain of quantum gravity for which we do not have a satisfactory theory. That curtain obstructs our understanding of the universe for times smaller than the Planck time which is about 10^{-44} s. So what the Big Bang really is we don't know, but that such a dramatic event took place some 13.7 ± 0.2 billion years ago is beyond doubt. This was established unequivocally from observing the aftermath of it. A first grand event is the period of *cosmic inflation* where our universe scaled up exponentially thereby generating an enormous amount of vacuum energy and making it homogeneous, isotropic and flat. The picture is that the latent vacuum energy of the inflated universe was converted into all the (dark)matter and radiation that fill the universe today.

Primordial baryogenesis. Shortly after the Big Bang the universe was presumably filled with the most basic forms of energy: a *primordial soup*! Matter in the form of quarks, leptons, their antiparticles and many types of radiation. The strong interactions were operative, however, the quarks and gluons were not in a confining phase, but in the *quark-gluon plasma* phase we mentioned on page 195 in Chapter I.4. A separate important question is the presence and role that dark matter may have played in the very early stages of the universe. This role strongly depends on what dark matter precisely is. What we know for sure is that it interacts very weakly with ordinary matter, and therefore it will not greatly affect the processes we will describe next. Ordinary matter and radiation are all interacting frequently enough to stay in equilibrium with each other. There is a simple rule, following on from special relativity that tells us that matter and anti-matter will *recombine*, and effectively annihilate each other if the temperature drops below twice the mass the particle type: $kT \leq 2mc^2$.

This in addition assumes that the density is large enough so that they will run into each other enough. Not much matter would be left if a slight asymmetry between matter over anti-matter did not develop at a very early stage, so that after the annihilation of all available anti-matter, a tiny surplus of matter (of 1 part in 10^9) remained and that is all the ordinary matter present in our early universe.

Primordial proton and neutron synthesis. When the universe was roughly 10^{-6} seconds old, the up and down quarks started binding into protons and neutrons due to the color force mediated by the gluon particles. The nucleon synthesis processes are

$$\begin{aligned} u+u+d &\rightarrow p \\ d+d+u &\rightarrow n \\ e+p &\leftrightarrow n+\nu \end{aligned} \qquad \text{(III.1.1)}$$

In this phase the universe was basically filled with a plasma consisting of protons, neutrons and electrons, and radiation consisting of photons and neutrinos.

Primordeal nucleosynthesis. After about 3 minutes the first nuclear fusion processes started to take place, the so-called *primordial nucleosynthesis* in which the lightest stable nuclei were produced like $^4\mathrm{He}$, $^3\mathrm{He}$ and tiny amounts of lithium ($^7\mathrm{Li}$) and beryllium ($^7\mathrm{Be}$). The process stopped there, basically because there were no stable nuclei with a higher atomic number. The typical sequence of fusion steps 're:

$$\begin{aligned} p+n &\rightarrow {}^2\mathrm{D}\ \ (\mathrm{Deuterium}) \\ {}^2\mathrm{D}+p &\rightarrow {}^3\mathrm{He} \\ {}^2\mathrm{D}+n &\rightarrow {}^3\mathrm{T}\ \ (\mathrm{Tritium}) \\ {}^2\mathrm{D}+{}^2\mathrm{D} &\rightarrow {}^4\mathrm{He} \\ {}^3\mathrm{T}+{}^4\mathrm{He} &\rightarrow {}^7\mathrm{Li} \\ {}^4\mathrm{He}+{}^3\mathrm{He} &\rightarrow {}^7\mathrm{Be} \\ &\cdots \end{aligned} \qquad \text{(III.1.2)}$$

Note that the process proceeded via unstable intermediates such as the hydrogen isotopes, deuterium and tritium, mostly ending up in stable $^4\mathrm{He}$ nuclei. After the first fifteen minutes the cosmic abundances settled to about 75% hydrogen ($H = p$) and 24% helium-4. The prediction of these primordial cosmic abundances was one of the important successes of using quantum (nuclear) theory in the context of the early universe. Many others were to follow.

Gravities opportunity: the seeds of large-scale structure. Only after about $300,000$ years the simplest atoms would form, meaning that the electrons would combine with the aforementioned nuclei to form electrically neutral atoms. At that point the universe was filled with a gas of neutral atoms. The photons decoupled, and the gravitational force became dominant. Inhomogeneities corresponding to local maxima in the mass density of particles attracted other particles more strongly than the low density regions and therefore high density regions started to build up mass. From a gravitational point of view all masses attract each other, and the more mass the stronger the attractive force. This means that pockets where the energy density is more than average will grow. These early density inhomogeneities are the seeds of the large-scale structure in the universe.

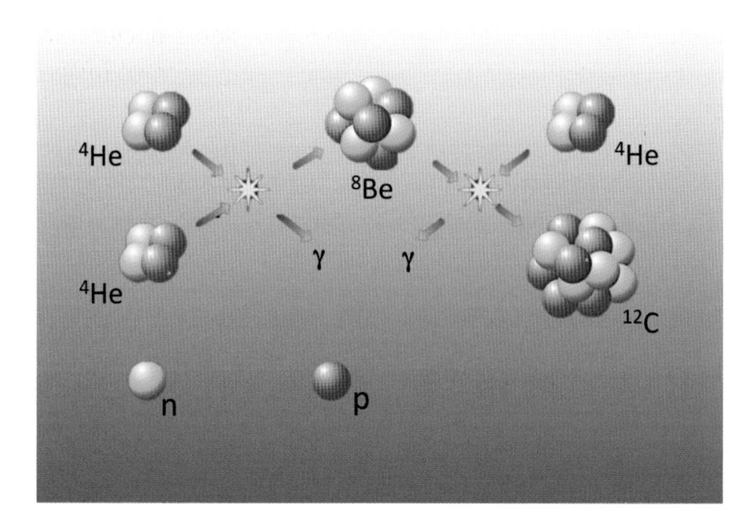

Figure III.1.4: *Carbon production.* It is shown how carbon nuclei were produced in the universe by successive fusion processes of ^{4}He inside stars.

From stardust we are made. In the center of these ever denser clouds, pressure and temperature started building up locally reaching again high temperatures of millions of degrees. This gave rise to a next round of nuclear fusion processes. That is how slowly the diverse array of chemical elements in nature was created in the core of many generations of stars, and the stockpile of basic chemical elements, indispensable for the later chemistry of life, was built. The truth is that all of us are made of stardust! It is interesting to be aware of the fact that this process took billions of years because several generations of stars were needed to build the heavy nuclei. And the fact that our expanding universe has to be old explains why it is also big and cold. It *has* to be, otherwise we could not be there to observe it. What feels like an utter inhospitable environment turns out to be necessary for life to be possible in the first place.

We see from the periodic table that in principle by adding on ^{4}He nuclei, elements like beryllium and the all-important carbon and oxygen can be reached, as indicated in Figure III.1.4. For example:

Chemical element	Milky way	Solar system	Earth crust	Human
H	73.90	70.57	0.14	10
He	24.00	27.52	-	-
O	1.04	0. 59	46.00	65
C	0.46	0.30	0.03	18
Ne	0.13	0.15	-	-
Fe	0.11	0.12	5.0	6×10^{-4}

Table III.1.1: *Mass abundances.* Abundances (in %) of some common chemical elements at different extraterrestrial and terrestrial levels.

$$\begin{aligned} {}^4\mathrm{He} + {}^4\mathrm{He} &\rightarrow {}^8\mathrm{Be} + \gamma \\ {}^4\mathrm{He} + {}^4\mathrm{He} + {}^4\mathrm{He} &\rightarrow {}^{12}\mathrm{Carbon} + \gamma \\ {}^{12}\mathrm{Carbon} + {}^4\mathrm{He} &\rightarrow {}^{16}\mathrm{Oxygen} + \gamma \end{aligned} \quad \text{(III.1.3)}$$

The way carbon is synthesized is remarkable to say the least. The effectiveness of the processes above is due to a subtle resonance which amplifies the second process. It remains mysterious that on the one hand all of life is carbon based, whereas the actual production of the carbon itself was a process depending on a delicate balance of values of the constants of nature. From this point of view one is tempted to conclude that life is a miraculous coincidence!

In Table III.1.1 you see what happened to the original galactic abundances, like in our Milky Way, on their way to become tiny parts of our physical bodies. The explanation of how these changes came about goes beyond the scope of this book.

Molecular binding

Atoms are electrically neutral because the positive charge of the nucleus is exactly cancelled by the negative charge of the electrons. Yet the charges are not exactly on top of each other so what you find if you go to short distances is that there are residual electromagnetic interactions (like dipolar forces) that become dominant. These residual interactions are to a large extent responsible for the fact that atoms bind in such a rich diversity of structures, be it molecules of varying complexity, or solids, or other types of condensed states of matter.

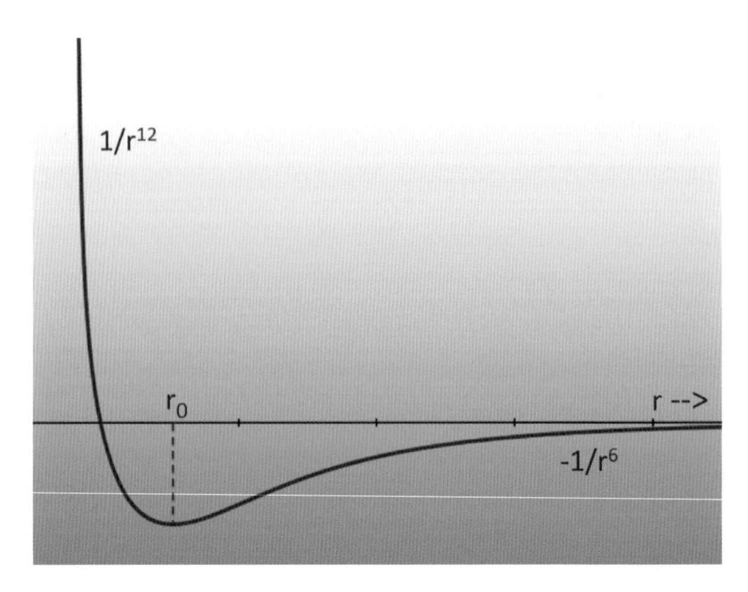

Figure III.1.5: *The interatomic interaction potential.* The interaction potential of two hydrogen atoms as function of their distance. For short distances the force is repulsive but for long distances attractive. This behavior is a consequence of the sharing of electrons which implies that a negative charge cloud forms between the two positively charged nuclei. The minimal energy configuration is achieved for a distance r_0. So free hydrogen spontaneously forms a gas of diatomic molecules H_2.

Repulsion versus attraction. Interactions are the mother of binding and binding is the father of structure. The secret of building spatially extended structures resides in the fact that the binding between atoms or molecules is the outcome of a delicate balance between a repulsive force that dominates at small distances and an attractive force that dominates at large distances. The typical behavior for the energy U of a pair of atoms as a function of their separation r is given in Figure III.1.5. Understanding the curve is not hard. Imagine releasing a marble on the energy curve, then starting at a small r it would roll away to large distances (that is the repulsive part of the interaction), but starting for large r it would role towards the origin (the attractive part). So, if the particle were to experience some friction then irrespective of where you start the marble would always end at a separation $r = r_0$, where the potential energy is minimal. This picture reminds us of the atomic binding of Figure I.4.5 at least in a qualitative sense. We conclude that also in this domain stability is based on a compromise between attraction and repulsion. This is a feature underlying the formation of structure on most levels of complexity.

Van der Waals binding. The basic attractive interatomic force is the Van der Waals force after the Dutch 1910 Nobel laureate Johannes Diderik van der Waals. It even works between two atoms that are called 'inert' like argon or neon. They have completely filled shells which means the charge cloud is spherical. However, if they get close these clouds become deformed and the molecule develops an (induced) dipole moment which just means that the resulting plus and minus charges have different spatial distributions. The induced dipole moments lead to a weak attractive force between the atoms. It is weak because the interaction potential drops off as $\sim 1/r^6$ that is much faster thus than the Coulomb potential ($\sim 1/r$) between two opposite charges. On the other hand, if the atoms are attracted they cannot come too close because then the electron clouds start overlapping and that causes a strong repulsion and a steep rise of the potential for short distances $(\sim 1/r^{12})$. That repulsion is due to the Pauli principle which holds for the electrons: it provides a hard core for the interactions. This potential is depicted in Figure III.1.5. At low temperatures the Van der Waals interactions may lead to the formation of a solid where all the atoms form a regular array, and the nuclei occupy the sites of a crystal lattice.

Polar (or ion) binding. Atoms have a certain number of electrons which form a charge cloud around the nucleus. The electrons subsequently have to occupy different states that is why the charge clouds differ from atom to atom. Now for the chemistry of atoms for example which molecules they can form, the shape of the clouds is all-important. The number of *valence electrons* is the number of electrons in the highest unfilled shell. The tendency of atoms is that they like to fill their outer shell. They can do that basically in two ways: one is that they can pick up the electrons of another atom in which case the atom that gives away electrons becomes a positive ion and the one that takes extra electrons becomes a negative ion. The ions have the same old nucleus but have a net charge because of an electron surplus or deficit. Clearly the ions made through this 'social' mechanism of giving and taking have opposite charges and will be attracted to each other because of the Coulomb force between them. But again, at small distances the repulsive interaction of the clouds takes over, and qualitative features of the picture of Figure III.1.5 remain valid.

A lot can be said based on the location of the atoms in the periodic table in particular the column they are in. Take the elements in the first column like hydrogen for example, they have one electron in the outer shell. As it happens these atoms are actually quite social: they are willing to give away their electron and to turn into a positively charged ion. Complementary behavior is obserbed in certain elements in the one but last column, like chloride (Cl), that like to receive an extra electron to fill their outer shell and turn into a negative ion. So indeed we see *polar binding* between atoms in the first column and the one-but-last column. And we see many well-known elementary molecules like HCl (hydrochloric acid) and NaCl (kitchen salt) that are held together this way.

Covalent binding. Simple atoms like hydrogen, oxygen or nitrogen, which are the main components of ordinary air, are bound in pairs. The question is how the pair-binding in the diatomic gases precisely comes about. How can it work because there are no ions to be formed? In these cases a different mechanism is operative that is also quite 'social', as it is based on the notion of *sharing*. Once close enough, atoms can lower their energy by sharing outer electrons; they spread as it were their negative charge clouds over the two nuclei, by sharing electrons. The cloud is mostly concentrated between the nuclei and that means that these become attracted to the cloud and therefore to each other. The binding that results from this mechanism is called *covalent binding*.

We have mentioned that what matters are the shapes of the charge clouds corresponding the outer (or valence) electron orbitals. They tell us a lot about the geometrical patterns of molecules and materials. On the other hand once we realize that the atoms are composites of nuclei and electrons and therefore by themselves complex objects, we should not be surprised to learn that in the behavioral diversity they exhibit, much will depend on the details of the atoms in question.

Hydrogen bonds. Once you know how atoms form molecules there is the next step up, which is to understand how molecules bind with each other or in case they become large, how they interact with themselves to produce more and more elaborate molecular structures. Here one exploits more intricate mechanisms that will do the job. A well-known example of this is the so-called *hydrogen bond* that plays a vital role in organic chemistry and therefore also biochemistry. It is based on the idea that molecules, or parts of molecules, may also behave like electric dipoles and therefore lead to an attractive force. The term hydrogen here refers to the fact that hydrogen, when it binds to a strong electronegative atom such as oxygen or nitro-

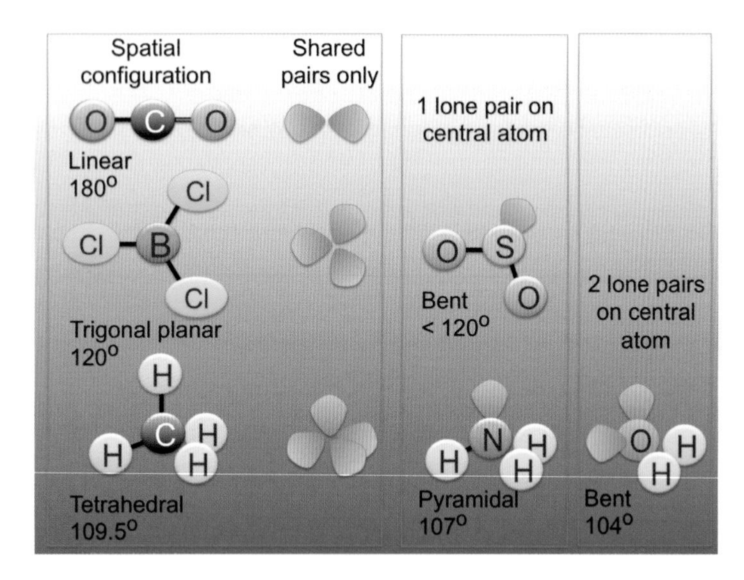

Figure III.1.6: *Molecular shapes.* We have depicted the spatial geometry of the atoms forming a molecule, and the charge clouds corresponding to the shared and lone electron pairs.

gen, like in water, gives a polar molecule that binds through these hydrogen bonds. This type of binding is what keeps the water molecules together in the liquid, and it for example explains the relative high boiling temperature of water. The hydrogen bond is thus structurally similar to the Van der Waals force, but it is stronger. These bonds play a vital role in understanding the spatial geometry of complex biomolecules.

It's all quantum plus electrodynamics. All this being said, I like to stress that all chemical binding mechanisms are a product of two fundamental ingredients. One is the set of underlying quantum principles as expressed by the Schrödinger equation, and the other set is formed by the laws of electromagnetism governing the forces between charges. It means that if – as is often done in practice – we were to put the constituents and their basic electromagnetic interactions in the Schrödinger equation and let a powerful computer turn the crank we would generate the structures we observe. Such calculations show that the theory is correct and have great value for applications. They do however not replace or satisfy our need to understand the basic physical and chemical mechanisms. Scientists have introduced many so-called forces and effective interactions and bonds, exactly because they provide a kind of elementary toolkit to effectively explain and predict chemical behavior. But we should remember that all of those new forces are nothing but residual electromagnetic interactions between objects like atoms or molecules or chemical 'groups' that have intricate charge distributions determined by the laws of quantum theory. It's all a matter of shapes and these shapes can be described as 'multipolar fields' of which the dipole is the simplest example. The quantum laws are strong, accurate and universal, and even though they don't allow us to understand all of chemistry directly from first principles, they do allow us to comprehend in detail the basic mechanisms that in a subtle balance give rise to the elaborate chemical structures we observe in nature.

The miraculous manifestations of carbon

The plug and play of organic chemistry. In this subsection we take a closer look at the element carbon and the remarkable structures it can form all by itself, as displayed in Figures III.1.7 and III.1.8. We start simple and add more complexity along the way.

The spatial geometry of simple molecules. Because the carbon atom sits in the fourth column of the periodic table, it has four valence electrons to share. Hydrogen has one to share so carbon can bind to four hydrogen atoms to form a methane CH_4 molecule, which as you probably know is a strong greenhouse gas molecule. Both atoms are happy because they made a perfect match in the one to four ratio. What about the other bad guy, carbon dioxide CO_2? Well, now the carbon shares two electron pairs with each of the oxygens to optimize its sharing strategy. And what about H_2O , just innocent water? Well the oxygen clearly shares one pair with each of the hydrogens and there are four non-paired electrons left on the oxygen.

The next question that naturally arises is what do these molecules look like? Can we from the binding mechanism decide what the spatial configuration will be? For simple molecules this is indeed the case as is shown in Figure III.1.6. The resulting shape follows from the mutual repulsion of the negatively charged electron clouds, which try to avoid each other as much as possible.

Shapes of simple molecules. So, for the methane or CH_4 it should not come as a surprise that it forms a perfect tetrahedron with the carbon nucleus at the center and the hydrogen nuclei at the four corners. The clouds on the bonds indeed maximally avoid each other meaning that the bonds will make angles of 120 degrees. For CO_2 there are two double bonds and we expect a linear structure with the carbon nucleus in the middle right in between the two oxygens. A detail is that indeed a double bond defines a plane, The two double bonds mutually repel and therefore the plane connecting to the first oxygen will be perpendicular to that connecting to the second. And what about the water molecule H_2O, is it also linear? Here there is another ingredient: the four leftover electrons of the oxygen form a cloud also attached to the oxygen. So in fact there are three clouds that will lie in a plane, and as the clouds are not identical the H_2O molecule has a bent structure. The lone pairs tend to be bulkier and therefore push the peripheral atoms down so that the angle between them will to be smaller than in the symmetric case. That explains why the two bonds to hydrogen make an angle, not of 120° but of about 104 degrees.

Greenhouse gases. Carbon dioxide is made by burning carbon containing materials. It is an enormously useful chemical compound but the problem is that we have produced and still produce far too much of it. It plays a hazardous role in our atmosphere as it is a greenhouse gas. This is the case, because molecules which have a certain structural complexity (like carbon dioxide, methane, but also water vapor) have many low energy, oscillatory quantum mechanical modes in which they can absorb and (re)emit radiation. In particular, modes corresponding to heat radiation. So the heat that is coming from the Earth's surface after being absorbed from the sun, or heat produced by human activities, gets absorbed by the CO_2 blanket in the atmosphere, and then reemitted. But the reemission is isotropic, meaning the same in all directions, and therefore half of the reemitted heat goes back to the earth and that is why the earth heats up.

Photosynthesis. One way to get rid of CO_2 is through vegetation; plants absorb carbon dioxide from the air, and in a process called *photosynthesis* combine it with water and light (photons) from the sun to produce carbohydrates and the oxygen we need in a process which can be summarized as $CO_2 + H_2O \rightarrow [CH_2O] + O_2$. Water vapor in the air certainly does affect the greenhouse effect in that it increases the warming up caused by carbon dioxide considerable. However water is engaged in all kinds of other climatological cycles like cloud formation and rain that make its role essentially different, the vapor concentration in the atmosphere changes by large amounts on a short scale of days or weeks.

Carbohydrates. Once you realize that carbon has four binding sites available you realize that there are extremely diverse ways to combine these molecules Carbon is an ideal example of a basic building block. And nature learned to play with it. Imagine you start with a tetrahedral *methane* CH_4 molecule, and you replace one hydrogen by another carbon then that is also a compatible configuration. Continuing this process two more steps you get the *butane* molecule of Figure III.1.7(a). It is evident thet *carbohydrates* like C_kH_{k+2} actually can in principle form for any value of k. These molecules correspond to long linear chains.

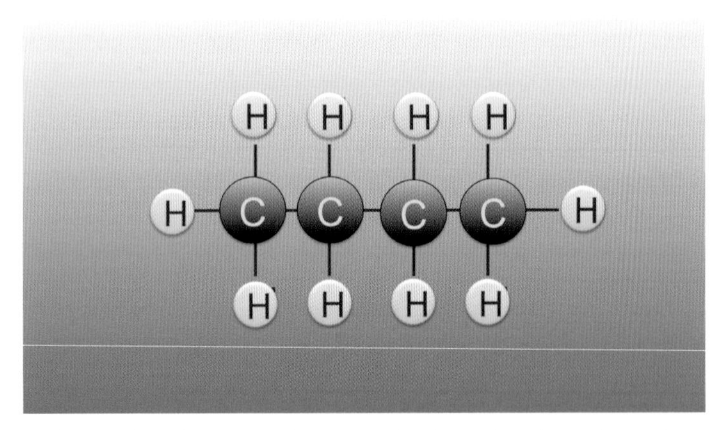

(a) Carbon has the powerful property that it can form long linear chains with hydrogen atoms on the side. This is the highly flammable gas butane for example.

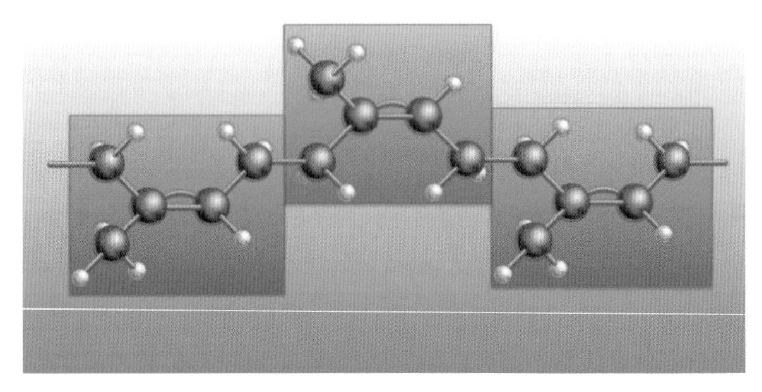

(b) A polymer is a linear chain made up of identical units.

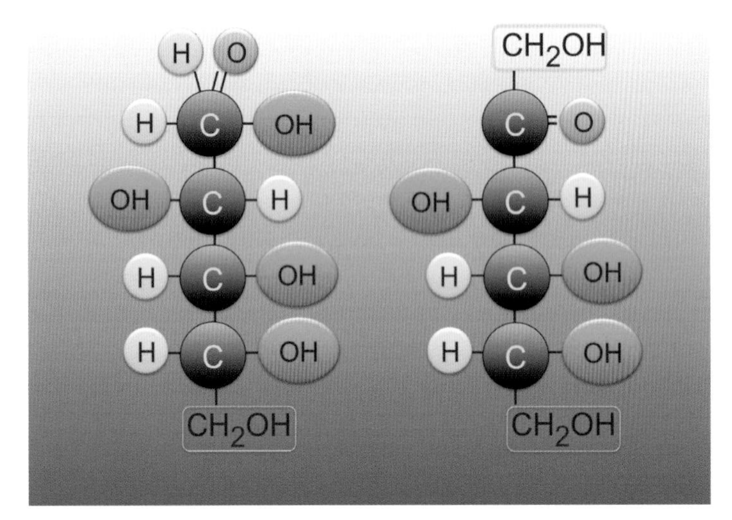

(c) The common sugars or carbohydrates glucose (l) and fructose (r). These have a chirality or handedness; there are two forms. The case where the bottom group is on the left or the right, is like a left or right shoe. They form mirror images that cannot be rotated into each other.

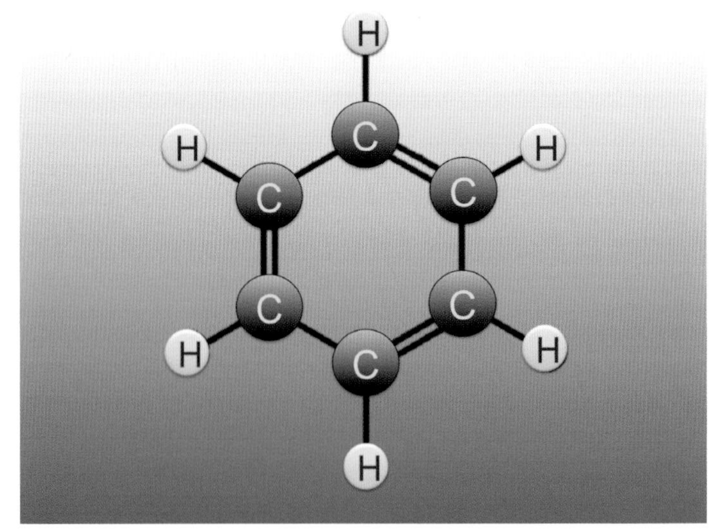

(d) If you can make chains you also can make cycles without extra ingredients. This is the benzene molecule C_6H_6 featuring the famous hexagonal ring structure with three double and three single bonds.

Figure III.1.7: *Miraculous carbon.* Carbon plays a central role throughout organic chemistry. With its four bonds it is remarkably versatile and can make linear, planar or 3-dimensional structures.

Polymers. One can go one step further, and build long linear molecules that are repetitive. Such long chains of of identical or similar units are called polymers as shown in Figure III.1.7(b), and it is a world on its own, to design polymers in such a way that they exhibit dedicated chemical properties, with particular applications in mind. This is what a substantial part of the bulk chemical industry is about.

Ring structures. There is not only the possibility of open carbon chains, you can also imagine the formation of cycles or closed chains like the so-called *benzene ring* C_6 which nature discovered and used over and over again. Ring structures like *cyclopentane, cyclohexane* and their polygon shaped relatives play an important role in the biochemistry of the base pairs in DNA and also in the *amino acids* from which the *proteins* are built. Furthermore, they are 'bread and butter' for the chemical and food industries.

Nano physics

Nano science. Carbon composites don't stop in the one-dimensional world of chains and cycles. Nothing keeps it from engaging in three valent bindings, meaning that a C atom has not just two C neighbors, but three that form an equilateral triangle. Such a connection opens the possibility of making two-dimensional structures with the topology of planes, tubes and balls, and two-dimensional surfaces that have holes in them, the simplest one being the torus or donut.

Mesoscopics. With the carbon structures we just mentioned we enter the unfolding world of nano-science and technology, where one is dealing with molecular structures on a nano scale, so typically involving up to a few hundred atoms. This domain is also called *mesoscopic*, just in between the macroscopic and microcosmic worlds.

Nature's LEGO. Every parent remembers the thrill of what happens after you hand a group of playful children a big box of the most basic LEGO pieces. It is amazing what kind of stable and metastable structures they come up with. In this sense evolution is like a room full of children with an overdose of LEGO pieces, and once you realize that, those elaborate carbon structures become little more than the inevitable outcome of a childlike but powerful methodology called trial and error.

Buckyballs. A most remarkable discovery was the buckyball or C_{60} gigantic molecule that is spherical rather than linear and made up of alternating pentagons and hexagons (see Figure III.1.8(a)). It was predicted by theoretical calculations to be extremely stable. Such large carbon molecules (not only C_{60} but actually a whole range going from C_{40} to maybe C_{240}) are now called *fullerene*s. This name refers to Buckminster Fuller, the American architect who pioneered the design and constructions of geodesic domes.

Nano tubes. Closely related are the nano-tubes depicted in Figure III.1.8(b) which have attracted a massive amount of attention because of their many potential applications. These tubes are thin: the smallest have a diameter of only a few nanometers. This makes them extremely strong in proportion to their weight. Large nano-tubes are hard to make and this has so far hampered their large-scale application in technology. Let us finally mention the materials that are only made from carbon atoms.

Diamond and graphite. As each C atom has four C neighbors, naturally located at the corners of a tetrahedron, it allows for the formation of wonderful three-dimensional lattices. One of those is quite exquisite indeed, because it is the diamond lattice. Diamond is pure carbon in a splendid guise, as it is extremely hard, highly transparent and very expensive. Diamond has relatively high density ($3.5\ g/cm^3$), does not conduct heat or electricity and is insoluble in any solvent.

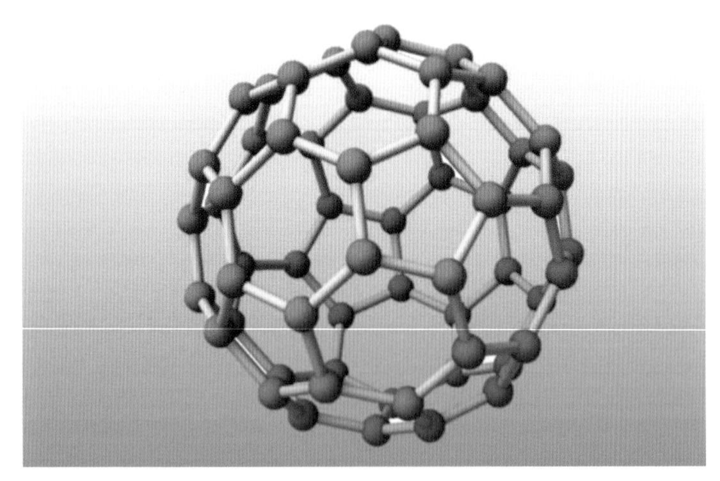

(a) The football shaped C_{60} molecule is an example of a *fullerene* after Richard Buckminster Fuller, the architect and pioneer in designing and building of geodesic domes.

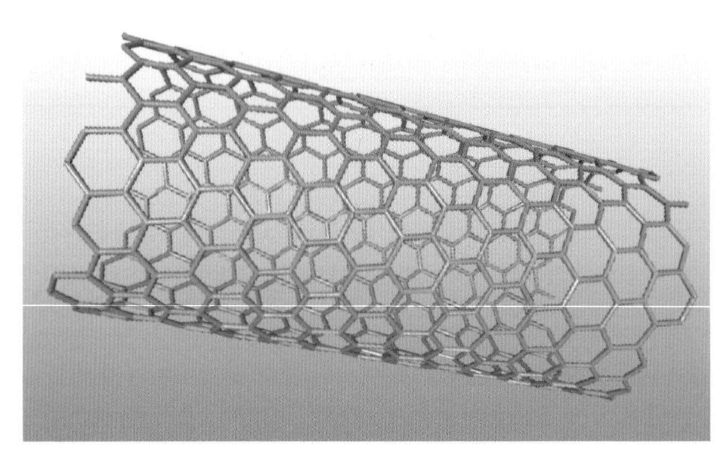

(b) A carbon nanotube.

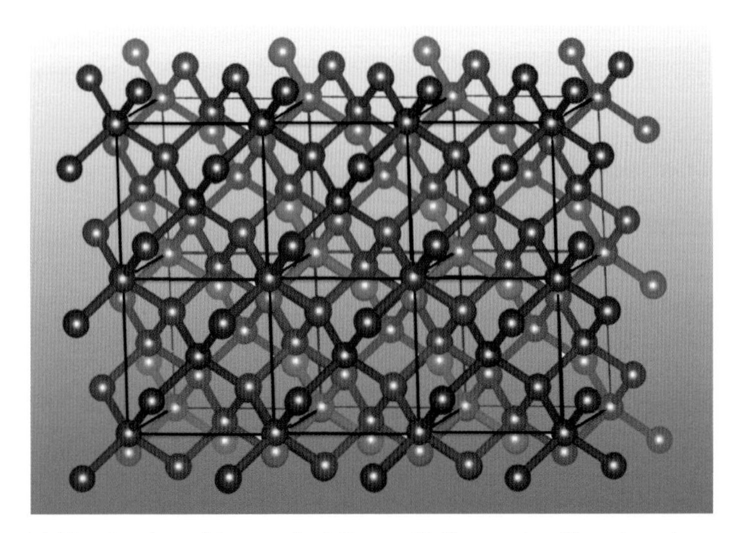

(c) The structure of the covalent diamond lattice made with carbon atoms on all sites.

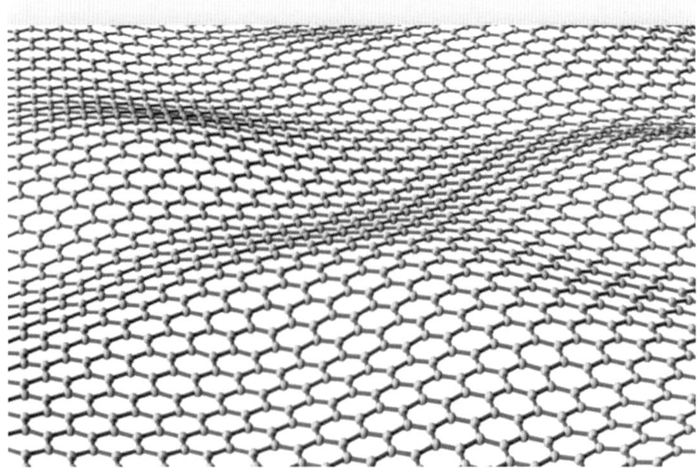

(d) Amazing graphene: only one molecule thick, and yet the strongest planar material. It is also transparent and an excellent conductor.

Figure III.1.8: *Carbon structures.* Some of the miraculous manifestations of carbon that all manifestly exploit the hexagon as basic building block.

Are there other three-dimensional carbon structures possible? Yes, there is one, much more common than diamond, and that is *graphite*, the stuff that sits in your pencil and makes drawing so easy because it is totally opaque (black), soft and cheap as well. These properties follow from the fact that graphite forms easily, it corresponds to a stack of two-dimensional honeycomb planes that are relatively weakly bound. Graphite is soft and greasy, it is relatively light ($2.5\ \mathrm{g/cm^3}$), a good conductor of heat end electricity and is soluble in most solvents. How different can members of one family be!

Graphene. Let us finally mention the recently discovered miraculous material called *graphene*; this is a perfect two-dimensional hexagonal honeycomb sheet which turns out to be extremely strong in spite of being only a single atomic layer (see Figure III.1.8(d)). It is furthermore transparent and has high thermal and electric conductivity. This highly unusual combination of qualities singles this material out for many exceptional applications in the future, varying from wearable electronics and displays to fancy wrapping materials. It may strike you that the structure is just like a single layer of graphite. The story goes that the Russian physicist Andre Geim and his student Konstantin Novoselov who received the Nobel prize for their groundbreaking work on graphene in 2010 made the first specimen just drawing with a pencil on the sticky side of sellotape.

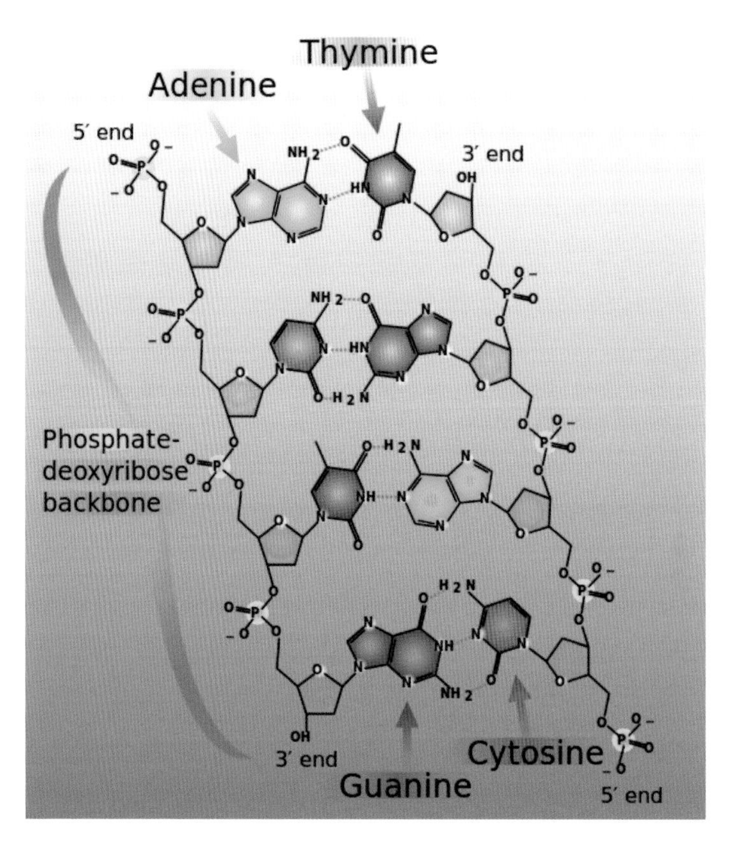

Figure III.1.9: *The chemical composition of DNA.* A fragment of the double-stranded DNA molecule. The picture also gives the molecular structure of the base molecules with the four letter code assigned to them. The four letters A, T, G, C are strictly paired as $A - T$ and $G - C$. The pairs are relatively weakly bound by hydrogen bonds indicated by the dotted lines. The DNA of the human genome contains about 3 billion base pairs, which contain among other things the genes that encode about 20,000 proteins. (Source: Wikipedia)

The molecules of life

The pinnacles of molecular structure are the molecules of life such as nucleic acids and proteins. It seems somewhat far-fetched to present these in an elementary book on quantum theory. The reason I do is that the structural hierarchy, as far as single molecules are concerned, really ends right there. And these structures are basically dictated by quantum theory. Therefore including them gives our review of the molecular hierarchy a sense of completeness. Let us therefore briefly summarize some structural aspects and not talk about the functional part. As a matter of fact the real tasks in the living cell are mostly performed by complex networks of proteins, and that is a level of emergence that transcends the one fully fixed by the basic laws of physics.

The complexity of biomolecules is relative in the sense that again it is a structural level in which a limited number of particular building blocks are used over and over again. Nature is brilliant in figuring out ingenious ways to apply a given structural element in many different ways. The structure of biomolecules is modular and the huge diversity is not as much in the variety of constituents, as it is in the way they are put together on a modular level.

The DNA molecule. A well-known example is the DNA molecule which is made of tens of billions of atoms. But its structure is highly repetitive so that one only has to show a little piece to see and understand what the building principles are. And once the architecture of the molecule is understood it is not so hard to explain the way it functions either. The structure of the molecule was discovered in 1953 by Francis Crick, James D. Watson at Cambridge University and Rosalind Franklin at King's College London. The Nobel prize for Physiology or Medicine was in 1962 awarded to the first two and Maurice Wilkins, a collaborator of Rosalind Franklin in London.

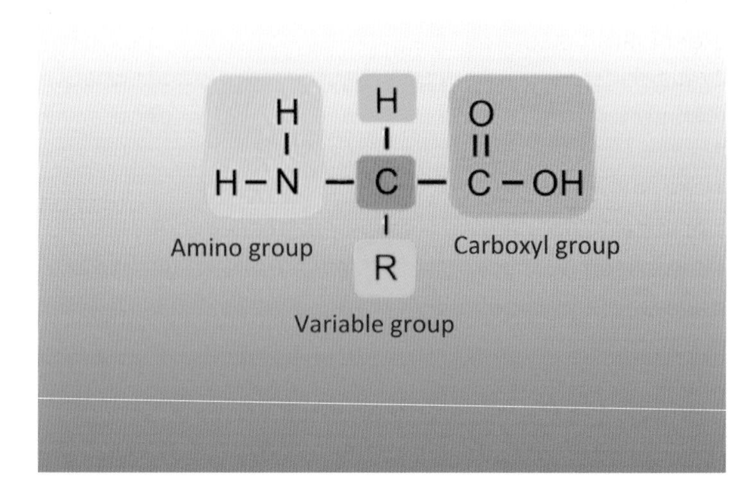

Figure III.1.10: *Amino acids.* The generic structure of an amino acid, with its amino and carboxyl groups. In the center is a specific group that characterizes the particular amino acid. Proteins are basically linear chains of amino acids.

We have illustrated a small segment of the molecule in Figure III.1.9, and it is clear that the molecule features two long strands that are kept together with hydrogen bonds to make a sort of ladder. The stiles of the ladder are just a backbone of some sugar that repeats itself some three billion times. The rungs of the ladder are made of pairs of *nucleobases*, of which there are only four, called *adenine* (A), *thymine* (T), *guanine* (G) and *cytosine* (C). It is the order in which these four type of rungs appear in the ladder which encodes the heritable traits of living oganisms. There is a strict pairing namely A always comes with T and G always with C, so if you know the left half of DNA it is easy to construct the complementary right half of the molecule. And it is this deterministic feature that allows us to understand how the heritable information can be reproduced after the cell division where the DNA molecule splits and the left and right half move to the two different daughter cells, which then are completed by synthesizing the complementary half within the daughter cell. The chemistry is in fact rather simple but extremely effective. If you think of the genetic information stored in DNA as a piece of text written in a four letter alphabet of some 3 billion letters long, then that would maximally amount to $N = 4^{3\,000\,000\,000}$ possibilities, which corresponds to six billion ($= {}^{2}\log N$) bits of information. That amount of data would easily fit on a DVD or USB stick, in fact a good deal less because most of the information is highly repetitive and not conserved at all and therefore believed not to be that important. Yet as we are talking about important hereditary data, we should realize that the same DVD is sitting in every nucleus of every cell of our body – you should imagine that you are carrying around trillions of backups of your genome. I must admit that it makes me feel some kind of important, The DVD of my personal 'feel good' movie is not for sale but nevertheless made in huge quantities. This is how the discovery of a deep secret of life ended up being a little more than a paean to painstaking reductionism.

Translation of DNA information to protein structure. DNA is crucial for the organism but it doesn't do very much, from a chemical point of view it is not very active. It functions as a template from which the data corresponding to a *gene* are transcribed by RNA molecules that also carry it outside the nucleus of the cell where the instructions are then performed by *ribosomes* (some enzyme) to translate the four-letter code sequence of the genes as a sequence of three-letter *codons*. A codon encodes for a specific amino acid and the codons therefore form the *genetic code* The ribosomes produce from that sequence of codons a linear chain of *amino acids* corresponding to a specific *protein*. This process is schematically represented in Figure III.1.11. The number of different amino acids that can be encoded by a three-letter codon (word) with the four-letter alphabet, can never be larger than $4^3 = 64$. In fact there are only twenty-one of them but most of them are represented by several different codons. This redundancy makes protein synthesis more fault tolerant against copying errors.

To make the structural hierarchy explicit and complete, I have displayed the generic structure of the amino acids in Figure III.1.10. Because of their modular structure they are in fact quite similar, consisting of an amino and carboxyl group and a specific variable group in the center. This group may contain five and six cycles and combinations thereof, somewhat similar to what we saw in the DNA segment of Figure III.1.9. A protein is just a linear sequence of amino acids that may run from ten to hundreds for small genes to hundreds of thousands for the big ones. And because of their characteristic charge distributions these proteins start to fold up in all kinds of interesting ways, as schematically indicated in Figure III.1.12. This is called the secondary structure, where one distinguishes so-called α *helices* and β *sheets* and simpler strings in between such as *turns* or *coils*. The helices are curled up and the sheets are more planar again with two strands bound by hydrogen bonds. The helices and sheets making up the protein are then again folded in characteristic ways into complicated and beautiful three-dimensional geometrical structures (see the rather random selection in Figure III.1.13). And again it turns out that their shapes determine to a large extent what biological functions the protein can perform.

Curling up. We should be aware of the fact that the gargantuan DNA molecule, which has a typical length say of 3 billion times a few nanometers ($= 10^{-9}$ m) equals some meters, apparently fits in a cell nucleus with a typical size of 10 micrometers ($= 10^{-5}$ m). This fact implies that nature must have developed some very clever folding tricks to make this possible. This is a generic feature of the big molecules of life, they are folded up in smart and elegant ways, and the way they are, usually tells us a lot about the biological function they may perform. DNA for example is curled up in different levels, first in small curls, then the curled up molecule curls up once more and then again etc.. Similar to what certain phone cords do when you don't want them to. But to read the code corresponding to a gene, the corresponding part of the DNA molecule has to be made accessible, i.e. certain genes have to be 'turned on', depending on what is needed in that particular cell at that time and place.

Epigenetics. At this point we enter the domain of *epigenetics* where one tries to understand how the gene expression in the organism is exactly regulated by means of other chemical mechanisms using *histones* and *methylation*. There are indications that also the methylation of the DNA is conserved, which means that it is somehow encoded in the DNA. It has been suggested to add a fifth letter to mark its positions along the molecule. Unsurprisingly, several meta-levels of regulation are operative to get from the *genotype* of the organism to the *phenotype*, to get from our DNA to who we are as an integrated being. Whether the development of an organism is primarily nature or nurture, chemistry is the language in which the explanation will ultimately be cast.

Conclusion. In this chapter we have shown how the complex hierarchy of matter came into being during the early

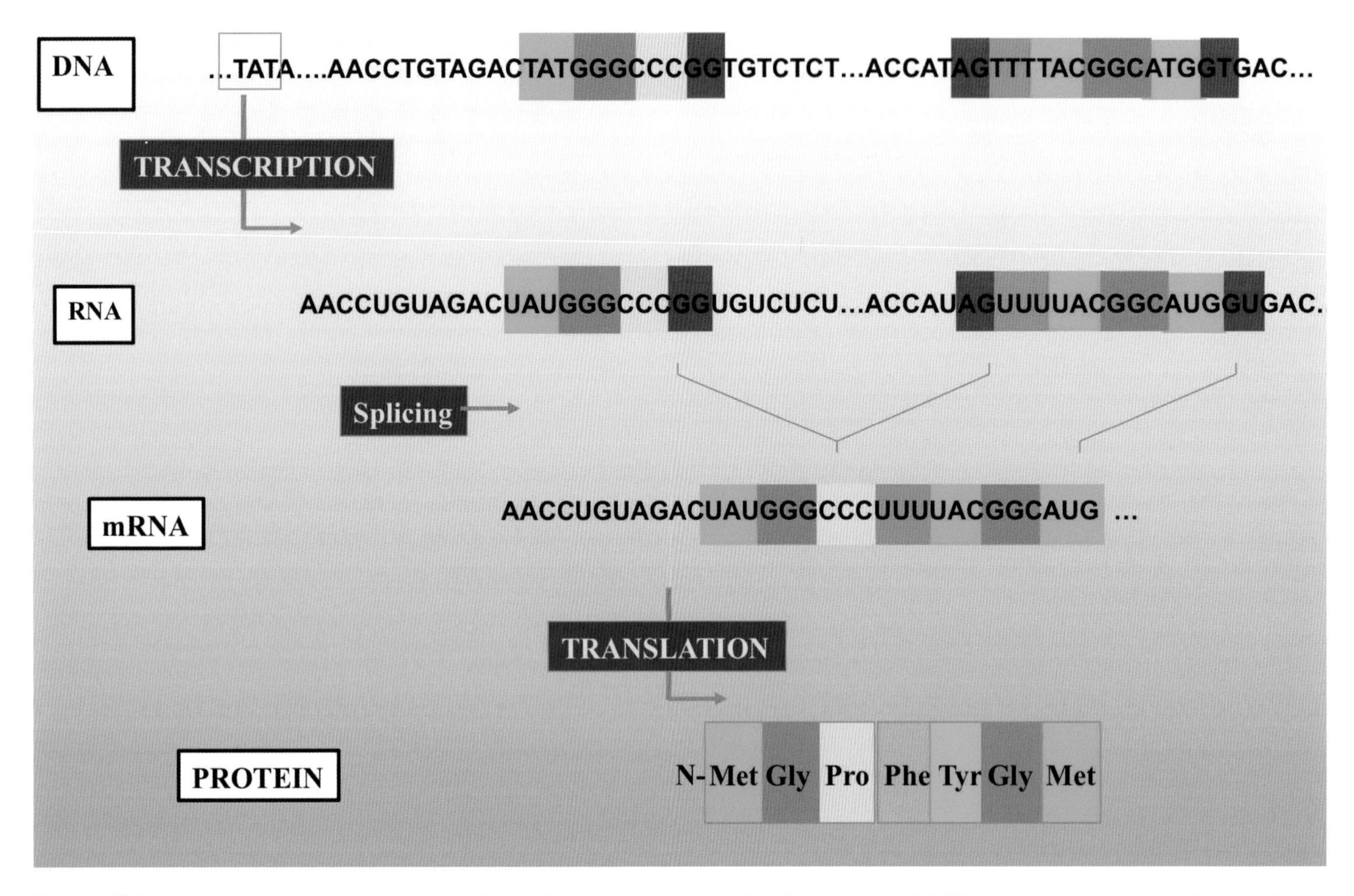

Figure III.1.11: *From DNA to proteins.* A schematic of how the linear four-letter code of DNA strand gets translated into a linear sequence of amino acids that form a protein. The four-letter code is copied on a single strand RNA. After splicing, which means cutting and copying the various pieces of the gene to a single sequence on a messenger RNA molecule, the messenger goes outside the nucleus of the cell. There the letter sequence is translated by Ribosome enzymes and the protein is synthesized. Each subsequent three letter sequence (called a *codon*) from the RNA gets translated into one of twenty-one amino acids, see Figure III.1.10.

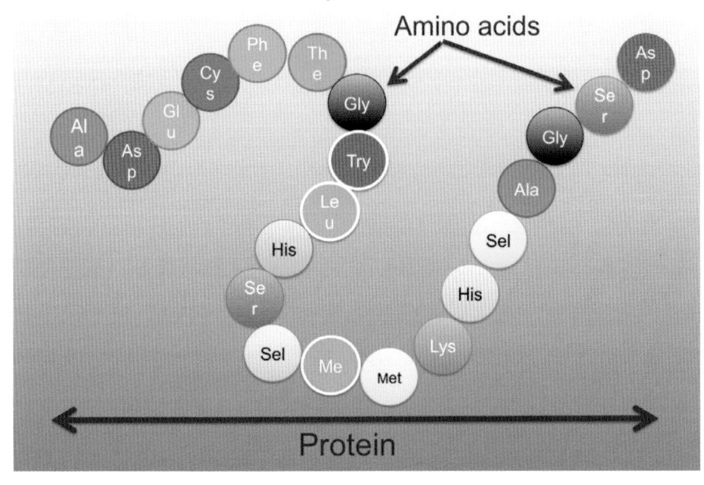

(a) Primary structure as a linear chain of amino acids

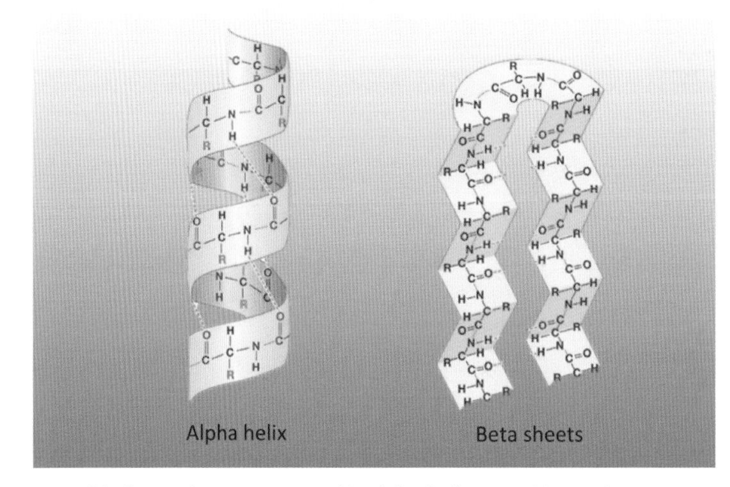

(b) Secondary structure with alpha helices and beta sheets.

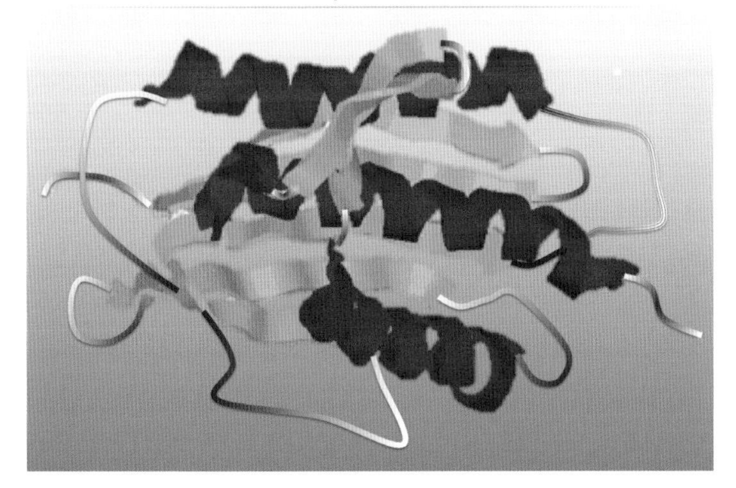

(c) Tertiary structure. The spatial structure consisting of folded helices and planes.

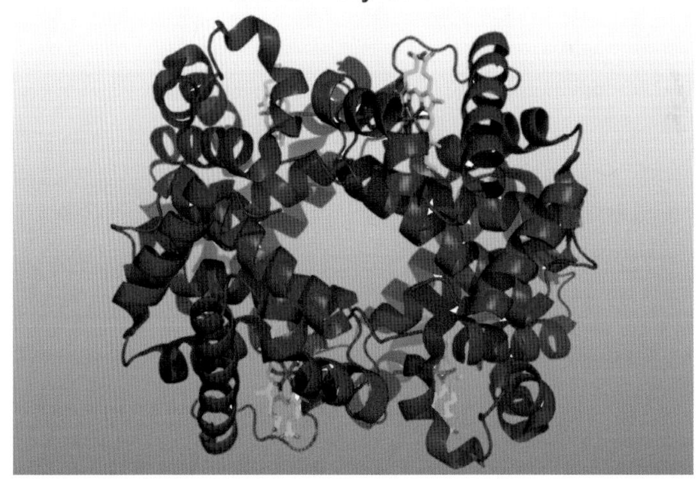

(d) Quaternary structure, representing a protein complex such as in this case *haemoglobin*.

Figure III.1.12: *Protein structure.* The four levels of protein structure.

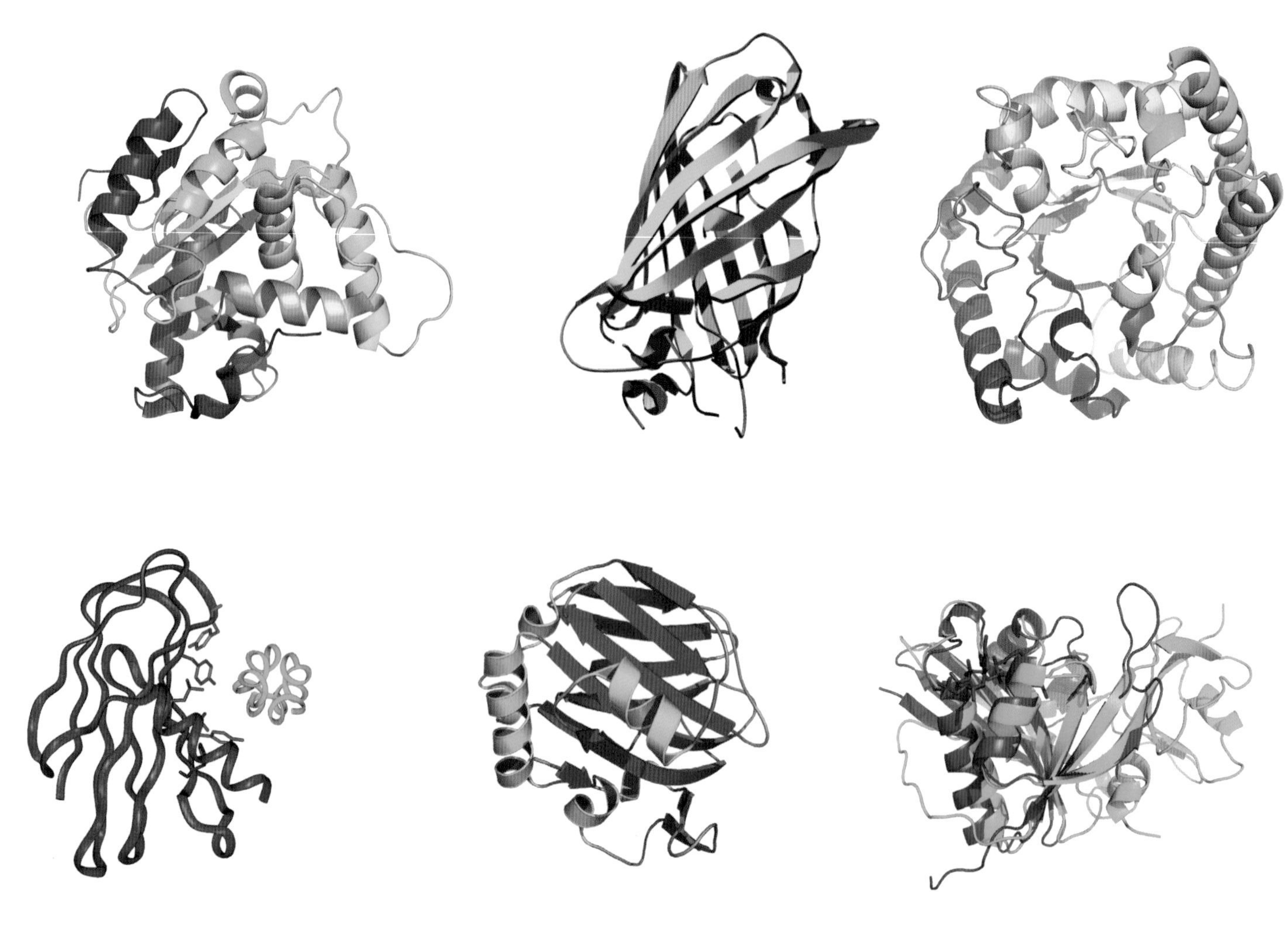

Figure III.1.13: *Proteins: the work horses of life.* Their tertiary three-dimensional structural complexity, diversity and beauty is where the quantum ladder reaches into the heart of life. One could easily imagine trendy fashion designers and hair stylists getting inspiration from these magnificent – all natural – dreadlock designs. For others it is just a splendid paean to reductionism.

stages of cosmic evolution. We have described the wonderful diversity that the flexibility of the carbon atom allows for and that is not only evident in the field of nano-science, but also in biochemistry and molecular biology. We have given examples of how nature has exploited the almost unlimited possibilities to create tremendous diversity from a very limited set of fundamental building blocks.

Further reading.
On molecular physics:

- *Molecular Quantum Mechanics*
  Peter W. Atkins and Ronald S. Friedman
  Oxford University Press (2010)
- *Molecular Physics: Theoretical Principles and Experimental Methods*
  Wolfgang Demtröder
  Wiley (2005)
- *The Molecules of Life*
  John Kuriyan
  Garland Publishers (2012)

Complementary reading:

- *The First Three Minutes: A Modern View of the Origin of the Universe*
  Steven Weinberg
  Basic Books (1977)
- *What is Life?*
  Erwin Schrödinger
  Cambridge University Press (1992)
- *The Double Helix*
  James D. Watson
  Signet Books (1969)

Chapter III.2

The splendid diversity of condensed matter

Water waves are called an emergent phenomena, because they are a property of the medium water but not of the individual water molecules. Emergent properties, which are ubiquitous in any form of collective, result from the combination of constituent properties and the nature of their interactions.

Condensed states of matter

Condensed matter physics is a research field with a wide scope, because there is a rich diversity of condensed states of matter that we have learned to distinguish and understand. Condensed matter systems are composed of large numbers of constituent particles or agents of various types, each with its own characteristics. When these particles are interacting all kind of unexpected things may happen, and their collective will exhibit a variety of emergent *properties. This raises a question that can be posed in two directions. On the one hand we may start from the observed macroscopic behavior and ask what the microscopic ingredients and mechanisms are that give rise to that collective behavior. On the other hand the microscopic constituents may be given and we are asked to 'design' a 'medium' that exhibits certain macroscopic properties. Condensed matter physics is the systematic study of widely different manifestations of order and disorder. It wants to understand what characterizes the different phases and what the underlying mechanisms are. We start this chapter with an introductory overview of some general concepts and will then focus on specific systems in the following sections. The next chapter is devoted to the properties of the electrons in solids.*

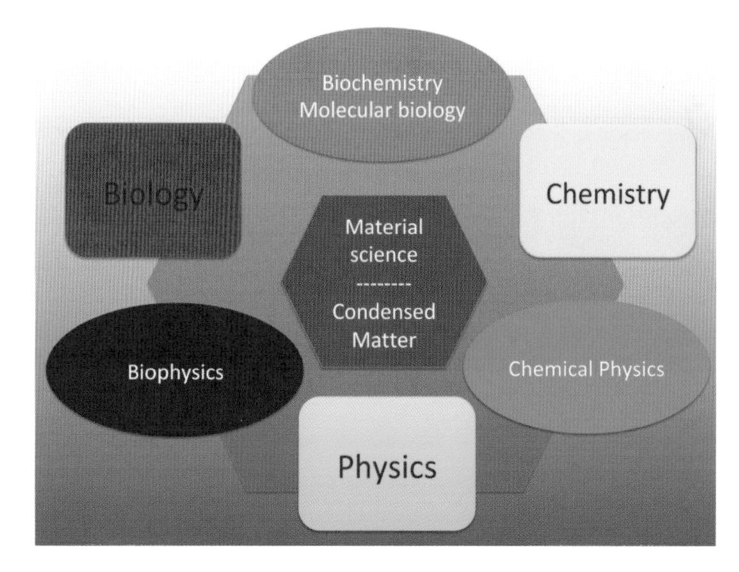

Figure III.2.1: *A science of complexity.* Condensed states of matter are studied in the three basic disciplines, and in the inter- and transdisciplinary fields that emerged in between those disciplines.

A multidisciplinary field. The study of condensed states of matter is by no means an activity only physicists are concerned with. Quite the contrary, it is an inter- or better transdisciplinary field, where the basic disciplines of biology, chemistry and physics, as well as other, interpolating fields, meet and inspire each other in many ways. This research environment is sketched in Figure III.2.1. Generally speaking the understanding of collective – often emergent – behavior, of large numbers of similar constituents or agents, is a principal objective of what is called *complexity science*. But the interactions typically go both ways; from individual to collective and back, from local to global and back. Characteristic for such systems is that they feature a variety of feedback mechanisms whose effects are notoriously hard to understand and model. The models and methodologies developed in statistical physics and condensed matter theory, offer possibilities for adaptation in a much broader context of complexity science – where they have demonstrated to be applicable in disciplines like economics, and other social sciences. Especially with the advent of large-scale computation, which allows large-scale data processing and model simulation (including the nonlinearities representing feedback mechanisms), these parallels can be explored quantitatively.

Just H_2O. Let me start with the familiar example of water. In Figure III.2.2 I have schematically displayed the different phases that can occur as a function of the temperature T. If we start in the middle, say at room temperature, and a normal pressure of one atmosphere, then it will be a liquid. If we heat it, it starts boiling at $100^o\ C$, and will make a transition to the vapor or gas state. And if we cool it, it will freeze and become ice. These phases differ by the way the molecules are aggregated.

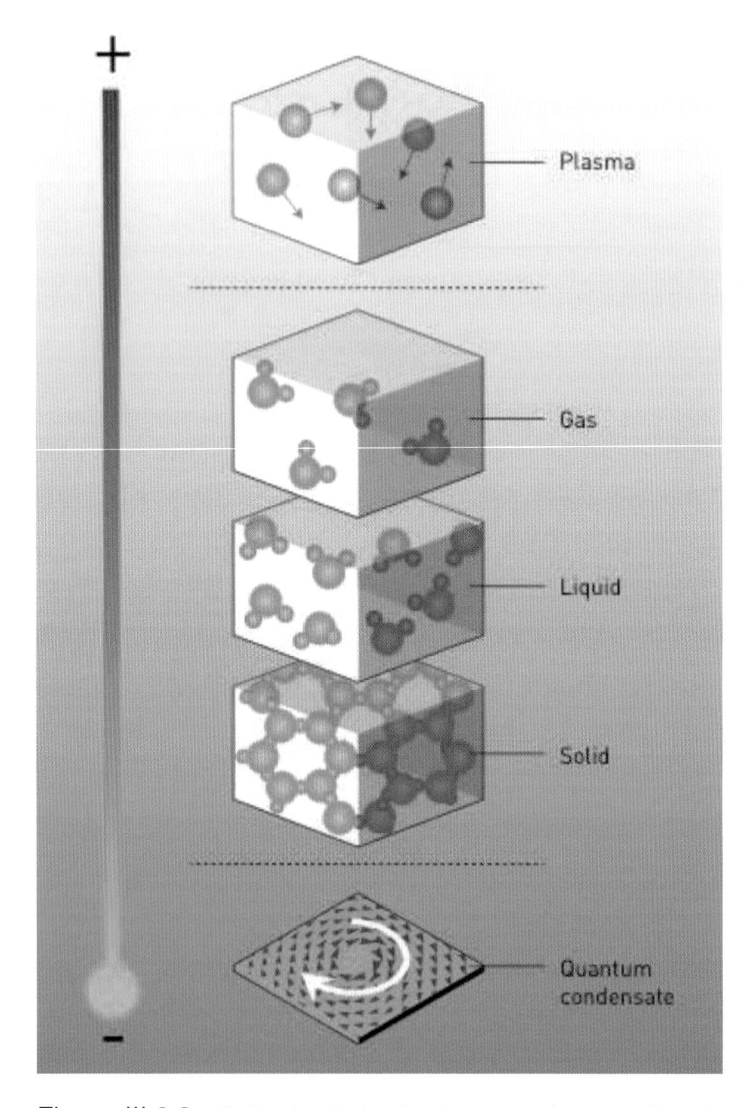

Figure III.2.2: Collective behavior becomes less predictable and harder to understand if we keep lowering the temperature. (Source: Nobel.org)

Collective behavior. In discussing collective behavior we distinguish a number of conceptual ingredients which we will briefly highlight in this section. On the one hand we have to know what the basic ingredients, often called *constituents* or *agents*, of which the system is composed, are. It is important to know what their individual properties or *internal degrees of freedom* are, but also what their *interactions* look like. On the other hand we have to determine what the possible *external control parameters* are, in the context of physics these are typically things like temperature, pressure and external fields.

The system may have different ways to aggregate, depending on the 'environment' and as a consequence enter different *phases*. We fix the environmental constraints by choosing the values of the external parameters in certain ranges. These external parameters already refer to macroscopic, that is, collective state variables. The temperature of a gas or liquid for example is linked to the average kinetic energy of the molecules, and can be regulated by putting the system in contact with a heat bath.

We are led to the notion of a *phase diagram*, where we draw the space of external parameters (or lower dimensional cross-sections thereof), and divide it into the domains corresponding to the different allowed phases.

Moving through parameter space one encounters boundaries that separate different phases, meaning that the system will go through a *phase transition*. The phases will exhibit different degrees of *order and disorder* on different levels. The question how to distinguish the various phases leads us to the notions of *order parameters* and *correlation functions*.

Finally, once a phase has been recognized, we have to identify the most relevant *effective degrees of freedom* of the system in that phase, these are generally emergent degrees of freedom which do not exist on the constituent level. On the one hand these are the low energy modes corresponding to so-called *quasi-particles*. You may for example think of density waves in a solid which are also called *phonons* or 'particles of sound'. On the other hand in macroscopic media one often encounters so-called *defects*, these are literally structural defects or imperfections in the medium. Defects can be localized (point like) or extended (like a line or a wall). Defects are robust for topological reasons, and they play a crucial role for understanding the properties of such materials. For example in a crystal one may have lattice defects, called *dislocations* or *disclinations*, as we will show later on.

Let us now zoom in on the concepts we just introduced.

Constituents and their degrees of freedom. When talking about condensed states of matter, we assume such states to be composed of many constituents. The constituents can themselves be composite as well, like ions, atoms or molecules. The constituents have certain properties like mass, charge, magnetic moments (spins), in fact any the attributes we have been discussing in previous chapters. The constituents will – depending on their properties – have interactions, and these interactions may be strong or weak, and may be long, short or intermediate ranged. For example if particles have spin one-half they are fermions and cannot occupy the same state, which has a huge impact on their collective behavior. Relevant is also to what extent the intrinsic degrees of freedom can be manipulated by external controls, like an applied magnetic field for example, which couples to all individual spins in the system. Needless to say that it is precisely the rich variety of constituents and their interactions (including feedbacks) that allow for the splendid diversity of possible states and phases of condensed matter.

In Figure III.2.3 I have indicated the substructures of the most common systems and their typical degrees of freedom which may or may not play a decisive role, depending on the question one is addressing. If we go down in scale the substance may consist of one type or various types of molecules, and much will depend on the *shapes* of the molecules, referring to the charge distributions (the molecular wave functions). These determine the electric and magnetic dipole and higher moments, and as the molecules are overall charge neutral, these moments are crucial and determine the rigidity of the individual shapes. And clearly these shapes are all-important for understanding how the molecules can fit together in a stable way, which in turn determines the allowed symmetries of a crystal to be formed. If the molecules become large, like polymers for example, one can imagine complex materials being assembled, like biological tissues made from large biomolecules.

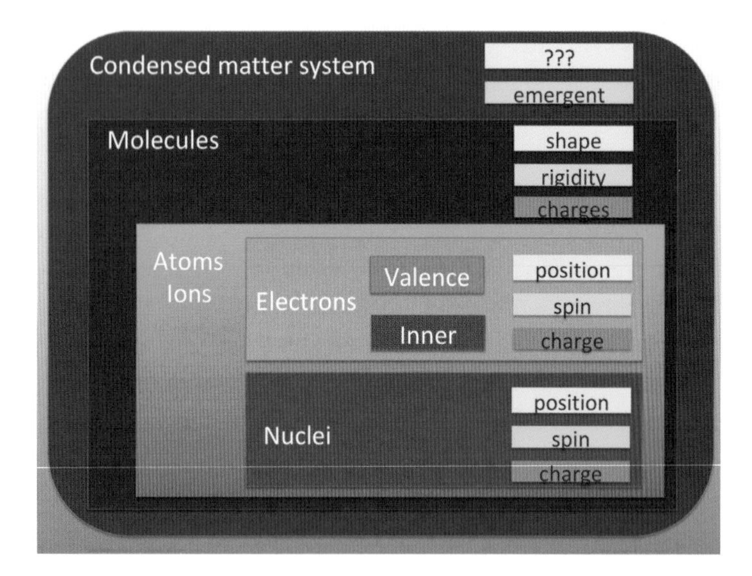

Figure III.2.3: *A hierarchy of degrees of freedom.* Building blocks of a condensed matter system (in white) and their 'degrees of freedom' (in blue).

The relevant constituents may also just be atoms, and they may form crystals, where they optimally balance their kinetic and potential energy, or alternatively their attraction and repulsion. The picture is that the nuclei sit on the sites of a lattice and the electron states may either be localized on the nuclei, or be spread out and extended. The electrons in the outer shell – so-called valence electrons – are relatively weakly bound and can hop to neighboring sites and in the case we are dealing with a conductor, they even have non-localized states that spread out over the whole lattice. So, the material is a highly ordered solid, but hidden in there are the electrons which form a freely streaming (not-ordered) fluid supported by the solid substrate of highly localized ions. Similarly we may have a solid where, say, the atomic spins are ordered, in which case we have a ferro or anti-ferromagnet, or the spins may be disordered – pointing in random directions – and there would be no overall magnetization. And indeed, these charge and spin degrees of freedom can be manipulated by imposing external electric or magnetic fields.

Control parameters and phase diagrams.

An important remark is that the 'relevant degrees of freedom' of the system as a whole are not known *a priori*, exactly because they will mostly be emergent such as sound, spin waves, currents, defects etc. These emergent degrees of freedom will strongly depend on the choices we make for the external parameters. These are for example the thermodynamic parameters such as temperature, pressure or chemical potential. Other parameters correspond to external electric and magnetic fields, or the chemical composition (or doping) of the material. Moreover, there is a dependence on the dynamic of preparation. If we cool a liquid rapidly (called *quenching*), then it may not have had enough time to achieve the optimal type of long range order. It would stay somewhat amorphous, in contrast with the perfect crystal which forms if we cool the liquid down slowly (called *annealing*).

There are still other options for manipulating the system. You may change the relative concentrations of components. You may replace certain components by similar, or not so similar ones. You can add components (like *solvents* or *interstitials*), or 'dope' the system by adding or removing charge carriers. These tools have been used in the most inventive ways to engineer materials with specific, sometimes most unusual, but highly desirable properties. This advanced form of 'legoism' makes certain corners of material science look like a kind of black magic: a form of witchcraft with the distinctive feature that it works!

The phase diagram. The parameter space may be divided into domains corresponding to the different phases, and this information is usually represented in a *phase diagram*. Often we are interested only in particular phenomena and we can restrict ourselves to smaller- and lower-dimensional cross sections of the parameter space. One axis that is usually present is the temperature (or energy) axis, and another is for example the pressure (or density) axis. If we add the pressure P, we can extend the Fig-

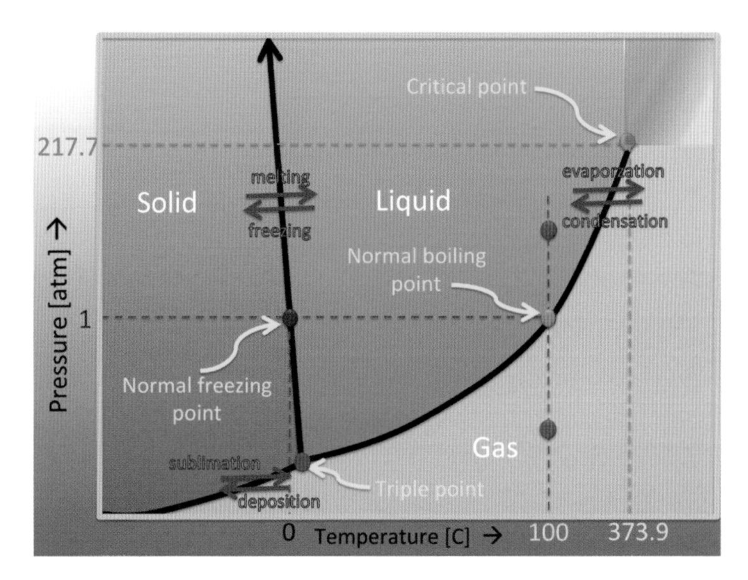

Figure III.2.4: *Phase diagram.* The standard phase diagram of ice/water/vapor with the triple point, and the standard definition of boiling and freezing point. Above the critical point there is a smooth crossover from the liquid to the vapor state.

ure III.2.2 to the two-dimensional $P - T$ phase diagram of Figure III.2.4. This adds novel features: the normal boiling and freezing points become lines, and as we see, these lines may join (or split) at a so-called *triple point*. Furthermore a line may terminate at a so-called *critical point*, where a clear distinction between the phases ceases to exist.

Equation of state. The state variables are usually not independent, since they have to satisfy a constraint, which is called the *equation of state*. For a fixed amount of stuff, say one *mol*, which means a total number of N_A molecules, one finds that in the diluted gas phase for example the 'ideal gas law' holds. This law states that $PV = RT$, which is a functional constraint on the macroscopic state variables P, V and T involving the universal or molar gas constant $R = N_A k$ which is just a fixed number (the product of Avogadro's and Boltzmann's constants). If we for example consider a fixed amount of gas in a container of fixed volume V, the equation tells us that lowering the temperature would lower the pressure proportionally (at least in a lower right-hand side corner of the diagram where the 'law' holds).

Phase transitions. Crossing a phase boundary in a phase diagram means that the system goes through a *phase transition*. Let us for a moment look at the dark blue line separating the liquid and gas or vapor phases. Crossing that line from blue to light brown means boiling the liquid. What you immediately see is that this may happen on any point on that line segment. If we boil an egg on a Sunday morning, what we do is that we have a fixed normal pressure of 1 atmosphere, and by heating the water we move to the right on the dashed red line until we hit the transition point at 100 degrees Celsius. But a less practical way to boil an egg would be start at high pressure with water at 100° C, the water is not boiling then but when we lower the pressure, sure enough when it hits 1 atmosphere the water would start boiling. This boiling process would correspond to crossing the phase boundary top down along the vertical dashed red line starting at the high red point moving to the pink straight below. High in the mountains the pressure of the atmosphere is lower and thus water boils at a lower temperature (about 4 degrees per kilometer elevation), which can make preparing your soft-boiled Sunday morning egg quite a hassle. Often phase transitions signal the occurrence of a tipping point in some (free) energy landscape of the system due to changes in the control parameters. And in that sense the phase diagram is a natural characterization for any multi-particle or multi-agent system.

Critical points. In a critical point, a phase separation line terminates. This means that the clear distinction between the two phases, and the marked transition between them, somehow disappears. We enter a critical region in which there is a smooth crossover between – in this case – the liquid and the vapor. In fact the usual clear surface separating them disappears and becomes a foggy layer.

Figure III.2.5: *A tabular iceberg.* In October 2018 a NASA inspection team discovered this huge, perfectly rectangular, so-called tabular iceberg in the arctic. Such bergs are formed naturally and have a strikingly rectangular geometry, reflecting the underlying crystal structure. They are not single giant monocrystals, though they look like it. (Source: NASA ICE)

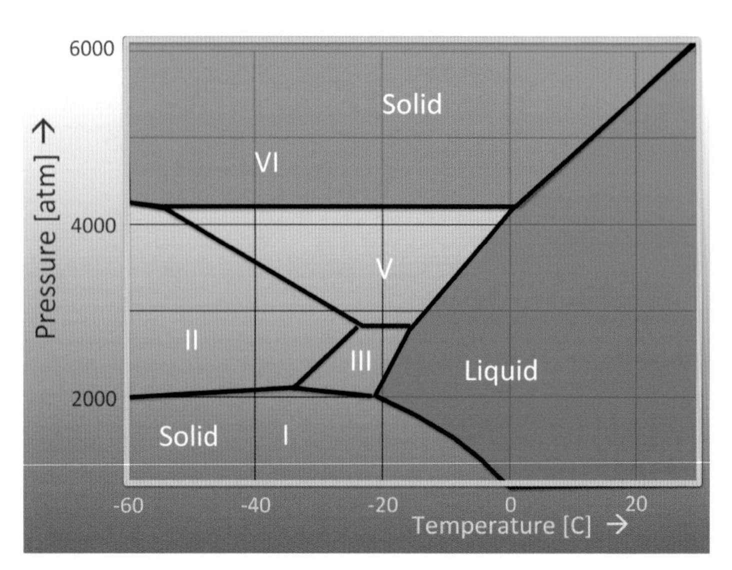

Figure III.2.6: *Ice varieties.* In the high pressure regime, high up along the vertical axis of the previous diagram, there are many distinct solid phases of water, where the water molecules happen to organize according to different symmetries.

Ice? What ice? In Figure III.2.6 we Souyrce:show a tiny corner of the phase diagram of water at very high pressures, and therefore not present in Figure III.2.4. It would have appeared high up on the left, in the direction where the arrow is pointing. The diagram shows that if you make the pressure large enough, the water will become solid even at higher temperatures. You furthermore see that there are actually many distinct solid phases up there. They are forms of ice that differ by their crystal symmetries. Some are *hexagonal* (I) others *tetragonal* (III,VI), *monoclinic* (V), *rhombohedral* (II) or *cubic* (not in the graph). A true *Baskin & Robbins* of structures, but – I am sure – all equally tasteless. Furthermore many of these fancy phases are metastable, so they tend to decay in more stable versions. Note also the impressive number of triple points in the phase diagram. Such is the hidden diversity of something as common as water. It shows its complex behavior only under extreme conditions.

Water versus Argon. It is interesting to compare the features of the phase diagram of water, with for example that of the noble element argon. The element $^{36}\mathrm{Ar}$ has 18 protons, and its 18 electrons completely fill all energy levels up to the $n = 3, \; l = 1$ shell of atomic states. These completely filled shells make the element stable and resistant to bonding to any companion. The noble elements are 'Einzelgängers', or 'lonely cowboys' so to say, they apparently have everything they need, and are like extreme individualists who love to ignore their neighbors. Under normal conditions it is an inert gas, and it has a phase diagram similar to that of water as depicted in Figure III.2.4, though the corresponding points are positioned at different locations. As is clear from Table III.2.1, for argon things happen at much lower temperatures, which indeed is a consequence of their 'nobility.'

If you would continue the phase diagram for argon to high pressures, one would surely see the melting line bend over to higher temperatures, meaning that liquid argon would

Table III.2.1: Comparison of water and argon.

Phase diagram	Water		Argon	
	T[K]	P[atm]	T[K]	P[atm]
Melting point	273.15	1	83.81	1
Boiling point	373.15	1	87.30	1
Triple point	273.16	0.006	83.81	0.68
Critical point	647.10	217.7	150.69	48.0

just like water solidify at very high pressures. This, however, only happens at pressures of tens of thousands of atmospheres! Furthermore, because this simple atom has so few degrees of freedom, it exhibits only one solid phase. This means that the phase diagram III.2.6 for argon would be rather boring, because it would just show one melting line going across from left to right.

At this point two observations can be made. On the one hand there are universals in phase diagrams, like that condensed matter will become solid under high pressure or at low temperatures (including the familiar triple and critical points). On the other hand, phase diagrams may exhibit a huge structural diversity that depends on the specifics of the constituents, whether they are simple spherical atoms, or composites with many internal degrees of freedom like water molecules.

Crystals. The reason that solids – usually crystals – form is that by bringing many atoms close together the orbits of the electrons start overlapping and the electrons start moving around changing nuclear partner so to say, which leads to an effective attraction. However, if they get too close the effect of the repulsion of positively charged nuclei starts to dominate. Balancing attraction and repulsion the atoms tend to organize themselves into an optimal pattern that minimizes their overall interaction energy. This is basically how crystals form. In a crystal the positioning of the atoms is strictly periodic which implies strong spatial correlations over large distances, corresponding to some discrete translational (and rotational) symmetries. Complexity and beauty apparently arise where attraction and repulsion strike a subtle balance.

Hard versus soft condensed matter. The field of condensed matter physics is divided up into two parts: soft and hard condensed matter physics comprising the topics we have indicated in Figure III.2.7.

Soft matter. With soft matter we think of liquids, coloids, gels, molecular materials like polymers and biomaterials. It is a diverse field that often involves physics at an intermediate – so-called mesoscopic – scale, like nano structures for example. This field mostly employs methods from classical physics, such as statistical mechanics and classical field theory, but also lots of chemistry. It is the branch of condensed matter physics most remote from hard core quantum theory, but it has become an innovative field with a wide range of applications. One of its most influential protagonists was Pierre-Gilles de Gennes of the École Normale Supérieure at Paris, who received the 1991 Nobel prize for his extensive oeuvre. This field has led to beautiful insights into the role of symmetry and its breaking. We will therefore in the following not just discuss crystals, but also *liquid crystals* and *quasicrystals*.

Hard matter. Hard matter is the present incarnation of what used to be called *solid state physics*. It studies properties of materials where quantum theory is absolutely indispensable. Quantum properties are vital for understanding the role electrons and lattice vibrations play. In the quantum realm these can rearrange themselves in collective quasi-particle degrees of freedom, with totally unexpected emergent properties, like *superfluidity*, low and high temperature *superconductivity*, and *topological order*. These latter phases, for example fractional quantum Hall systems, include new degrees of freedom called *anyons* with exotic spin and statistics properties. Towards the end of Chapter III.3 we will take a closer look at them.

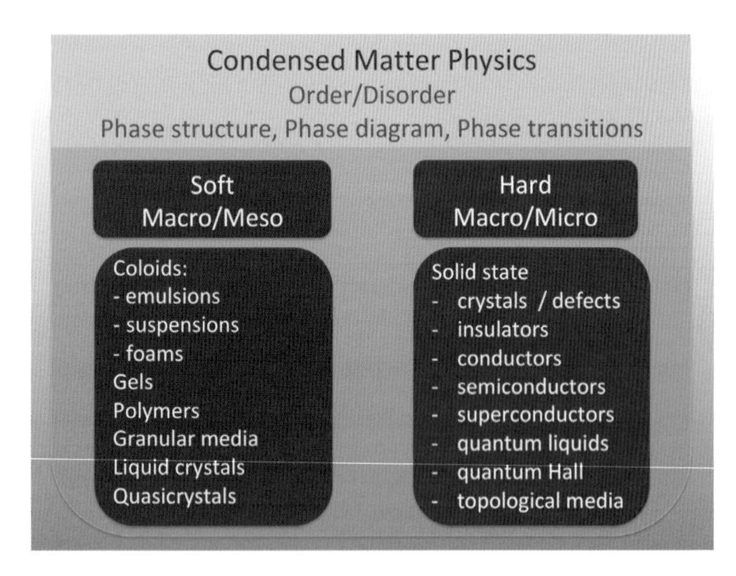

Figure III.2.7: *Hard versus soft.* Condensed matter can be roughly divided up into 'soft' and 'hard' matter. Both are of great technological importance.

Plasma. We have seen that for large pressures most systems become solid. There is of course also the other extreme regime, corresponding to high temperatures, which is of interest as was already indicated in Figure III.2.2. For very high temperatures, there is yet another phase transition: the water molecules will ionize, which means that they will break up in two oppositely charged components, the OH^- and H^+ ions:

$$H_2O \rightarrow OH^- + H^+$$

This is again a quite different state of water. It is still overall electrically neutral, but it will couple strongly to electric and magnetic fields, because the individual components (and constituents) do. If you apply a voltage over the plasma, currents will flow, and clearly, the positive and negatively charged components will run in opposite directions.

In Chapter I.3 where we talked about fusion, we mentioned the crucial role played by the tritium plasma as a 'fuel'. And in the previous chapter we alluded to the state of the very early universe as a *primordial soup*, this refers to a universal plasma made up of bare 'charges' for all interaction types. Of special interest is the colored component of the soup called the *quark-gluon plasma*, which is nowadays studied experimentally by smashing lead ions into each other in the Large Hadron Collider at CERN, by the so-called ALICE collaboration. In that experiment one tries to recreate for a tiny period of time, a tiny bit of early universe. It is fascinating to realize that not only with space observatories but also with big accelerators one is trying to get ever closer to the Big Bang and thus contributing to cosmology.

Order versus disorder

We have indicated the importance of identifying different phases. These are roughly characterized as ordered and disordered phases, but also phases that sit in between. Solids are highly ordered, gases are disordered, and simple liquids tend to be more like dense gases, but if the constituents are more complicated they can be both. Both ordered and disordered! How can that be? Well, it depends on which degrees of freedom you are talking about. In a liquid crystal for example, the positions of the molecules are not frozen into a crystal (disorder), but the orientations of the molecules are all aligned (order). Glass appears to be solid, but is in fact an extremely viscous liquid. And what about gels, polymers, and biomaterials, are they ordered and in what ways? In a conductor the nuclei have fixed positions in the crystal lattice, yet at the same time the conducting electrons form a liquid that flows freely through the material. The diverse topics we have mentioned so far used to belong to different fields of study but are more and more integrated because similar techniques are used to study them.

One of the fascinating results from classical physics, in particular statistical thermodynamics, is that certain disordered equilibrium states like a gas of atoms or a liquid can still be rather easily described if one applies statistical methods to them. After all, the behavior of a *mol* of a dilute gas consisting of some 10^{23} atoms in equilibrium, can to a first approximation be described in terms of only a few macroscopic variables like pressure P, temperature T and a volume V and an entropy S, that have to satisfy the *ideal gas law*, $PV = RT$. Such a drastic reduction of variables can be performed if one is only interested in the most relevant degrees of freedom that effectively describe the equilibrium states of the collective in a given phase.

The gas molecules bounce around randomly, yet, even though the individual behavior of the atoms is highly erratic, the collective is surprisingly well behaved and highly predictable. As every insurance company can tell you, as long as the number of clients is sufficiently large, statistics becomes an extremely reliable tool for predicting the probability of certain events. In the classical theory of somewhat less diluted gasses, where one takes the size of the atoms and the presence of walls of the container into account, one arrives at the *Van der Waals equation of state*. This equation is an important generalization of the ideal gas law from a conceptual point of view, because it predicts a phase transition to a liquid state. We will return to this equation shortly.

It turns out that the most complicated behavior is observed near a phase transition. There the distribution of thermal fluctuations broadens; fluctuations apparently occur on all scales which means that they are not distributed like a Gaussian distribution with a well-defined mean and variance around the mean. No, the distributions behave like *power laws*, where compared with the Gaussian, the venom is in the tail of the distribution. Whereas the exponential distribution tends rapidly to zero, the power laws have so-called *fat tails*. These tails describe so-called 'high impact, low probability' events, but the point is rather that in spite of the fact that these events are far away from the average, their probability is actually *not* so small after all, in fact gigantic compared to an exponential distribution With power laws extreme events in the tail of the distribution cannot be discarded at all. Indeed, under such circumstances, insurance brokers are not that eager anymore to sell you an insurance policy, and if they do, they will certainly make you pay a good deal more to cover their substantial risks.

Phases, order parameters and correlations. So what then determines in what sense a system is ordered or disordered?

Order parameters. There is a special set of observables important for the identification of different phases: these are denoted as local *order parameters*, which are called local because they depend on the position x. To probe the difference between a vapor and its liquid state, the order parameter would be the local density $\rho(x)$. In the transition it would make a sudden jump from a tiny to a large constant value $\rho(x) = \rho_0$. For magnetic systems the order parameter is the magnetization M, which is the spatial average of the local magnetization $M(x)$, which in turn corresponds to a local average of a sizeable number of spins centered around the point x. In metals spontaneous magnetization occurs at the so-called Curie temperature, which means that the magnetization M acquires a non-zero value below this temperature. So, to conclude, order parameters are specific observables that probe for a structural change in the state of the system when it goes through a phase transition.

First- and second-order phase transitions. We distinguish two types of phase transitions called first- and second-order transitions. For the second order transition the order parameter changes continuously (but not smoothly) from zero to a non-zero value. A typical example is spontaneous magnetization which we just mentioned and will discuss in more detail shortly.

Correlations. The order parameters correspond to the average property of a local quantity. But a measure of order can also be more subtle and correspond to probing multi-local correlations in space or time in the system. For example, if you have a crystal, then many of its properties are periodic, and strongly correlated spatially. Measuring such correlations can then help you identify the spatial structure and symmetries of the crystal. A famous technique, X-ray diffraction, does exactly that: it yields a diffraction pattern in which such spatial correlations are encoded, and from which the three-dimensional crystal structure can be reconstructed.

First-order transitions. In a first-order transition the order parameter jumps discontinuously. A nice example is the liquid-vapor transition (evaporation or boiling), where there is a region in parameter space where both phases can coexist, but where one of them becomes unstable. The transition then often takes place through bubble nucleation, as we know too well from the ordinary boiling phenomenon. Inside the bubbles we have the new phase and outside the bubble is still the old liquid phase. Because of thermal fluctuations, bubbles spontaneously form in the liquid, and if they have a sufficient size they will start growing. The threshold occurs when the energy it costs to make the wall (proportional to the surface area of the bubble) becomes equal to the energy gain which is given by the energy difference between the two phases, and this gain is proportional to the volume of the bubble. Clearly, if the bubble is large enough the volume term wins and the bubble will start expanding. If you transfer more heat to the liquid, more and larger bubbles will form, and those may furthermore coalesce. This process continues until the transition is completed and there is no fluid left.

In the Figures III.2.8 and III.2.9 we have depicted the liquid-vapor transition from two complementary points of view. The first figure shows the transition in a pressure-volume (P, V) diagram. The colored curves are different isotherms (curves of constant temperature). The yellow one corresponds to a high temperature and reproduces the ideal gas law, $P = RT/V$. The orange isotherm where $T = T_c$

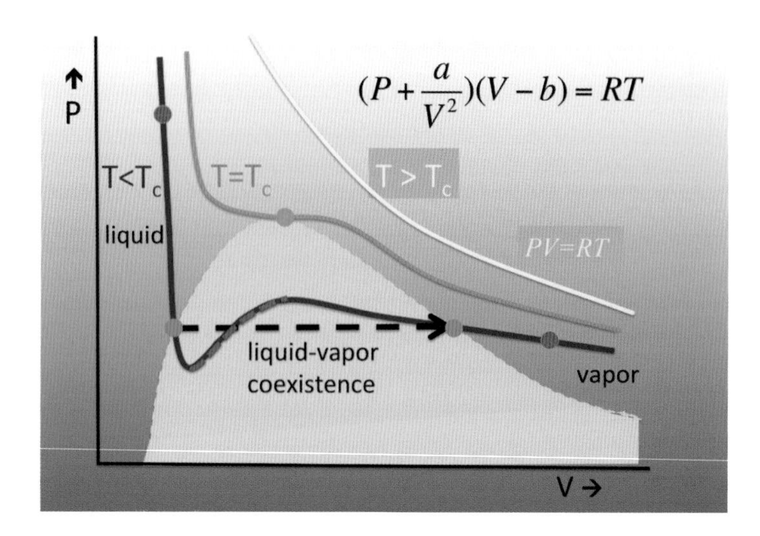

Figure III.2.8: *Van der Waals equation of state.* We have sketched three isotherms meaning P as function of V with T fixed. The yellow one for $T > T_c$, where we recover the ideal gas law. The orange one is for $T = T_c$, and the purple one corresponds to the boiling process as described in the text.

is special because all lower isotherms have a minimum and a maximum. The purple curve is the 100° Celsius isotherm and describes the process corresponding to the vertical transition marked in Figure III.2.4. The points on an isotherm supposedly correspond to equilibrium states, but that cannot always be the case. The segment highlighted with the dashed red line cannot represent physically acceptable states because increasing the volume would also increase the pressure, but for physical states it is the other way around, the 'compressibility' in those points has the wrong sign. So only the descending parts of the isotherm represent allowed equilibrium states. What makes these curves interesting is precisely that for $T < T_c$, we see that for a certain pressure range there are two possible states: the left one corresponding to the liquid and the one on the right to the vapor. The picture does immediately suggest the explanation. We can slowly descend the 100° isotherm by increasing the volume and thereby lowering the pressure, keeping the system in equilibrium until we hit the dot-

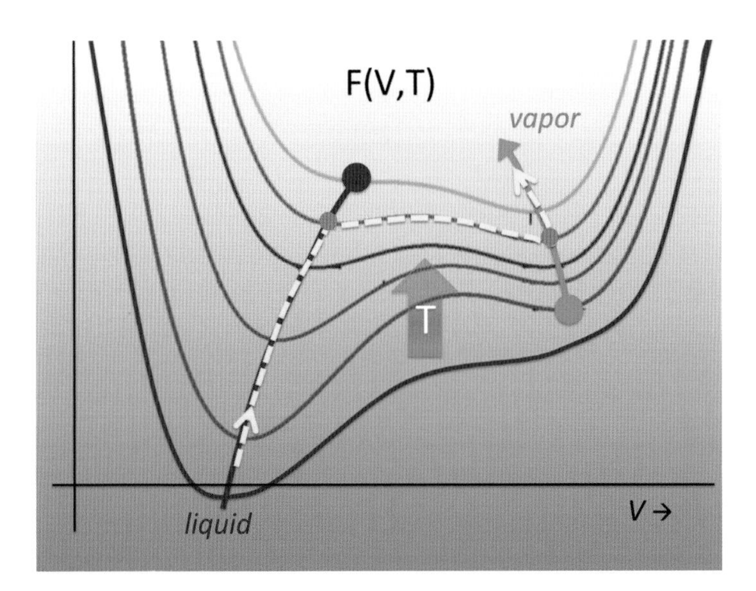

Figure III.2.9: *Free energy landscapes for different temperatures.* The minima correspond to the equilibrium liquid and/or vapor states. The yellow trajectory corresponds to horizontal 'boiling' trajectory in the phase diagram of Figure III.2.4. The liquid state is stable, until we hit the red curve where the vapor minimum has lower energy and the system makes the boiling transition to that stable vapor state.

ted line at the pink point (where $P = 1\ \mathrm{atm}$). This is where the boiling transition starts, and as we all know this is a pretty violent non-equilibrium type of process that works through bubble nucleation, and continues until all the liquid has vaporized and the system can restore equilibrium in the vapor state on the isotherm (corresponding to the the pink point on the right). From there the system may move down again if the volume is further enlarged. In the intermediate region during the crossing we have two coexisting phases in the system, part is liquid and part is vapor. The whole transition trajectory marked by the dashed black arrow between the two pink dots, thus corresponds to the single pink dot in the phase diagram III.2.4. This teaches us that the phase diagram certainly tells us that there is a transition, but does not inform us in any way about how that transition actually takes place, and whether it is a first- or second-order transition.

Minimizing the free energy. Now in the second figure, Figure III.2.9, we look at the first-order transition from the point of view of the free energy $F = F(V, T)$ of the system, and this time it is convenient to take the horizontal trajectory in the phase diagram, corresponding to the familiar boiling process we witness in the kitchen.[1] In the figure we plotted the free energy as a function of volume for increasing temperatures. The equilibrium states correspond to minima of the free energy and we see that there is a range of temperatures where we have two minima. We have a fixed amount of matter, so the left minimum is the small volume or liquid state, and the right minimum is the vapor state. We start at a low temperature equilibrium state corresponding to the unique minimum. If we start raising the temperature, we see that the energy landscape is changing. Once we arrive at the light blue isobar it develops a second (local) minimum, but it has higher energy and is therefore unstable. If an outlandish fluctuation somewhere in the liquid happens to create a tiny vapor bubble, this bubble would instantly collapse because there is nothing to gain (energy-wise) by being a bubble. However by going to higher temperatures the values of F for the two minima become equal, and on the red curve the vapor minimum has become clearly lower than the liquid one. Then indeed, the liquid state becomes metastable. Even moderate fluctuations will create bubbles that are big enough to start growing, thereby executing the actual vaporization process. You also see that even if we are careful and succeed in overheating the liquid, then you hit the dark blue point where the minimum corresponding to the liquid disappears. At that point the liquid state becomes unstable and the transition necessarily takes place.

Tipping points. It is worth pointing out that the free energy diagram is quite universal for understanding the origin of tipping points in all kinds of multi-agent systems. The free energy would correspond to some relevant 'util-

[1] This is a process at fixed pressure, and is naturally presented by equal pressure lines or so-called *isobars* in a (T, V) diagram.

ity function' the system wants to minimize (environmental constraints, costs, etc). The 'fitness' landscape will in general depend on other (control) variables. For example we have a society burning fossil fuels which provides us energy for $X per kWh. Around 1970 the landscape started to change in that another possibility appeared, namely solar power. It is still expensive, and without some local subsidies a local effort easily collapses. However the price comes down rapidly, and the second minimum of the utility function starts competing. Ambitious countries, states and cities may create successful local bubbles that are economically feasible and start to grow. And that is how the energy transition will presumably take place in the present age. The energy transition is typically a first-order transition, and as a matter of fact we see it happening all around us! This shows you the metaphorical power of the boiling process as a model for certain types of transitions and the visualization with the two competing minima as a powerful analogy.

Collective degrees of freedom: quasi particles. Once the system has chosen a different ground state corresponding to a new phase and another minimum of the free energy, we should ask what other aspects of the physics of the system have changed. Most importantly, we should find out what the low energy excitations of the system in the new state are. The low energy excitations are of interest because they are the first that will get excited if we perturb the system, and as such they determine more then anything else the *emergent* properties of the system in the new phase. These modes help also to identify and label the collective states. Whether it is a conductor to heat or electricity, or whether it is a magnetically ordered ferromagnet, for example.

What happens to a crystal if I hit it? This is like probing the system by locally deforming it and observing the response of the system to that deformation. We study how the deformation propagates through the system. How the deformation energy starts spreading. The resulting propagating modes are the low energy excitations, in this case they are longitudinal density waves, which correspond to sound. Sound is an emergent phenomenon because an individual atom does not know what sound is, it cannot make sound by itself. It needs the ordered collective to propagate, and in that sense it is just like the 'wave' that can be excited in a football stadium: to let it propagate through the crowd requires a collective effort. And if a large fraction of the audience are fans of the opposing team, it will definitely not propagate. The point I am making is that by studying the response of the system to perturbations we get to know a lot about its ground state or phase.

In reality the molecular systems we consider are more omplicated and we do not only have to worry about the positions of the nuclei in the crystal lattice. For example, the nuclei may have a tiny magnetic moment, called *spin*, which means that they are like tiny bar magnets. If the system is at a relatively high temperature these little magnets will point in arbitrary directions. They are highly independent, and thus their orientations are uncorrelated even on short distances. So in this case we have that the nuclei are strictly ordered because they form a crystal, while their spins are not ordered at all. Apparently we have to be specific if we say that a system is ordered.

The behavior of electrons. Another crucial ingredient of most condensed matter systems that we have not mentioned so far are the electrons. Given the underlying lattice structure of the nuclei, what is the quantum behavior of the electrons in that given background? Do they stay localized, close to 'their' nucleus, or do they start hopping around freely, or do they form a conducting fluid of some sort? It turns out that the behavior of the collective of electrons in condensed states of matter is highly diverse and keeps surprising us up to today. Understand this behavioral variety is one of the main drivers of condensed matter physics. These problems have been studied for decades and time and again new fundamental properties are discovered often leading to important technological innovations. We fo-

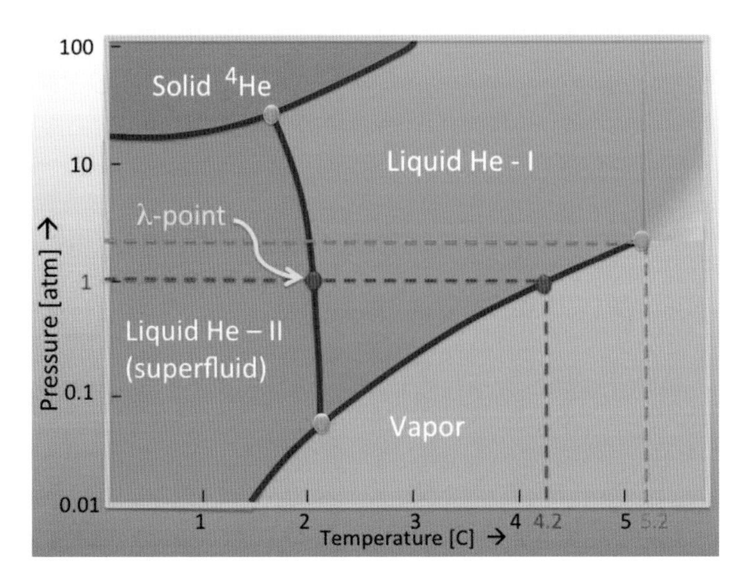

Figure III.2.10: *Phase diagram of* $^4\mathrm{He}$. Comparing this phase diagram with the conventional one of Figure III.2.4, a new superfluid phase has opened up at low temperature, splitting the triple point into two triple points. The critical point is marked in green.

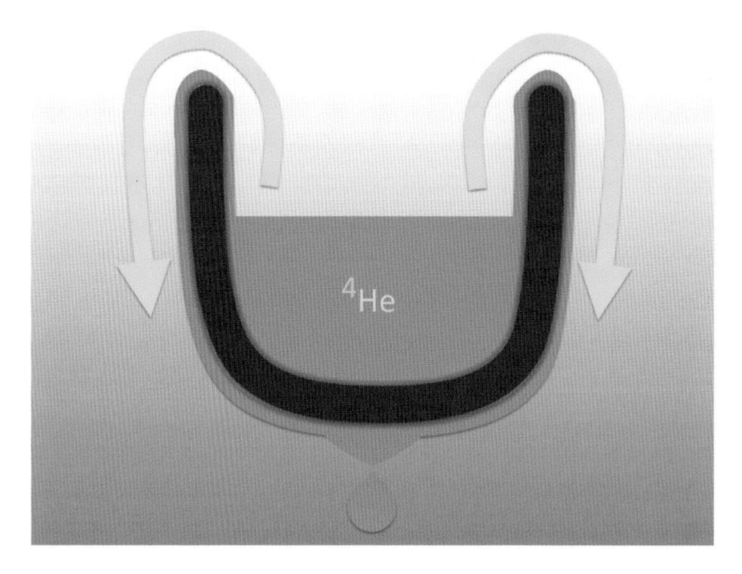

Figure III.2.11: *Superfluidity.* The vessel filled with liquid $^4\mathrm{He}$ that will turn into a frictionless superfluid. When cooled below the λ−point, it will spontaneously creep over the wall of the vessel until it is empty.

cus on some of these types of behavior in the remainder of this section. A more thorough analysis is given in the next chapter.

The quantum regime. In Chapter I.3 we discussed scales and units, and pointed out that at low energies quantum theory necessarily comes into play, which leads to another plethora of conceivable physical states that can have highly unusual properties like superfluidity and superconductivity.

In the quantum regime we should expect that the quantessential spin and statistics properties of particles come into play but also that the Heisenberg uncertainty relations will manifest themselves in the collective behavior. Of special interest is the possibility that bosons can occupy the same state. What typically happens is that once you lower the temperature far enough, a macroscopic number of the bosonic particles will occupy the same lowest energy state. The system forms a so-called *Bose condensate*, a special quantum coherent state, which means that the system will go through a phase transition. Systems where this happens will exhibit 'macroscopic quantum' behavior. Quantum matter phases have been in the centre of attention for quite a long time, and still many novel phases are discovered, which pose formidable puzzles for the theorists to understand, like for example high temperature superconductivity. There are still many open questions with regard to understanding collective quantum phenomena from a microscopic, first principles point of view.

Superfluidity. Let us consider the famous example of Helium-4, a boson, where you can see how the quantum behavior, the formation of a Bose condensate, adds a new phase to the phase diagram. The phase diagram of Figure III.2.10 shows the actually not so recent discovery of *superfluidity* by the Russian physicist Pjotr Kapitza in 1937 (and independently by J.F. Allen and D. Misener).[2]

[2]The discovery was made at a time of international tensions, and therefore credentials have been somewhat controversial. An interest-

He received the 1978 Physics Nobel prize for his landmark contributions to low temperature physics, of which this discovery clearly was an outstanding one. We see that compared to the standard phase diagram of Figure III.2.4, in the low temperature region the superfluid phase has been added. Kapitza discovered that phase by just lowering the temperature of some ^4He vapor under the standard pressure of one atmosphere, so he came from the right at the height of the horizontal red dotted line in the diagram. He first crossed the 'standard' transition from vapor to fluid, but then at a temperature of 2.17 K at the so-called λ point he witnessed the transition to the superfluid phase. The ordinary triple point had 'opened up' and with the appearance of the new phase it split up into two triple points. A superfluid displays the curious property of frictionless flow, and therefore behaves rather 'creepy' in the literal sense. If you watch an open container filled with superfluid, you will see the fluid all by itself creep over the rim and run down the outside of the vessel. In Figure III.2.11 we have sketched an experiment along these lines: the self emptying mug! Thank heaven there is friction! Thank heaven that our superdrinks are not superfluids!

Magnetic order

Magnetization. Magnetic properties of atoms are the combined result of three components: (i) the electrons have spin with an associated magnetic moment of one Bohr magneton μ_b; (ii) the atomic orbits of electrons correspond to states with a magnetic quantum number m, which means that the magnetic moment of the orbit equals $m\mu_b$; and (iii) finally there is the nuclear magnetic moment which turns out to be a factor thousand smaller. We will not enter in any detailed discussion of how these interact but will just assume atoms, ions, or electrons to have some overall spin or magnetic moment. For the spins we can now also introduce an order parameter, it is called the *magnetization* $\mathbf{M}(x)$, the average magnetic orientation of certain number of spins around the point x. If the temperature is high we know that because of the random orientation of the spins, the average magnetization $\langle \mathbf{M}(x) \rangle$ in the ground state will be zero. But if we cool the medium down, then the disturbances in the lattice become smaller and the magnets will feel each other and can lower the energy of the state by aligning, in which case a phase transition will take place.

ing historical account can be found in *S. Balibar, The discovery of superfluidity, Journal of Low Temperature Physics, Vol. 146, Nos. 5/6, 2007.*

Phase transition at the Curie point. At a certain temperature called the Curie point there will be a *phase transition* to a state where all spins will spontaneously align. Order is spontaneously created and the order parameter will acquire a non-vanishing constant, that is to say a position independent value: $\langle \mathbf{M}(x) \rangle = \mathbf{m}_0 \neq 0$. This emergent form of order is called *spontaneous magnetization*, and the system is in a ferromagnetic phase and as a whole behaves like a single big magnet. So we may conclude that ordinary permanent magnets are made of materials of which the Curie temperature lies far above room temperature. And as expected the order parameter thus signals whether the system is ordered or disordered.

Low energy modes: spinwaves. The low energy modes associated with the magnetic spins in a ferromagnet are the so-called *spin waves*. You may compare them to the waves that a light breeze can excite in a field of grain as we described in the section on symmetry breaking in Chapter II.6. These are again collective excitations of the ordered spin system with a wavelength that is long compared to the distances between the spins and because they have a long wavelength they are low energy excitations indeed. If we quantize these waves we get particle like excitations or quasi-particles called *magnons*.

The Ising model

Let us take some time to discuss an absolutely iconic model that instantly comes to the mind of any physicist when you mention the word phase transition. It is called the *Ising model*, cherished for its simplicity and its depth, which was introduced by Wilhelm Lenz in 1920. He suggested it as a problem to his student Enst Ising, who then solved the one-dimensional version of it and found that it had *no* phase transition. Moreover, he erroneously concluded that there would be no phase transition in any dimension. How ironic that Ising's 'fame' in physics is based on drawing a wrong conclusion from an elementary calculation. It is precisely that two-dimensional version we are going to discuss, which has for a long time been the canonical model for a (second-order) phase transition. It was solved exactly by Lars Onsager in 1944, who reportedly at a conference just wrote down the exact answers on a black board without further explanation, leaving the learned audience flabbergasted, and with a nice problem to work on! The problem of figuring out how he did it. It is one of those models to which a tremendous amount of work has been devoted. It has popped up in all subfields of physics and beyond.

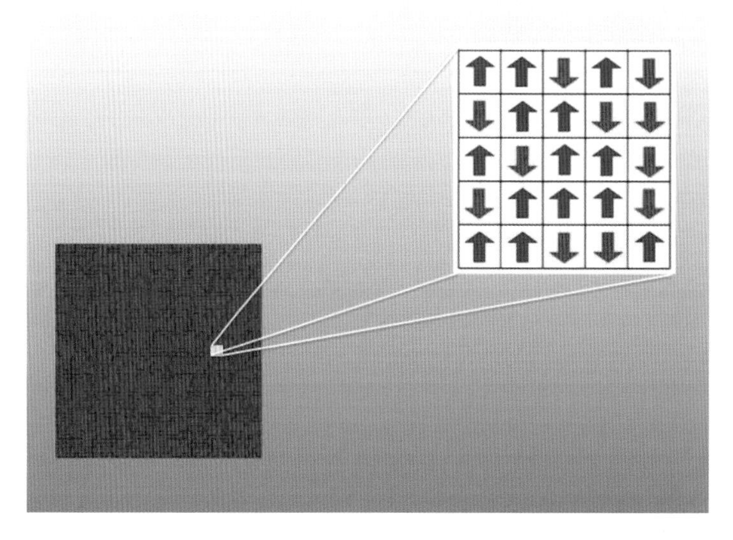

Figure III.2.12: *Ising model.* A two-dimensional Ising system of spins that can only point up or down. Here the system is in a disordered state, where the spins are randomly pointing up or down. If you think of these as nuclear spins you see that the spins are neatly ordered spatially on a cubic crystal, but that the spin orientations are disordered. So order and disorder can peacefully coexist if they refer to different degrees of freedom.

As mentioned before, we distinguish the ordered *ferromagnetic phase* where all spins are aligned, and the *non-magnetic phase*, where the spins point in random directions. Here the order does not concern the spatial positioning but the orientation of the spins. As we pointed out, in the ordered phase the magnetization is some non-zero constant while in the disordered phase it is equal to zero. To be precise there is a different ordered phase which is called anti-ferromagnetic, where the spins at neighboring sites are anti-aligned.

The Ising Hamiltomian. The classical Ising model has an *infinite array of spins that can only point up or down.* A two-dimensional Ising model configuration is depicted in Figure III.2.12. The spins $\sigma_i = \pm 1$ only interact with their nearest neighbors, and the contribution to the energy of any pair of neighbors is,

$$H(\sigma) = -\sum_{ij} J_{ij}\, \sigma_i \sigma_j,$$

where J_{ij} is the interaction parameter. If $J_{ij} = 0$ there is no interaction, whereas if the coupling is constant and positive, $J_{ij} = J > 0$, then we have a ferromagnetic system, and if the constant J is negative we have the anti-ferromagnetic case. If the couplings J_{ij} are chosen randomly, then we speak of a *spin glass.* For simplicity we have left out a term for the coupling of the spins to an external magnetic field. Let us consider the ferromagnetic case, If a pair of neighbors has the same spin, the contribution to the energy is minimal, whereas if the spins are opposite the contribution is maximal. The total energy equals the sum of all pair contributions. For the ferromagnetic case, the minimal energy configuration is therefore the one where all spins are the same, either all up or all down.

The Ising partition sum. The probability for a configuration to occur is given by the Boltzmann factor we introduced in the section on Statistical Physics in Chapter I.1:

$$P(\sigma) = \frac{e^{-\beta H(\sigma)}}{Z_\beta},$$

where the normalization factor Z_β is the *partition sum*:

$$Z(\beta) = \sum_\sigma e^{-\beta H(\sigma)}.$$

Having the probability distribution of configurations, we can define averages, or expectation values. The free energy is defined as $F = -\beta^{-1} \log Z$, and the thermal equilibrium states correspond to the minima of the free energy.

Ising magnetization. To obtain the magnetization we first average the spin over all sites in a given configuration: $M_\sigma = \sum_i \sigma_i / N$, the thermal average is then given by

$$M = \langle M_\sigma \rangle_\beta = \sum_\sigma M_\sigma P_\sigma .$$

In Figure III.2.13 we have depicted three configurations, representing the ordered and disordered phases, wich a critical configuration in between.

Order. In the ordered, low temperature phase the domains are macroscopic (the lowest energy configuration is just a single domain with all spins up or all spins down). In the ordered phases the magnetization would be $M \neq 0$.

Disorder. On the right we see a configuration corresponding to the high temperature disordered phase, where there are basically no domains. The individual spins are just randomly pointing up or down, and consequently the magnetization would equal zero.

Critical. In between is the critical case where the temperature equals the critical temperature T_c, where there are domains of all possible sizes. In fact this critical case is special in the sense that it is *scale invariant*, meaning that

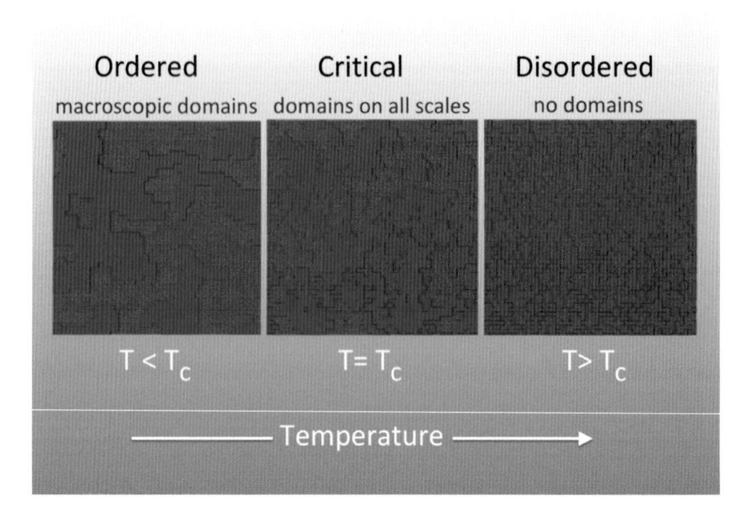

Figure III.2.13: *Magnetic order and disorder.* We see the states of an Ising model without external magnetic field. At low temperatures the state is ordered, and spins are aligned over macroscopic distances, while at high temperatures the state is disordered and there are no domains, just individual spins randomly pointing up or down. In between there is a critical point, where there are domains of all sizes. The critical Ising model is scale invariant.

if you enlarge the picture and cut out a piece of the original size, it would not be possible to distinguish it in a statistical sense from the original one. It is self-similar in a statistical sense.

Mean field theory. One can make an illuminating approximation of the model as a *mean field theory*. One approximates the spins by the local magnetization field $M(x)$. Clearly this approximation will break down for small distances. It is possible to write an effective free energy $F(M,T)$ in terms of this field $M(x)$ this is known as the Landau theory. Because of the symmetries in the model it will only have even powers of the field and in low order it will look like:

$$F(M,T) = \mu M(x)^2 + \lambda M(x)^4, \tag{III.2.1}$$

where the parameter $\lambda > 0$ (the free energy is bounded)

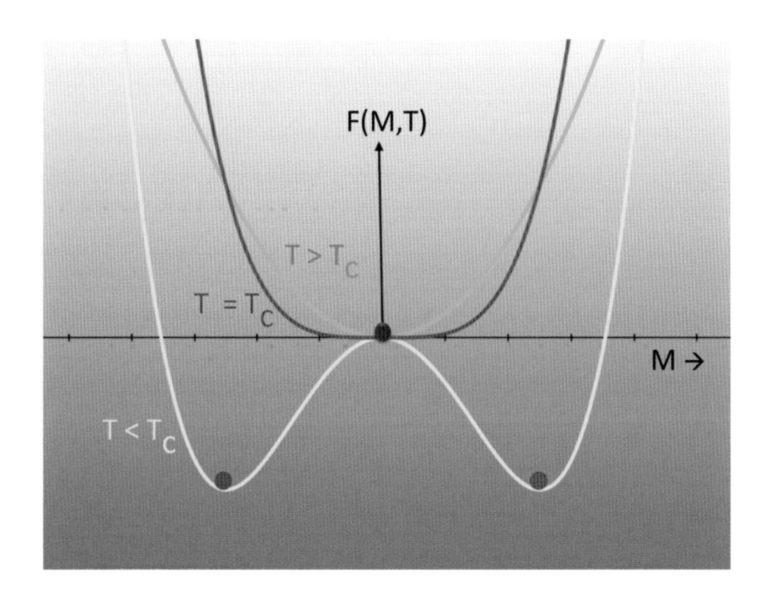

Figure III.2.14: *Second-order transition.* We have plotted the free energy F as a function of the order parameter M (magnetization) for three values of the temperature. At $T > T_c$ the symmetric minimum is at $M = 0$ (no magnetization). At $T < T_c$ the minimum is at $M \neq 0$ (spontaneous magnetization), and the system will 'choose' the red or the blue minimum. This is an example of *spontaneous* symmetry breaking.

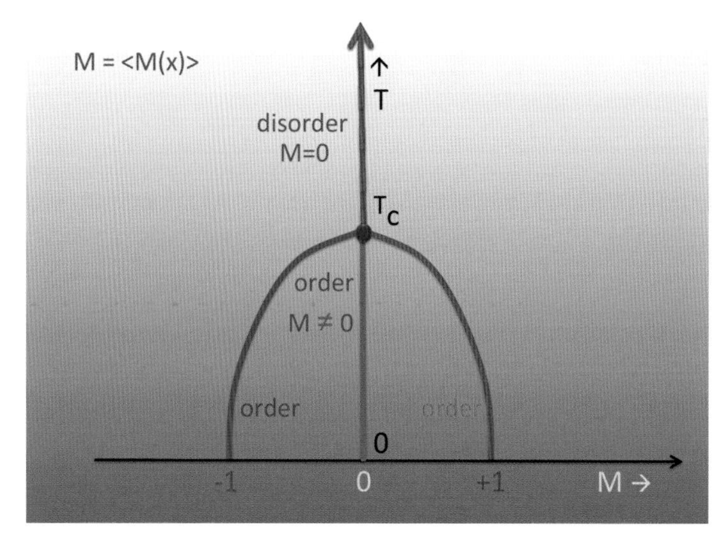

Figure III.2.15: *Ising model phase diagram.* The vertical axis is in fact the phase diagram of the Ising model (without external field). It has only one control parameter which is the temperature. We have plotted the average spontaneous magnetization as a function of temperature. If we lower the temperature the minima of the free energy in the previous figure trace out the blue and red curves giving M for $T < T_C$.

and the other parameter μ has a temperature dependence which near the critical point is given by $\mu = \mu_0(T - T_c)$. In Figure III.2.14 we have plotted the free energy $F(M, T)$ of the system as a function of the average magnetization and the temperature. We see from the figure that the minimum of the free energy for $T > T_c$ yields the value $M = 0$, and for $T < T_c$ we see that the minimum of the free energy corresponds to a non-zero value for M. The latter is the situation where the symmetry of F is spontaneously broken in the sense that the system has to choose one of the two degenerate groundstates, with all spins up or all spins down. For $T = T_c$ the system is in the critical state, where the free energy curve flattens out ($\mu = 0$). The vanishing of the quadratic curvature term means that the spin wave excitations have effectively a zero mass (they are 'gapless'). And this is what gives rise to the power law behavior of the correlation functions as we will discuss next.

In Figure III.2.15 we have summarized the results. Along the vertical axis we have a one-dimensional phase diagram with temperature as the only control parameter. For low temperature the phase is ordered, and above the critical temperature it is disordered. In the same graph we have plotted the order parameter, which is the magnetization M along the horizontal axis. The magnetization tends to $M = \pm 1$ as temperature goes to absolute zero. We see that the order parameter as a function of temperature changes continuously in this case, which means that we are dealing with a second-order phase transition.

Correlation functions. A meaningful probe of order and in particular of critical behavior are the spatial correlation functions for large distances. For the Ising model, one calculates the thermal average of the product of two spins σ_i and σ_j but now as a function of their separation $|i - j|$. The

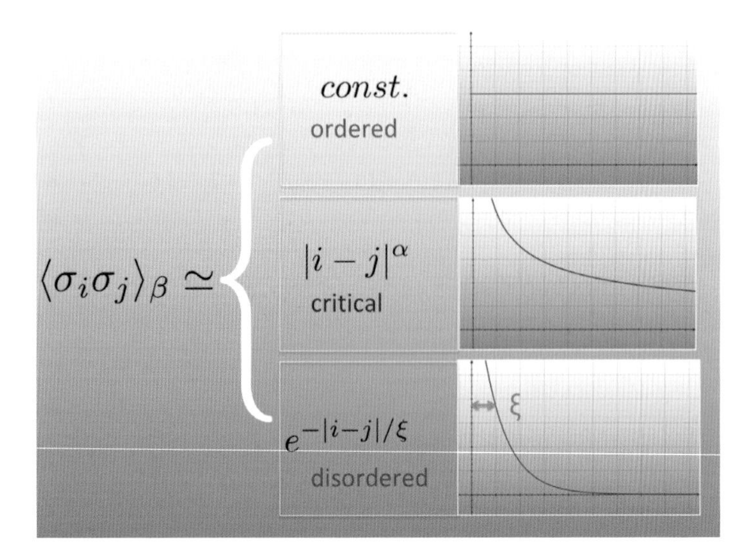

Figure III.2.16: *Correlation functions.* The typical behavior of the spin-spin correlation function $\langle\sigma_i\sigma_j\rangle_\beta$ in the three regimes of the Ising model.

expression is as follows:

$$f(i-j) = \langle\sigma_i\, \sigma_j\rangle_\beta\,. \qquad \text{(III.2.2)}$$

It is simplest to first consider the case at low temperature where there is long range order. This would be reflected in the correlation function to be a non-zero constant. On the other hand, if the system is disordered one expects the correlations to be short range, and indeed the the correlation function can be calculated to decay exponentially over a characteristic length called the *correlation length* ξ. We have summarized the distinct functional behavior of the correlation functions in the three regimes in Figure III.2.16.

Critical behavior. The behavior at the critical point, the phase transition itself, is of great interest. It turns out that the transitions show a high degree of *universality* The correlation functions for example, behave as *power laws*, which means that for large x they behave like $f(x) \simeq x^\alpha$. Such functions are characterized by a power α which is called a *critical exponent*. These exponents express the characteristic quantitative behavior of correlation functions in the critical state, between the ordered and disordered phase. In fact as we approach the critical point from the disordered side on finds that the correlation length $\xi(T)$ diverges, so, $\lim_{T\to T_c} \xi(T) \to \infty$. This is precisely why the exponential decay law in the disordered phase changes to a power law at the critical point.

Universality. It turns out that different types of systems have identical critical behavior meaning that they have the same set of critical exponents at the critical point. These exponents do not depend on the microscopic details of the model but rather on the number of dimensions and the symmetries of the system. The fundamental symmetry underlying second-order phase transitions is *scale* and *conformal invariance*, which can than be extended in various ways to obtain the different universal behaviours. So the critical behaviour of the 2 dimensional Ising model can for example be described on a free massless (Majorana) fermion field. Which means that the spin and energy correlation functions of the two models show exactly the same critical exponents. So it is also in this field of research that symmetry arguments can greatly advance your understanding observed phenomena. The critical exponents label the representations of the group of certain conformal symmetries in two-dimensions.

Anti-ferromagnetism. Now in magnetism there could be another type of order referred to as anti-ferromagnetism, where the neighboring spins tend to point in opposite directions. This corresponds to choosing the coupling parameter J in the energy expression to equal $J = -1$. The ordered, low temperature, lowest energy configuration now corresponds to a red/blue checkerboard configuration. And the magnetization as defined above would also give zero for this ordered phase. This just illustrates the fact that one has to have some clue or make an educated guess, about what the state looks like before one can come up with a sensible type of order parameter. Here we can the repair

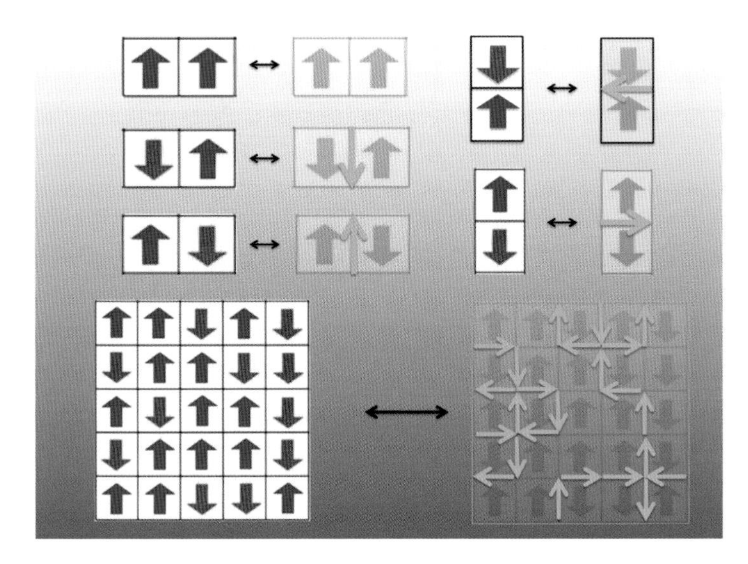

Figure III.2.17: *The loop representation of the Ising model.* We illustrate an equivalent or 'dual' representation of the Ising model where the states are represented as connected oriented paths along the links of the lattice. For any possible pair of neighbors there is a unique prescription. If the paths cross at some vertex there are always two arrows pointing towards and two arrows pointing away from the vertex.

the definition of the magnetization quite simply by adding an extra minus sign on all odd sites, for example. And – as we will see – there are ordered phases in the quantum regime where there no local order parameter can be defined.

Domain walls and defects. If we think again of the energy associated with a neighbouring pair, we have $\varepsilon = 0$ if the spins point in the same direction and $\varepsilon = 1$ if they are different. Now with this we can construct a *dual representation* of the Ising model, in terms of oriented contours along the edges of the (dual) lattice. We have depicted this correspondence in Figure III.2.17, For any pair of neighbors we draw an arrow along the edge they have in common if the spins are opposite, or no arrow if the spins are the same. If you now look at a large configuration, then the spin configuration uniquely corresponds to a configuration of oriented lines. There is one subtlety that is clear from the last picture in the figure, if two lines cross, then you always have two arrows pointing in and two out, and this in turn means that there are two options for how to connect the lines at the crossing. If we have a blue domain inside a red domain, that would yield a closed boundary oriented anti-clockwise, and if we exchange the colors, the orientation would flip to clockwise. This representation in terms of these boundary contours or *domain walls* immediately makes manifest where the energy is located. The walls cost energy (because they coincide with a pair of differing neighbors), and the total energy equals the total length of the domain walls. In the ferromagnetic ground state there are no walls, and therefore a domain wall is called a *defect*. It is a *topological defect*, away from the boundaries of the sample the walls form closed loops which cannot break. The loops can grow or shrink, they can join or break up, they can disappear or being created, but a wall cannot have an endpoint in the sample. So you can also think of the Ising model as a 'gas of loops', with the additional property that the loops don't intersect. You may check this by looking at any would-be intersection of the walls, and note that the two ingoing arrows can be connected to the two outgoing arrows only in two ways. Drawing these one finds that they do not cross, indeed. the loops avoid themselves and others.

A dual representation. The two dual representations, one by spin and the other by loop configurations, provide two complementary perspectives on order versus disorder. Starting in the ferromagnetic phase from zero temperature, there are no defects, and it is by raising the temperature that the loops are created, and by the time we are in the disordered state, the loops have 'condensed,' there are defects everywhere. A maximal energy state is one where there is a defect on every link which happens to correspond to a perfectly anti-ferromagnetic state. And indeed changing the sign of the neighbor-coupling J exactly exchanges the highest and lowest energy states of which there are two each.

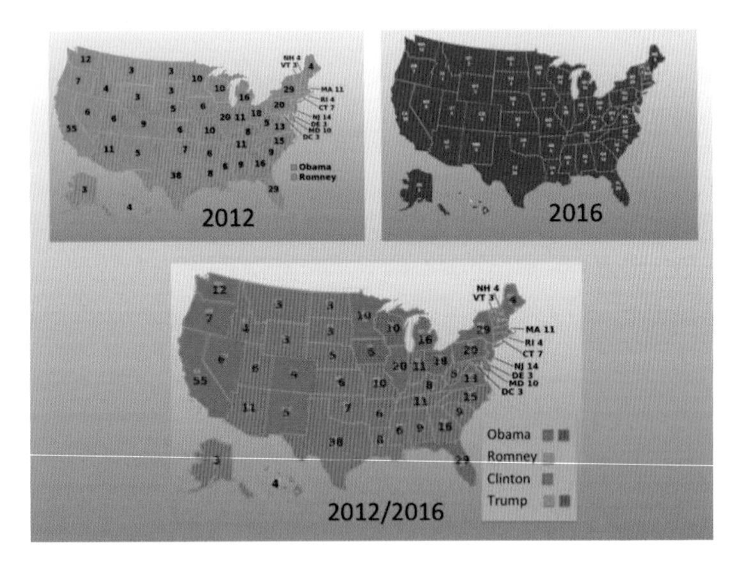

Figure III.2.18: *US voting patterns.* An Ising model representation of voting patters of the 2012 and 2016 elections. In the bottom figure you see the shift. Indeed the swing states are on the boundary, the shift involves moving the 2012 boundary. If you create a new island you are considered a defect and it costs a lot of energy, there is a high threshold. Building domain walls is also costly but not as expensive as creating a new domains.

These considerations illustrate a quite general principle, that defining a certain type of order in a system usually also implies the existence of certain types of defects, both topological and non-topological. This is not only true for spin systems but for most forms of order. As will be discussed in the next section, crystals for example have all kinds of defects, of which the *dislocations* and *disclinations* are the most well-known. These defects have their own dynamics, for example if we prepare the spin system starting from high temperatures by *quenching* it, meaning cooling it fast, then the loops will not have time enough to annihilate and the defects get frozen in. If, on the contrary, we cool it slowly, then we may end up with a perfect ground state as the defects had enough time to pair up and annihilate each other.

Swing states

G: Hey Orange! I really like that stuff you are talking about.
O: Thank you Green. It took me quite some effort to master this subject, so I am glad to hear you like it.
G: You know, Orange. I think this stuff may have great applications.
O: But Green, this is pure science just for the sake of ....
G: All that blue and red, that order and disorder, those arrows up and down. It really did make me think of the elections!
O: But Green, ...
G: Those walls, you know. And how hard it is to create blue bubbles in the red domains.
O: But Green, ...
G: You see, if you take the voting patterns of 2012 and you take those of 2016, and you look at what happened.
O: But Green, ...
G: Yes, Orange, yes! Look at that, the swing states are right there bordering on the walls. That's exactly where all their campaign money and energy went, and yes, that's where they got the walls moving. Chr chr.
O: Green! Stop it.
G: And no red bubbles in the blue, and no blue bubbles in the red. Just like you said.
O: That's no science, Green!
G: Hey those swing states are just defects, and nothing happens elsewhere.

O: Stop it!
G: I wouldn't call that a landslide! It's all in the margins, Orange. In spite of all excitement and heated discussions, we are dealing with Ising system at low temperature, with some domain walls frozen in. Don't you think that is a comforting thought.
O: Oh, Green, I wished I never told you.
G: The Ising model of voting! Chr chr. Maybe we should start working on that phase transition, Orange! I mean, what would it be like to live in an anti-ferromagnetic country? They call it disorder, but didn't you just say that it just a different type of order? You know, the colors mix well, and I didn't see a glass ceiling either. There are so many walls, that it is just like having none!
O: Oh no....
G: Oh Yes. I think we should start working on 2020 and 2024 elections including terms for fraud and outcome denial! Chr chr. □

It directly follows from simple energy considerations that it costs more to create a red site in the middle of a blue domain (four units of energy), while moving a red boundary, which means changing a blue to red site at a boundary always costs less. From this local energy perspective it is also clear that domain walls will have the tendency to straighten out.

Defect condensation and dual order. The state we have described as disordered, where the spins are randomly distributed, can be considered from the dual point of view as a state where there are defects all over the place. If we were to define a dual order parameter measuring the average number density of wall segments or links on the dual lattice, it would be non-zero. In other words, it is a kind of dually ordered phase where the defects have condensed.

Crystal lattices

Symmetry reigns. At low temperatures or high pressure atoms (or ions) tend to settle down in periodic arrays which correspond to a crystal lattice. A characteristic of such a lattice is that it is periodic, and there is a certain basic geometric pattern – called a *unit cell* – that repeats itself over and over again. So if you move the (infinite) lattice over a certain distance in certain directions it looks exactly the same, and the same is true if one rotates around certain axes by particular angles or reflects the lattice about in certain planes. The lattice can be characterized by the set of symmetry operations that leave the lattice invariant. These operations form intricate infinite discrete groups, consisting of discrete translations and rotations.

Wallpaper groups. The five basic space filling lattices in two dimensions and their corresponding space groups have been constructed, they form the so-called *wallpaper groups* and there are a total of seventeen of them.

The Bravais lattices. The space-filling crystal lattices have been classified by the nineteenth century French mathematician Auguste Bravais. In two dimensions there are five different lattices. In three dimensions there are seven basic lattices to which special points may be added, making a total of 14 Bravais lattices. Not surprisingly there is an awesome jargon that comes with them in order to distinguish them, involving terms like *cubic-face-centered, orthorhombic, triclinic, rhombohedral* and so on. In particular *cubic-face-centered* sounds to me like a fancy AI surveillance algorithm!

For the 14 space-filling, three-dimensional lattices, the space groups have been fully classified and everything is known about all 230 of them. This means that also the point groups preserving the unit cell in three dimensions are known and there are 32 of them.

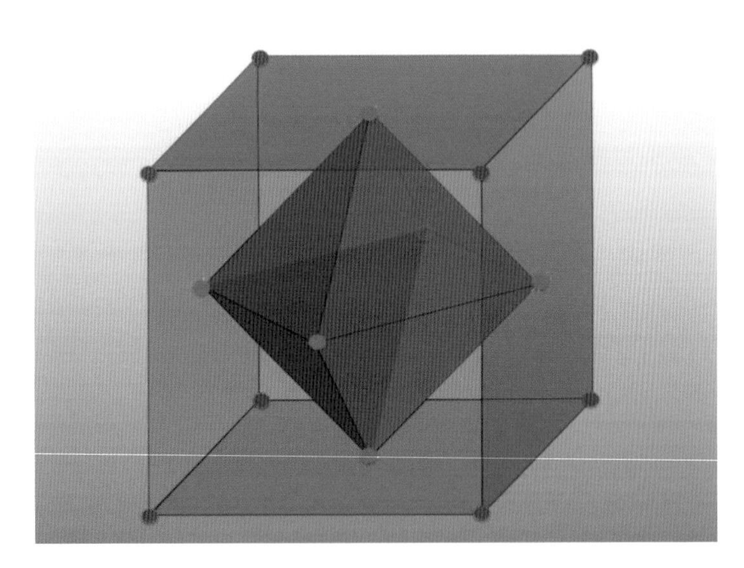

Figure III.2.19: *Symmetries of octahedron.* The embedded octahedron has the same symmetry group as the cube.

X-ray diffraction and more. Crystal lattices can be studied experimentally by short wavelength photons (X-rays). The X-rays scatter from the nuclei on the lattice sites and the scattered waves will interfere with one another. So whether we get reflection of diffraction depends on whether the interference of the many scattered waves is constructive or destructive. The crystal has planes of atoms in various directions and the photons may be diffracted or reflected depending on whether their momentum satisfies certain conditions which are determined by the specific geometrical properties of the lattice. From the reflection and diffraction patterns one can then reconstruct the geometry of the lattice.

This widely applied technique of studying molecular order whether it is lattices or complicated molecular structures like DNA[3] was invented by the British physicists William Henry Bragg and his son William Lawrence who shared the Nobel prize for Physics in 1915. The application of the technique to the complicated molecules of life was pioneered by Max Perutz, an Austrian refugee, who got a position at the Cavendish laboratory in Cambridge with the Braggs. Nowadays we can probe the surface of solids on atomic scales by advanced microscopes, the *scanning tunneling microscope* (STM) or the *atomic field microscope* (AFM). But the 3-D imaging is still of the diffractive type. These probing techniques are – not surprisingly – based on quantum principles themselves.

There is the remarkable fact that if you want to probe nature at some scale then nature often also provides you with the tools which are operative at the same scale, that allow you to build suitable probing devices. It is a matter of giving and taking. This is true for atoms with visible light, for nuclear structure using nuclei (alpha particles), and is true for genetic manipulation using all sorts of enzymes etc.

Kitchen salt or the cube. Let us now look in more detail at some three-dimensional lattices. A well-known example in three dimensions is the kitchen salt or sodium chloride (NaCl) crystal, which is a simple cubic lattice with the sodium and chloride atoms occupying alternating sites (see Figure III.2.20(c)). The *point group* of the cubic lattice, which is the symmetry group of the cube, is surprisingly rich and consists of 24 elements. As indicated in Figure III.2.20(d), it has four threefold axes (rotations around main diagonals), three fourfold axes (around lines through centers of opposite faces), and six twofold axis (through centers of opposite edges). This group is denoted by O and called the octahedral group, because it is also the symmetry group of the octahedron obtained by drawing the planes through the face centers of the cube, as one may see from Figure III.2.19. Indeed, correcting for the identity element we verify that the group has indeed $1+3\times 3+4\times 2+6\times 1=24$ elements. The transformations we discussed so far are all rotations, but there is one more transformation that leaves the cube invariant,

[3]There is the (in)famous story that Francis Crick and James D. Watson discovered the structure of DNA in 1953 after Maurice Wilkins had shown them a diffraction pattern measured by Rosalind Franklin at King's College London. It held the clue to the spatial structure of the double helix.

(a) The *Cubic Space Division* by M. Escher. It is invariant under translations by the lattice constant a along the x, y and z axes. (© 2023 The M.C. Escher Company.)

(b) Kitchen salt crystals of about 10 micrometers. Image taken with environmental scanning electron microscope (ESEM) at 950° C.

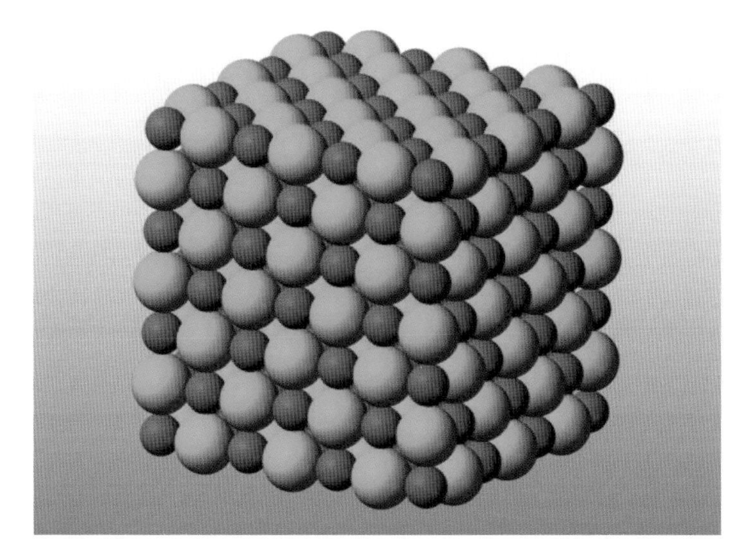

(c) The crystal of kitchen salt or sodium chloride ($NaCL$). It is a simple cubic lattice with alternating sodium (purple) and chloride (green) ions.(Source: MIF Univ. of Calgary.)

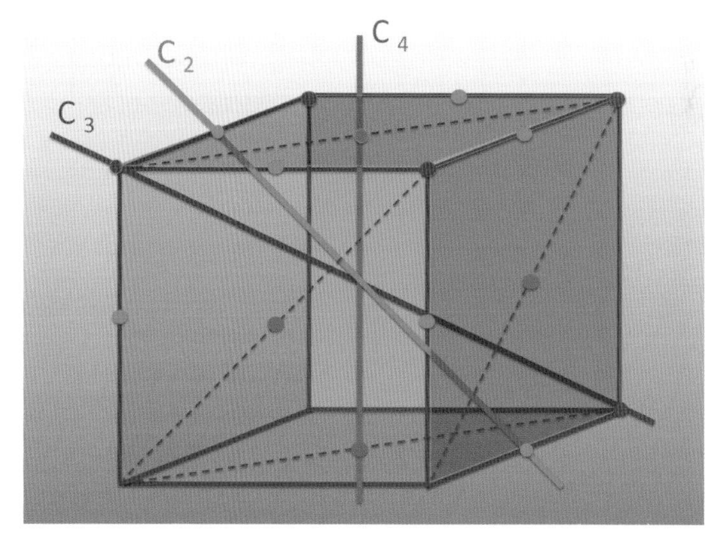

(d) The symmetries of a cube. It has three fourfold axes (blue), four threefold axes (red) and six twofold axes (green). The set of all transformations that leave the cube invariant is the *orthohedral group* O; it has 24 elements.

Figure III.2.20: *The symmetries of the cube.*

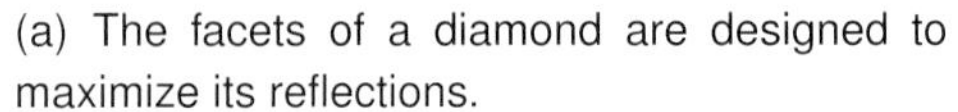

(a) The facets of a diamond are designed to maximize its reflections.

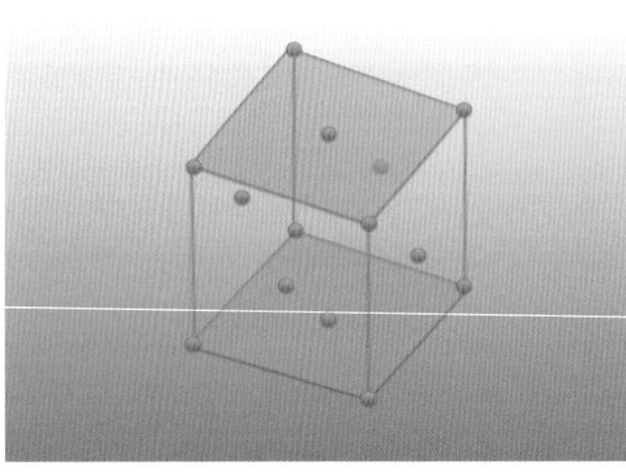

(b) A cubic face-centered (fcc) lattice cell.

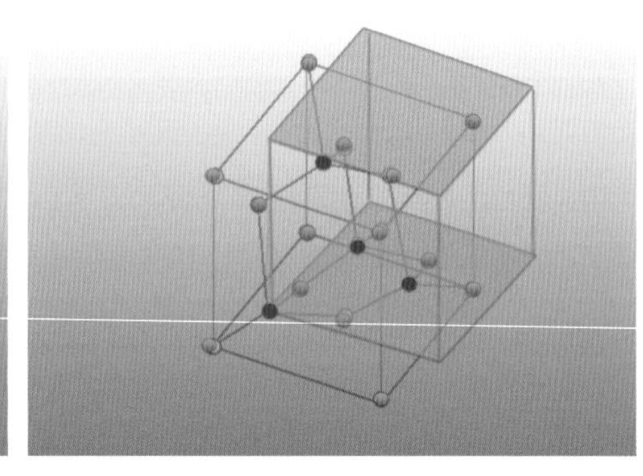

(c) A second fcc lattice superimposed at the point $(\frac{1}{4}, \frac{1}{4}, \frac{1}{4})$ in blue.

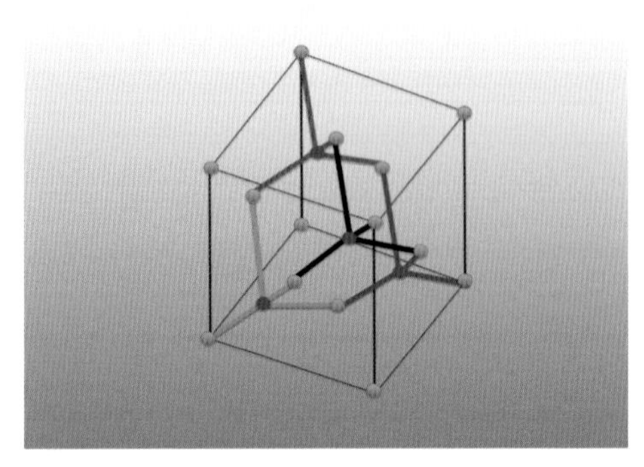

(d) The resulting diamond lattice as a stacking of tetrahedra.

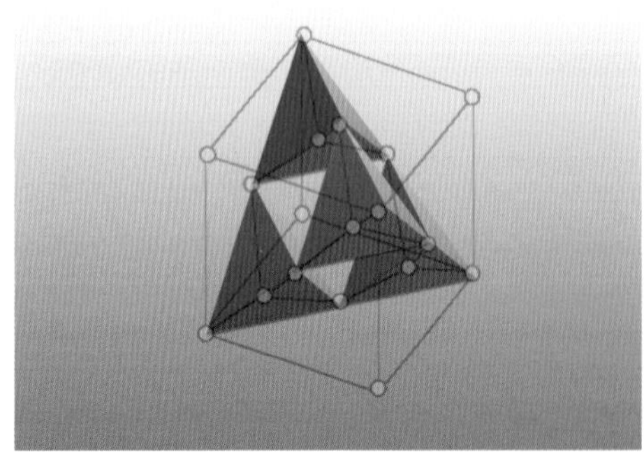

(e) The lattice as a stacking of planes with tetrahedra (with center).

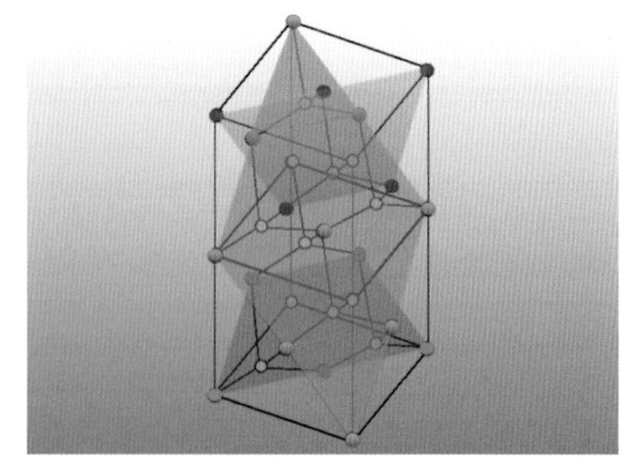

(f) The lattice stacking of planar triangular lattices.

Figure III.2.21: *The diamond lattice.* The intricate diamond lattice and some ways to look at it which display different aspects of its symmetry.

namely inverting all coordinates, which amounts to mirroring every point of the cube in the origin. This is called the *inversion* or *parity* operation P. If we add this transformation, we get a group denoted by $\mathrm{O_h}$ with 48 elements. This group is non-abelian (not all elements commute with each other) as one can easily check.

Diamond. Crystal lattices clearly exhibit intricate and aesthetically pleasing features and coincidences. A nice example is the diamond lattice which is more involved and we explore different perspectives on it in Figure III.2.21. The structure is built-up of two cubic face-centered (fcc) lattices which are shifted with respect to one another (III.2.21(b) and III.2.21(c)). The result is a perfect three-dimensional stacking of tetrahedra (III.2.21(d) and III.2.21(e)): the corners are all on the first fcc lattice while the centers are on the second fcc lattice. The lattice can therefore also be viewed as a stacking of planes with tetrahedra. One can go one step further and think of the whole lattice as a stacking of pairs of strictly identical triangular lattices, one of each fcc lattice. In Figure III.2.21(f) we show the three top layers of subsequent pairs, which all belong to the first fcc lattice. Projecting all the points down along the body diagonal, which is perpendicular to the layers one finds that there are three inequivalent triangular lattices in the figure corresponding to the blue, red and green layers.

The uses of symmetry. It turns out that the symmetry group tells us a lot about the physics of the system; it not only characterizes the stable equilibrium or ground state, but also provides a natural labelling of the low energy modes that can propagate through the system. The symmetry teaches us also about properties of the spectrum of electrons. And finally the symmetry group of the lattice determines the possible lattice imperfections or *defects* that may occur.

As we live in three-dimensional space most of us will agree that our analysis should stop there. The classification of space groups and lattices in higher dimensions is to be considered a mathematical pastime at best. But nature had a surprise in store. Who would have expected that higher-dimensional regular lattices would rear their heads also in our three-dimensional world in the guise of so-called *quasicrystals*.

This provides another striking example of the 'unreasonable effectiveness of mathematics in the natural sciences,' which refers to the title of a famous lecture by Eugene Wigner who got the Physics Nobel prize in exactly for his work on group theory and its many applications in quantum theory. We will return to quasicrystals towards the end of this section.

Crystalization and symmetry breaking

We introduced and expanded on the concept of symmetry breaking in Chapter II.6. It has many beautiful applications in condensed matter, and in particular also in the theory of crystallography. In this section we explore two representative examples.

The concept. Suppose one of the atoms in a simple cubic lattice is of a different type, say it is has a different color, then we may ask for the transformations that leave not only the cube invariant but also keep the colored atom in place. For this case the answer is quite obvious from Figure III.2.20(d). If we ask which transformations leave not only the center but also one of the red dots in place, then we are only left with a single threefold axis. This means that the rotation group $\mathrm{G} = \mathrm{O}$ is reduced to, or as is often said, *broken* to, $\mathrm{H} = \mathrm{C}_3$. This reduction of the symmetry from a group G to the so-called *residual symmetry group* H, which is a subgroup G, means that certain degeneracies in the spectrum that occurred in the unbroken situation will now be lifted. So one could say that breaking the symmetry allows for less uniformity and more differentiation.

Symmetry breaking is therefore an invaluable tool to analyse and interpret experimental data. In particular if we have certain external parameters we can change, like temperature or electric or magnetic fields, it may be that what appeared as one state breaks up in a set of different states. Then different states with the same energy may split up in states with different energies, much in the way we discussed in Chapter I.4 in relation to the Zeeman effect. There the spherical symmetry of the atom was broken by the direction of the external magnetic field, and the spectral line was split because the degeneracy of the states was lifted. Symmetry breaking may also happen spontaneously if one lowers the temperature, as is the case with 'spontaneous magnetization' in a magnet as described by the Ising model. Even without an external magnetic field the spins may line up because of their local ferrromagnetic interactions.

You now may also understand that the formation of a lattice itself, the process of crystallization, is an example of spontaneous symmetry breaking. You should think of starting with a liquid which we envisage as a continuum. If you are at some point in the liquid it looks the same, independently of what point you chose, and it looks also the same in all directions. A simple fluid is therefore said to be *homogeneous* and *isotropic*. This translates in the statement that the symmetry of a simple liquid consist of all rotations by any amount about any axis, and also of translations in any direction by any amount. Clearly this group is continuous and is called the *Euclidean group* E_3 of three-dimensional rotations and translations we mentioned before. It is the symmetry group of empty three-dimensional Euclidean space. So crystallization is a process where the symmetry gets broken from the Euclidean group to the symmetry group of the lattice, which is a discrete subgroup of E_3.

Goldstone modes. We have in the section on symmetry breaking of Chapter II.6 mentioned how breaking of a continuous (global) symmetry leads to the existence of massless modes. This is precisely what happens upon crystallization, where the Euclidean group gets broken to the discrete lattice group. The low energy modes correspond to the sound modes that can propagate through the crystal. They are the Goldstone modes which are associated with the breaking of the continuous translational symmetries of the perfect fluid. In Figure III.2.22 we give the pictorial account. From (a) to (b) the crystallization takes place. In Figure (c) we have sketched a sound mode corresponding to a longitudinal pressure or density wave that propagates through the crystal.

Topological defects. There is an additional observable consequence of broken symmetry in the situation we are discussing. Broken symmetries manifest themselves not only in lifting degeneracies and the presence of particular low energy modes, but also in the presence of *defects*, called lattice defects in the case at hand. The theory predicts that if we break the continuous group E_3 to the discrete group of the cubic lattice, we have line defects that we in principle can label by the elements of the symmetry group of the lattice. In a crystal we typically distinguish two kinds: translational defects called *dislocations* and rotational defects called *disclinations*. We have illustrated them for a two-dimensional lattice in the pictures (d) and (e) of Figure III.2.22.

Dislocation. In the bottom left Figure III.2.22(d) the dark atom is special, since it marks the endpoint of an extra vertical layer that does not go all the way up. Note that far away from the marked atom the lattice has restored itself to its normal unperturbed form. The marked atom is an irregularity, a defect. How do you quantify the defect? In this case you should compare the near environment of a normally positioned atom with that of a defect. If you walk around a normal atom like the one marked in the upper left corner, following the blue arrows you see that it takes 8 steps to get back. If you take 8 steps around the defect site, you go one step too far, and you have to move back by one lattice vector (marked in yellow). This translational

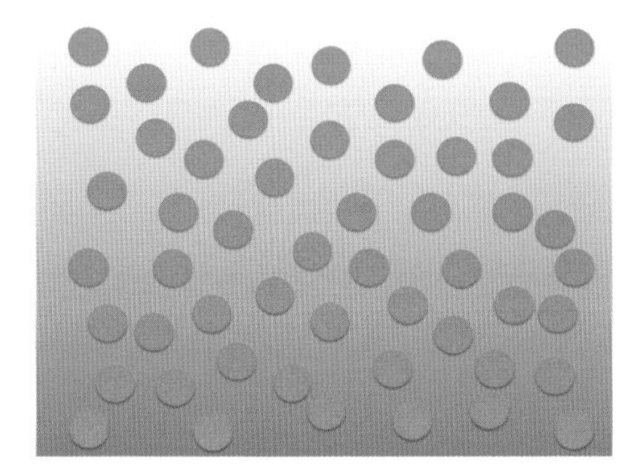

(a) A gas or liquid made of simple atoms. It has no long range order and therefore effectively a continuous translational and rotational symmetry.

(b) Upon cooling the atoms may 'freeze' and form a regular lattice. The symmetry corresponds to a *space group* consisting of discrete translations and rotations.

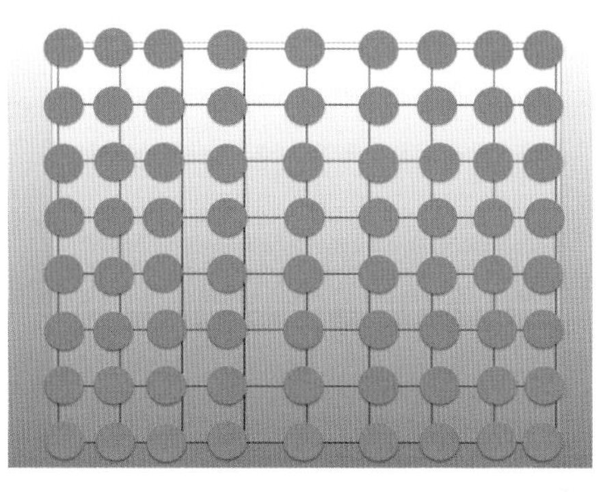

(c) A sound wave propagating horizontally. Sound is a periodic density fluctuation in the direction of the motion (longitudinal). The atoms are coherently moved out of their equilibrium position.

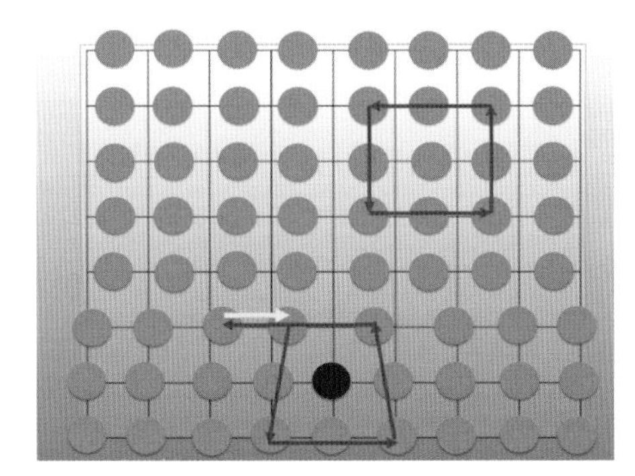

(d) The empty site is a *translational defect*, also called a *dislocation*, because when going around it in 8 steps one's position is shifted by one lattice distance. As indicated, away from the defect the lattice is restored.

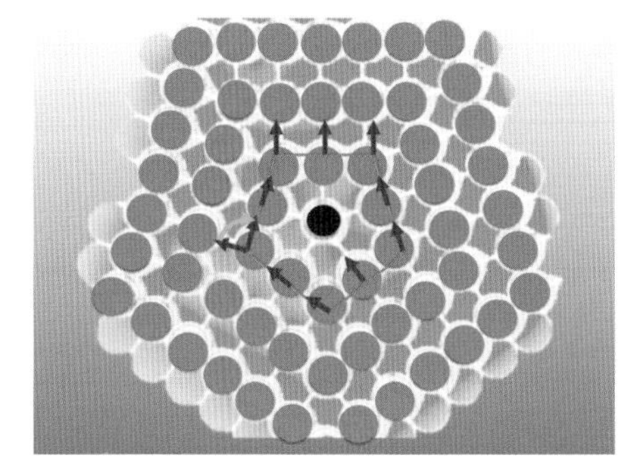

(e) A *rotational defect* (disclination) related to a rotation over an angle of 90° . One sees the defect angle if one carries a little vector tied to the local lattice frame around the defect. Starting on the left we obtain a defect angle of 90° .

Figure III.2.22: *Defects and broken symmetry.* We show two types of lattice defects in a simple two-dimensional crystal.

defect is thus labeled by a translation vector (also called a Burger's vector), and that elementary translation corresponds to a basic element of the discrete translation part of the lattice group. One encounters this one step dislocation on *any* loop around the defect location. Therefore the defect is uniquely labeled by this group element.

It is easy to imagine that in the process of crystallization such dislocations may form spontaneously. The number of dislocations one finds will depend on how fast we cool the system down. It is clear from the picture that the defect locally deforms the lattice and therefore will carry a certain amount of extra energy. The dislocation in two dimensions is a point defect, and it is stable for a topological reason. You may be able to move it around, but you cannot smoothen it out locally. You can think of the dislocation to be connected (via the extra layer) to either the boundary of the sample or to an 'anti-defect', which means that these defects are locally stable but can annihilate with an anti-defect.

Disclination. In the bottom right picture we show a disclination or rotational defect. This defect is labeled by the 'defect angle' you encounter as you parallel transport a local lattice vector (or frame) around the defect. If in the figure we take the local blue vector smoothly along the green path around the defect and return to the starting position, the vector has rotated over an angle of 90°, and again this is an element of the symmetry group of the lattice. This analysis reminds us of our considerations in the section on curved spaces in Chapter I.2, where we discussed this characteristic and called it a non-trivial *holonomy*. It requires a lot of energy to make a disinclination. They may spontaneously form in small samples, and alternatively you can also imagine 'growing' the crystal starting from the impurity outward. That way the fivefold symmetry would be introduced 'by hand.' It is not a lattice in the normal sense because the translational symmetry is broken right from the start of the growing process, that is the price for having a fivefold rotation symmetry in the plane.

Liquid crystals

We have alluded to the importance of the shapes of constituent particles for understanding their collective behavior. This hidden underlying geometry is one of the keys to the diversity that is displayed in properties of materials. In the previous section we showed that these shapes can often be translated into symmetries or their breaking. A splendid example of this are the types of order/disorder that arise in soft condensed matter physics, in particular the subject of *liquid crystals* and *nematics*. With the language of symmetry at hand we are able to give some qualitative characteristics of the materials straightforwardly. The examples are quite easy to visualize and are used to further illuminate the rather abstract notion of symmetry breaking.

Partial order. As mentioned, an ordinary lattice is an example where we break the continuous Euclidean group E_3 down to an infinite discrete group of translations and rotations. It is not so hard to imagine that media can have strange mixtures of order and disorder which are in between a liquid and a crystal. In such cases the translational symmetry is not broken but the rotational symmetry is: the system is partially ordered. These types of systems can easily be visualized by assuming that the building blocks have simple geometric properties, for example they are like tiny rods or pancakes or tetrahedra.

Nematics and smectics. In Figure III.2.23 we illustrate various possibilities if the constituents are rod-shaped. They can form an ordinary liquid or a fully ordered crystal, with both translational and rotational order. In Figure III.2.23(c), however, they form a two- or three-dimensional structure which preserves orientational order with translational symmetry, which is a liquid crystal called a *nematic*. The next picture shows another realization: the rods are oriented along the z direction. Furthermore the rods form strict horizontal layers, but within the layers there is free motion.

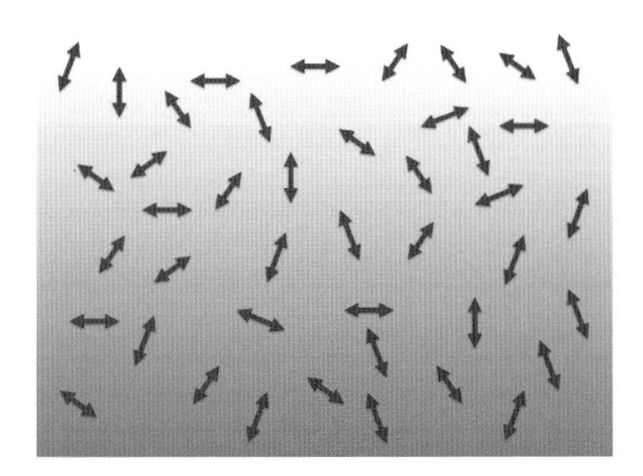

(a) A nematic liquid made of simple rod-shaped atoms. It has no long range order and therefore effectively a continuous translational and rotational symmetry.

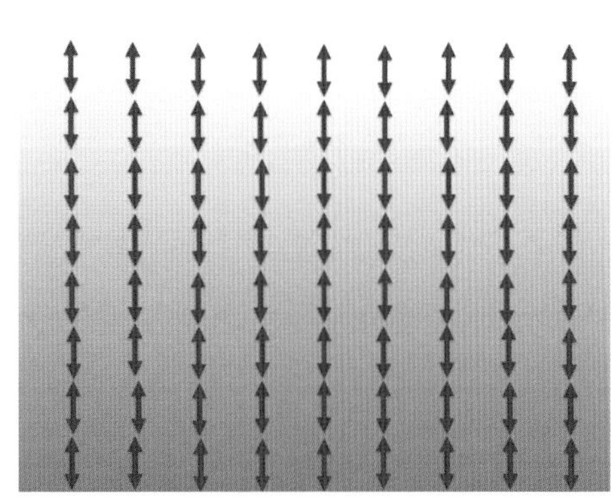

(b) Upon cooling the atoms may 'freeze' and form a regular lattice. Translational and rotational symmetries are broken to a discrete space group consisting of discrete translations and 180° rotations only.

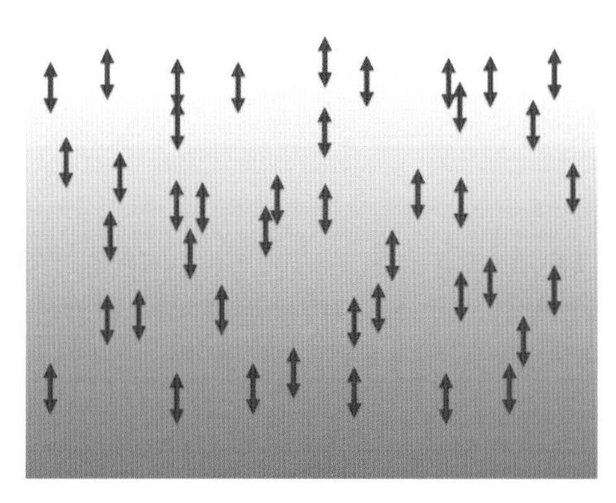

(c) A liquid crystal in which there is still complete translational symmetry, but the rotational symmetry is broken. Such a phase is called *nematic*. There is no positional order but there is orientational order.

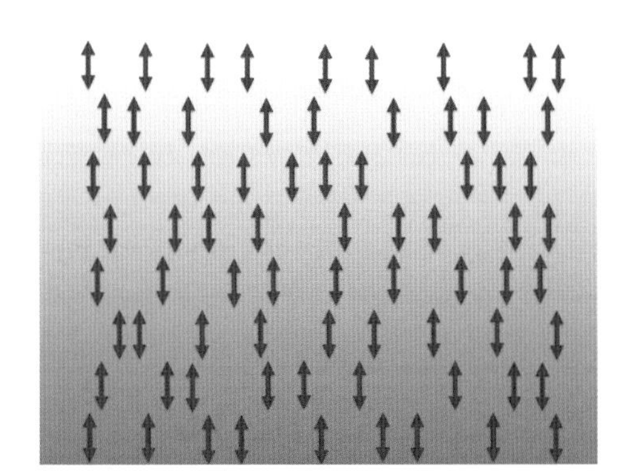

(d) This system is called a *smectic*. It is anisotropic, as it is made up of independent layers in which the horizontal translational symmetry is still manifest, but in the vertical direction it is ordered. There is complete orientational order.

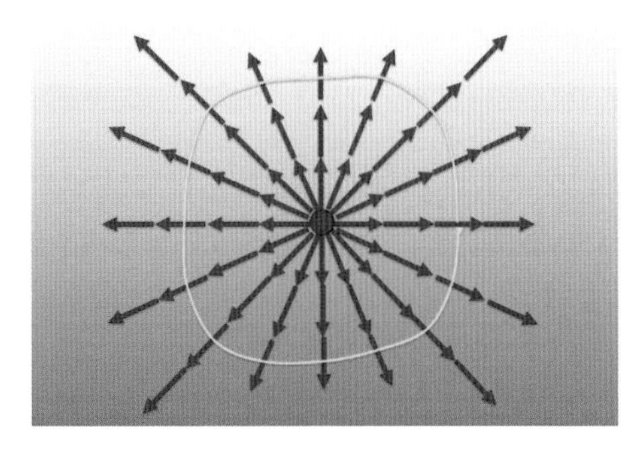

(e) A rotational defect (a *vortex*) as it exists in an ordered spin system (represented by ordinary arrows), related to a rotation over an angle of 360°. This is observed if one follows the direction of the spin vector if one moves around the defect.

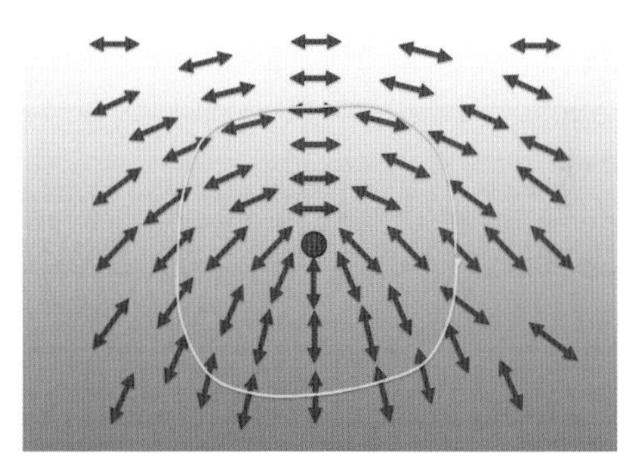

(f) This is a rotational defect in a nematic of rods. It is called a *half-vortex* as it corresponds to a defect angle of 180°. This defect is not possible in a spin system like in (e), going around the direction of the spin arrow would point in the opposite direction.

Figure III.2.23: *Nematics.* Various types of two-dimensional order in a *nematic* system made up of rod-shaped molecules.

This structure is called a *smectic*. A third possibility (not depicted) is called a *uniaxial nematic*, where the rods are vertically stacked in thin filaments. In the direction of the filaments there is the translational order of stacking, but there is no horizontal order across the filaments.

Defects. In Figures III.2.23(e) and III.2.23(f) we have depicted two rotational defects, the first one is an ordinary point defect one may encounter in a two-dimensional spin system or vector field, but of course it can also exist in a nematic. The signature of the defect is that parallel transporting a vector along a closed loop around the defect the spin rotates over 360° as indicated in the figure. The last picture shows a 'half-vortex', and we see that the configuration is smooth in spite of the fact that the rod rotates only over 180° when taken around. So it is a point-like defect. This configuration will not form in a spin system because there would necessarily be a discontinuity along a line starting from the defect and ending at the boundary. Such a line would cost much energy and that suppresses the formation. One way to look at this is to say that the half- vortices are 'confined' in the ordered two-dimensional spin system. Indeed, if one cools a spin or nematic liquid rapidly through the transition one usually finds many of the allowed point defects in the (partially) ordered system.

We have illustrated the idea of liquid crystals with a very simple example, but it should be clear that there is an unlimited arsenal of variations and alternatives that has been very actively been pursued for example under the name *polymer physics*. As we mentioned Pierre-Gilles de Gennes of the College de France made many invaluable contributions to the early exploration and further development of this field of research.

Quasicrystals

Tilings of the plane. In Figure III.2.24 we have depicted some tilings of the plane by simple regular polygons.[4] It works perfectly for triangles, squares and hexagons, but with pentagons (Figure III.2.24(c)) it doesn't quite fit and one cannot tile the plane. A consequence of this is that in the diffraction patterns there can be no signature of a fivefold symmetry. In three dimensions something similar happens, since it is not possible to fill space by stacking dodecahedra which do have fivefold symmetries. The Bravais lattices we discussed before do not admit any fivefold axes and therefore the diffraction patterns of periodic crystals can only have two-, three-, four-, and sixfold symmetries and not have a fivefold symmetry.

It was a big surprise therefore, when in 1982 the Israeli physicist Daniel Shechtman actually observed a clear diffraction pattern that appeared to come from a perfect crystal but nevertheless showed a manifest fivefold symmetry, like the pattern displayed in Figure III.2.26(c). How could that be? Could there be a nice Bragg diffraction pattern coming from some non-periodic structure? Yes indeed, it turned out that a nice but not perfect diffraction pattern could be generated not only by a perfectly periodic, but also by a non-periodic structure. The system of Shechtman was clearly perfectly ordered, otherwise there would not be such a clear diffraction pattern, but could not be periodic, because that is incompatible with the fivefold symmetry. With his observations the new field of quasi(periodic)-crystals was born. Shechtman received the Nobel prize in Chemistry in 2011 for his remarkable discovery which caused a paradigm shift in the well-established field of crystallography.

Non-periodic tilings. An instance of a quasi-periodic structure is a tiling of the plane by two types of *rombhi*, de-

[4] A regular polygon has equal angles and is equilateral.

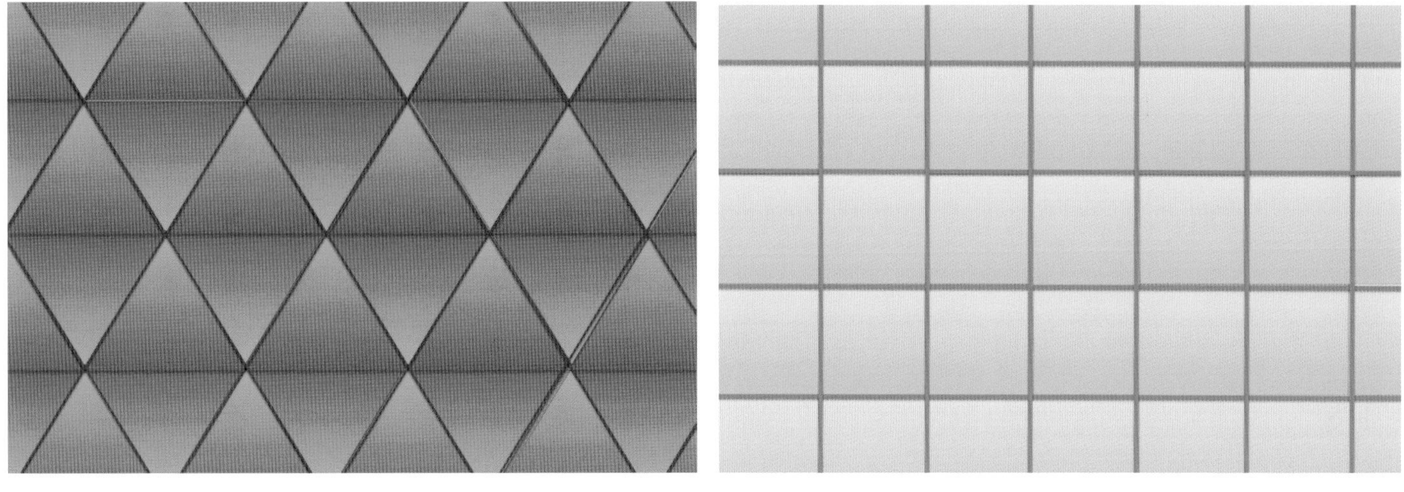

(a) A triangular tiling of the plane.

(b) A square tiling of the plane.

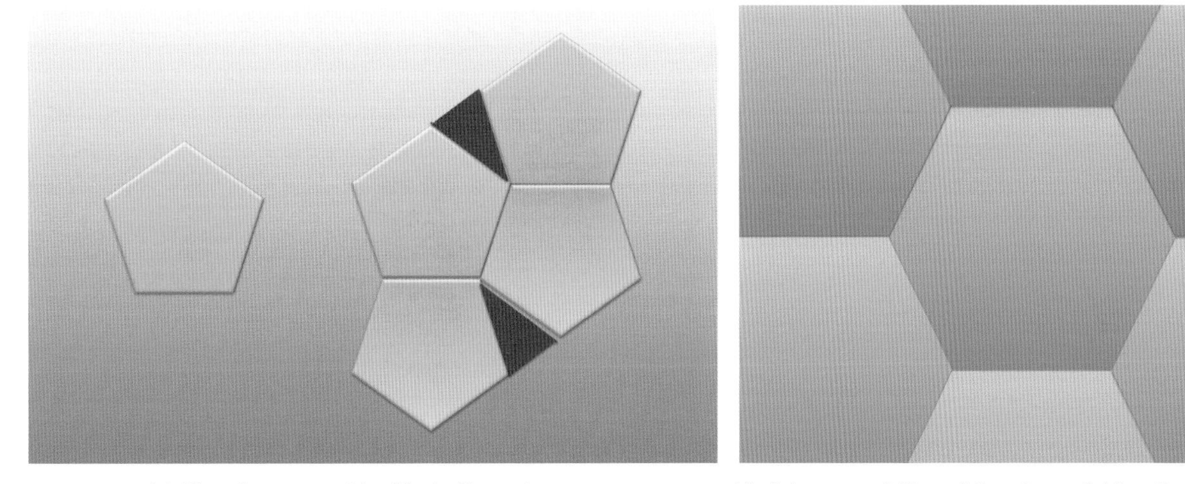

(c) The plane cannot be filled with pentagons.

(d) A hexagonal tiling of the plane. Adding the centers would make it a triangular lattice like (a) again.

Figure III.2.24: *Polygon tilings.* Possible and impossible polygon tilings of the plane. The regular tilings have discrete translational and rotational symmetries plus reflection symmetries in certain planes.

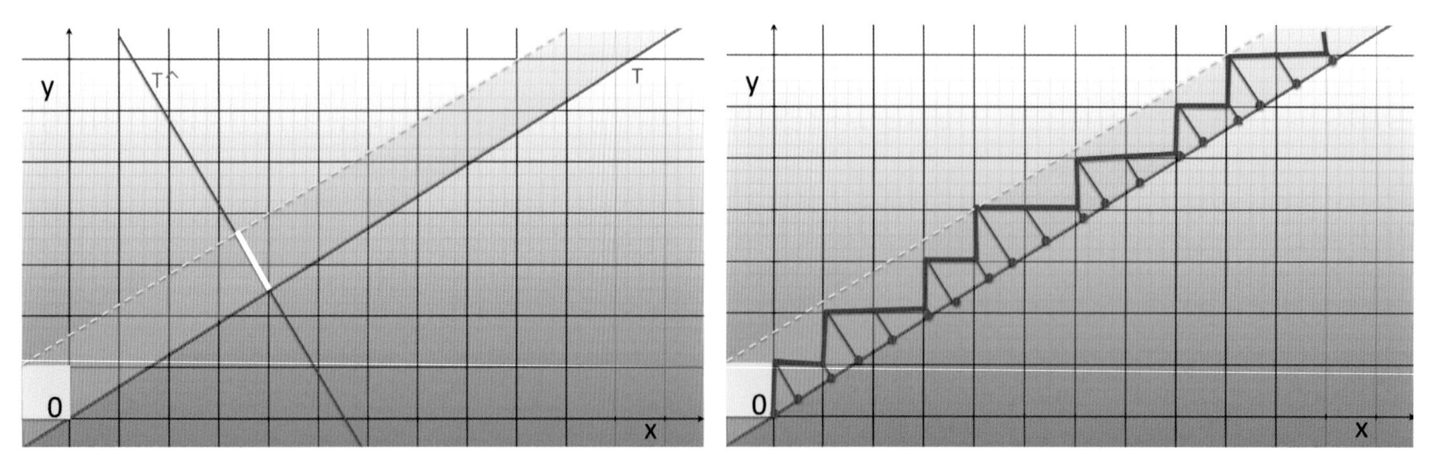

(a) The projection method to obtain a non-periodic tilings. A strip is constructed shifting the basic cell along the subspace T on which one wants to project, and the white segment (subspace) is the intersection of the strip with $T^{\perp}$.

(b) All lattice points in the strip are projected on T producing a non-periodic 'tiling' of the red line (space).

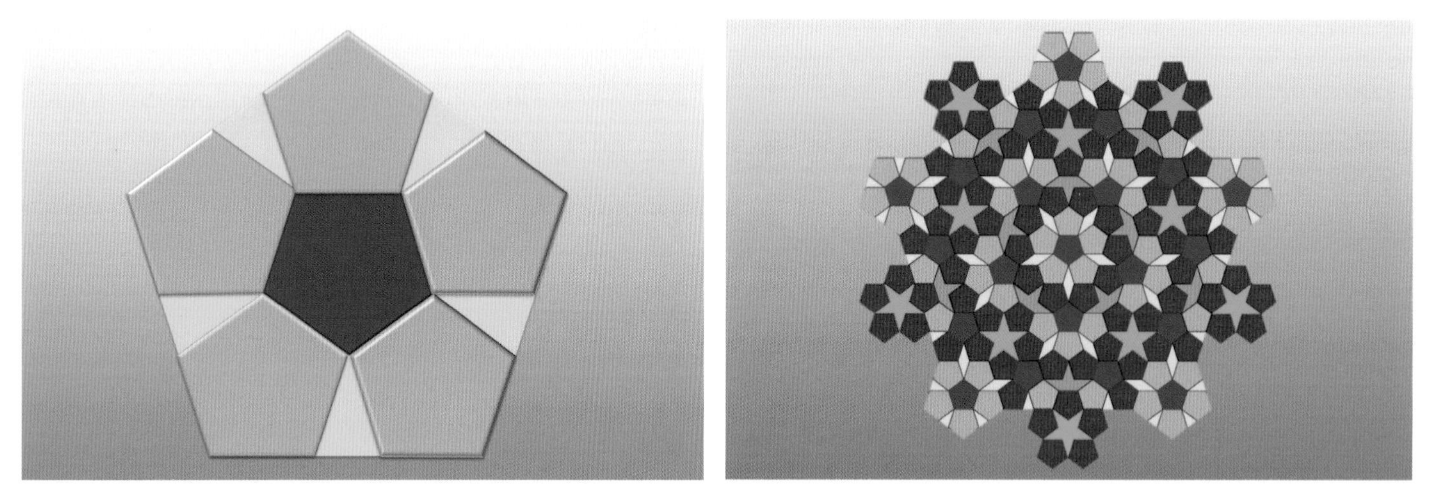

(c) A pentagon filled with six smaller pentagons. Embedding six pentagons into a larger one can be repeated indefinitely, to generate the Penrose tiling P1.

(d) The Penrose tiling P1. The tiling is *self-similar* and basically a *fractal*. Translational invariance has been given up in favor of scale invariance.

Figure III.2.25: *Non-periodic tilings.* Non-periodic but scale invariant tilings of the line and of the plane.

picted in Figure III.2.26(a). This tiling has an approximate fivefold local symmetry. The mathematics of these non-periodic tilings has been developed by the British mathematical physicist Roger Penrose in the early 1970's.[5] They are remarkable in that there is no translation which leaves the tiling invariant. They can have reflection symmetry and for example a fivefold rotation symmetry. But the Penrose tilings have another more subtle so-called scaling symmetry, which means that from any point in the tiling you can blow up or shrink the tiling by a certain amount and it will fit again. This means that such patterns are *self-similar*: they repeat themselves on larger and larger scales and are therefore a special kind of so-called *fractals*.

A one-dimensional Fibonacci tiling. One way to obtain quasicrystals or quasi-periodic tilings is by projecting regular periodic lattices from higher dimensions. We have illustrated this in Figure III.2.25. The top two pictures illustrate the method of going from a simple two-dimensional square lattice to a non-periodic one-dimensional 'lattice'. One first defines the 'physical' one-dimensional space T like the red line in the figures. In this example the line has a slope $2/(1+\sqrt{5})$, which is equal to the inverse of the Golden Mean. This slope is an irrational number which ensures that it will never go through a point of the lattice and that guarantees that the sequence is not periodic. The following step is to shift the two-dimensional unit cell along T, and this defines the light shaded strip along T. Next one projects all lattice points in the strip parallel to the orthogonal subspace $T^{\perp}$ on T and one gets a non-periodic covering of the line by line segments of only two distinct lengths, being the two different one-dimensional tile types. The sequence of short (s) and long (l) segments forms a so-called *Fibonacci chain*: sl, sll, $slsll$, $sllslsll$, $\ldots$. Each next entry of the sequence is obtained by joining the previous two, which makes the sequence as a whole 'self similar'. Every finite sequence is repeated an infinite number of times, but that does not imply that the chain is periodic. There is also an alternative way to construct the sequence through some 'growing' algorithm. This is a general method that can be used to generate any Penrose tiling, and is referred to as the *substitution* or *inflation method*. This is beyond the scope of this book and we will not discuss it in any more detail.

[5] Penrose received the Nobel prize for Physics in 2020, not for his 'tilings' but for 'his discovery that black hole formation is a robust prediction of the general theory of relativity.'

The two-dimensional Penrose tiling P1. Let me now give you an idea how one can obtain a non-periodic tiling in two dimensions with a fivefold symmetry by the projection method. We start with a five-dimensional simple cubic lattice. This lattice evidently has a fivefold symmetry rotating about the diagonal of the hypercube, where the corners on the five coordinate axes are rotated into each other. This is just like the threefold axes of the three-dimensional cube depicted in Figure III.2.20(d). We choose the physical space as a plane that is orthogonal to the fivefold axis. We then move the hypercube over the plane to obtain a five-dimensional layer. All lattice points and edges in that layer can now be projected orthogonally on the two-dimensional physical space, and then a tiling like the Penrose tiling $P1$ of Figure III.2.25(d) results. The figure shows that $P1$ needs four types of tiles to fill the plane: the 'pentagon', the 'star', the 'boat' (half star) and the 'lozenge'. The tiling has an approximate 'local' fivefold rotational symmetry.

The projection method allows us to generate all the two- and three-dimensional Penrose tilings. From the figure one may correctly guess that also the $P1$ tiling also can be constructed from a concentric 'growing' algorithm. Not surprisingly the topic of quasicrystals has given rise to a prolific mathematical literature.

The projection method is due to Paul Steinhardt of the University of Pennsylvania, while the growing algorithmic approach was worked out in detail by the British mathematician John Horton Conway and Roger Penrose himself.

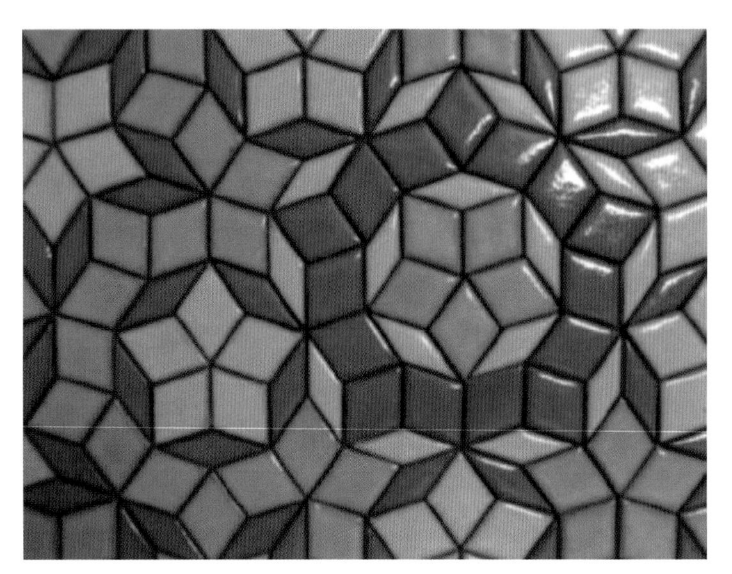

(a) A quasi-periodic tiling of the plane with fivefold symmetry with two types of rhombi. The sharp angles of the rhombi are 72 and 36 degrees.

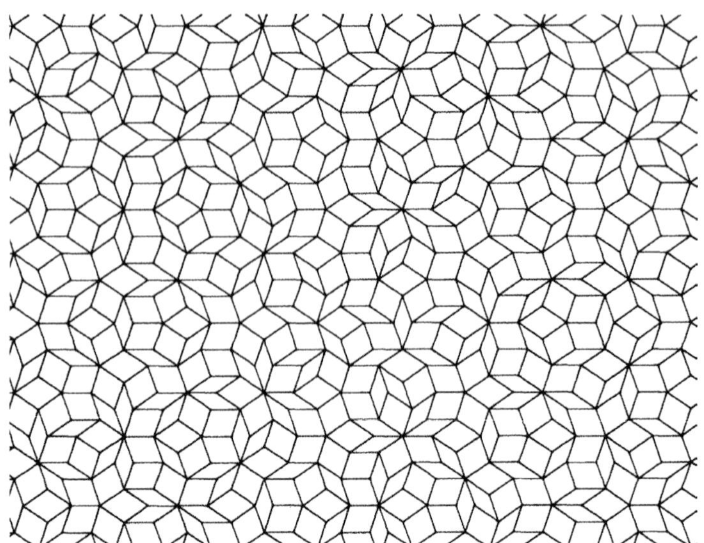

(b) The (Penrose) quasi-periodic tiling (P3) of the plane with a *'local'* fivefold symmetry. It is possible to completely cover the plane by this arrangement with only two different types of tiles.

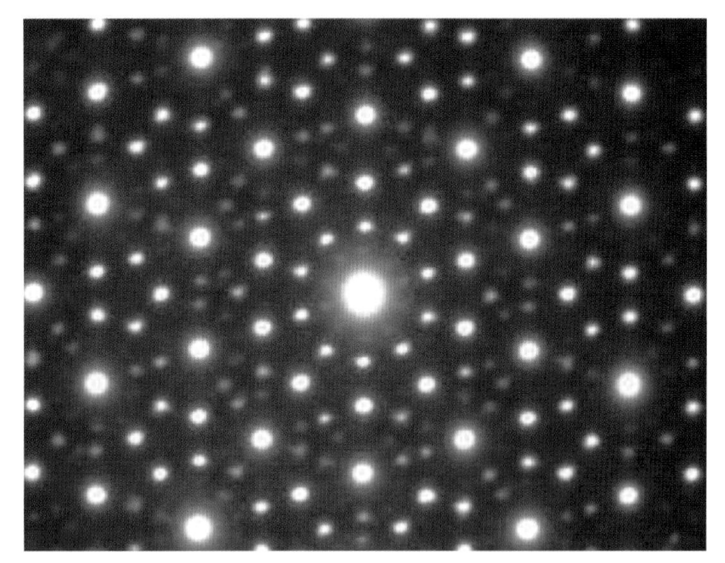

(c) The diffraction pattern of a quasicrystal (the Al_16Mn alloy) having a fivefold symmetry.

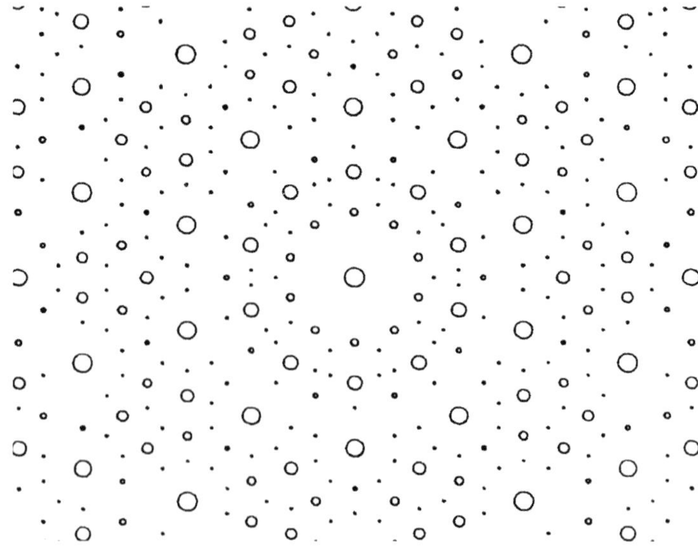

(d) The calculated diffraction pattern from a projected higher-dimensional lattice, in a direction orthogonal to a fivefold axis (as in Figure (b)).

Figure III.2.26: A quasicrystal with fivefold symmetry.

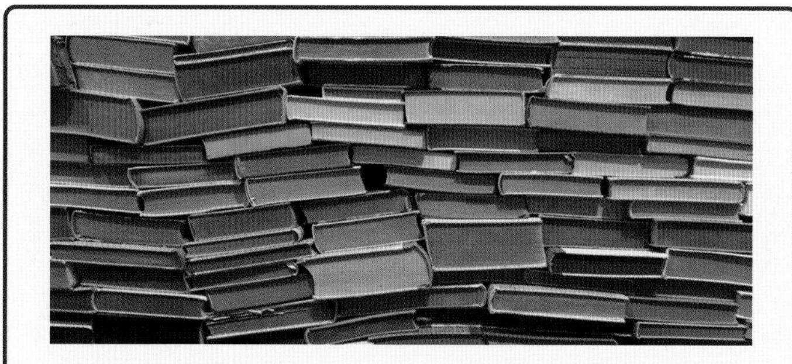

Further reading.
On condensed matter physics:

- *Introduction to Solid State Physics*
  Charles Kittel
  Wiley (2004)
- *Solid State Physics*
  Neil W. Ashcroft and N. David Mermin
  Thomson Press (2003)
- *Principles of Condensed Matter Physics* P. M. Chaikin and T. C. Lubensky
  Cambridge University Press (1995)
- *Modern Condensed Matter Physics*
  Steven M. Girvin and Kun Yang
  Cambridge University Press (2019)

On quasicrystals:

- *Quasicrystals: The State of the Art*
  D.P. di Vincenzo, P.J. Steinhardt
  World Scientific (1991)
- *Quasicrystals and Geometry*
  M.Senechal
  Cambridge University Press (1995)

Chapter III.3

The electron collective

Bands and gaps

Electron states in periodic potentials

Two limits. If the nuclei are positioned on the sites of some regular cubic or hexagonal crystal lattice, the electrons no longer move in a spherical electric field of a single nucleus which would give rise to the atomic bound state orbits, rather the electrons experience a periodic electric potential due to the nuclei on the lattice. You may imagine some set of energy wells with a characteristic depth $-V_0$ separated by a distance a. To get an idea of what may happen in this situation we can approach it from two sides as I indicated in Figure III.3.1.

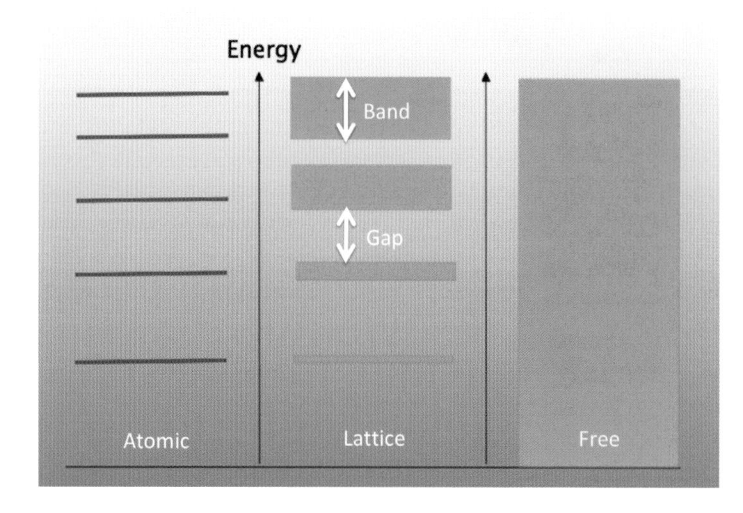

Figure III.3.1: Energy levels, bands and gaps. For individual atoms (l), free electrons (r), and for a periodic lattice of ions (m).

The first approach starts on the left-hand side where we assume that the separation a of the nuclei on the lattice would be large compared to the sizes of the electron clouds of the individual atoms. Then the electron states stay localized around each atom and would maintain the typical atomic spectrum as given on the left. For a solid of N atoms each level would be N-fold degenerate. Now if we start making the separation a smaller, then at a certain point the clouds of neighboring atoms would start overlapping, and the electrons would start feeling each other's presence due to both their charge and the exclusion principle. This repulsion would deform the clouds and therefore the energy levels would start to split. As a consequence energy bands of narrowly split levels start showing up in the spectrum as indicated on the diagram in the middle.

We could also approach the problem from the right-hand side where we start with V_0 small. Then we would just have the spectrum of free electrons moving through space, and these can have any energy. In other words the spectrum is continuous as indicated in the diagram on the right. Now letting the size of the potential barrier grow energy

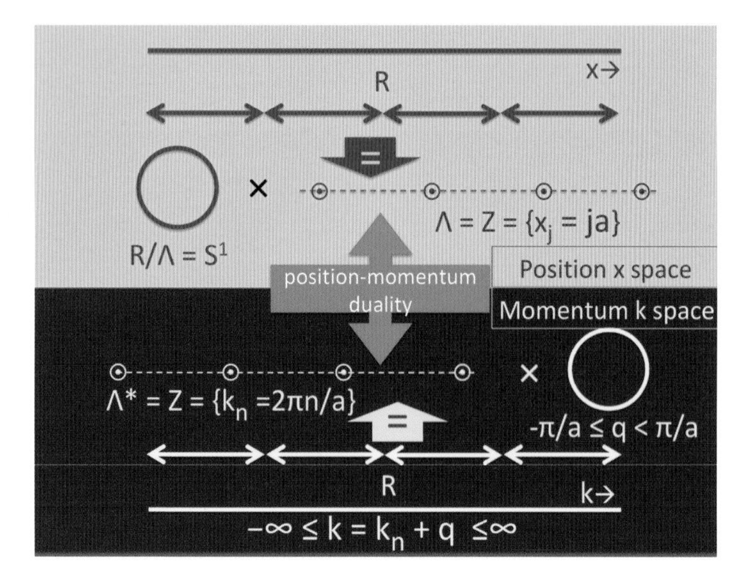

Figure III.3.2: *Position-momentum duality.* In this figure we explain the real space- momentum space duality in the case of a periodicity with period a in the potential for example. We know position space we have $R = -\infty \leq x \leq \infty$ while the free particle momenta are also unbounded $R = -\infty \leq k \leq \infty$. Working top down: (i) divide x-space up in identical pieces of size a which are periodic so we can think of them as little circles (ii) relabel the coordinates a map $x = ja + \varphi a/2\pi$. on a pair (φ, j) where $S^1 = 0 \leq \varphi < 2\pi$ is the angular coordinate of a circle with radius $a/2\pi$, and $j \in Z$ an integer with $-\infty \leq j \leq \infty$.

gaps would open up and we would again end up with the spectrum in the middle. So coming from the left it is bands that form and coming from the right it is gaps that open up.

Periodicity and the reciprocal lattice. Let us consider the one-dimensional case where the electrons will move in the periodic potential of the ions on a lattice. The periodicity implies an invariance of the potential under translations over the lattice distance a. And the electron wavefunctions will then carry certain representations of that symmetry. The fact that the potential is periodic does *not* mean that the wavefunctions themselves have to be periodic. The situation is similar to the case of the single atom where the potential is spherically symmetric around the nucleus, but the quantum states are generally *not* spherically symmetric. They form representations of the rotation group labeled by the quantum numbers l and m.

The situation we have depicted of the right hand-side of Figure III.3.1 is illuminating. Let us consider the free particle limit of the spectrum and think of them as states in a periodic (though vanishing) potential. This perspective is visualized in Figure III.3.2 where the top and bottom half are dual to each other. We start in ordinary position x-space which in one dimension is just the real line R. We think of it as a periodic sequence of intervals of size a, the lattice distance. This means that we interpret periodic x-space as a product of a circle with circumference a and a infinite lattice $\Lambda = Z$ with points x_j labeled by an integer j and where $x_j = ja$. So we may now quantize the free particle on this product space, and try to recover the free particle spectrum on the real line, being a continuous spectrum $-\infty \leq k \leq \infty$, as indicated by the real line at the bottom of the figure. The free particle quantization on the circle of radius a yields states that correspond to the discrete 'reciprocal' lattice $\Lambda^* = Z$, labeled by set of integers $\{-\infty \leq n \leq \infty\}$ and corresponding $k-$values $k_n = 2\pi n/a$. It is strictly analogous to the simple Bohr atom. The quantization of a discrete position lattice produces states labeled by a continuous set of values q that form a circle, a periodic interval $-\pi/2 \leq q < \pi/a$. This fundamental domain of $q-$values is called the first *Brillouin zone*. Combining these plane wave quantum numbers we indeed recover the overall k spectrum by simply multiplying the individual exponential (wave functions) which leads to the identification: $k = k_n + q$, corresponding to adding the exponents.

The Brillouin zone. The procedure just outlined is actually quite general, and works in any dimension. You start with an d-dimensional periodic lattice Λ in R^d where we basically identify the points of the x-lattice. This means that the space R can be thought of as a 'product' of a d-

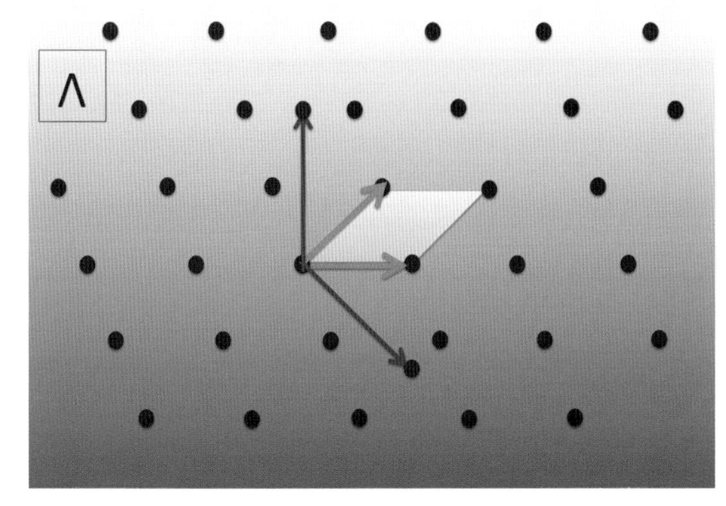

(a) The lattice Λ in x-space.

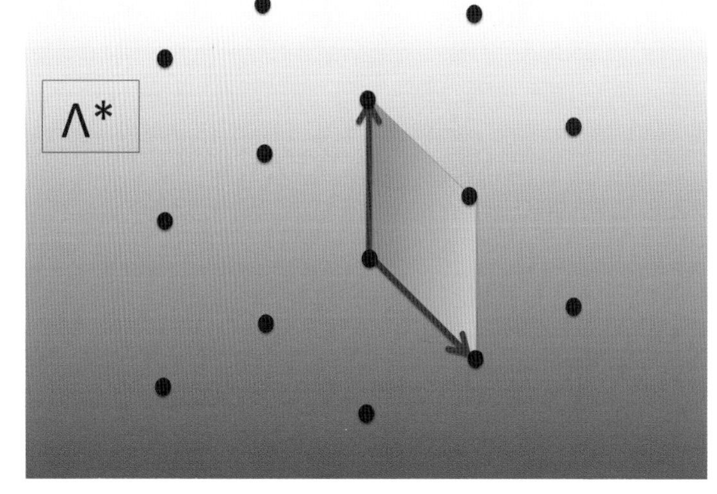

(b) The dual (reciprocal) latice Λ^* in k-space.

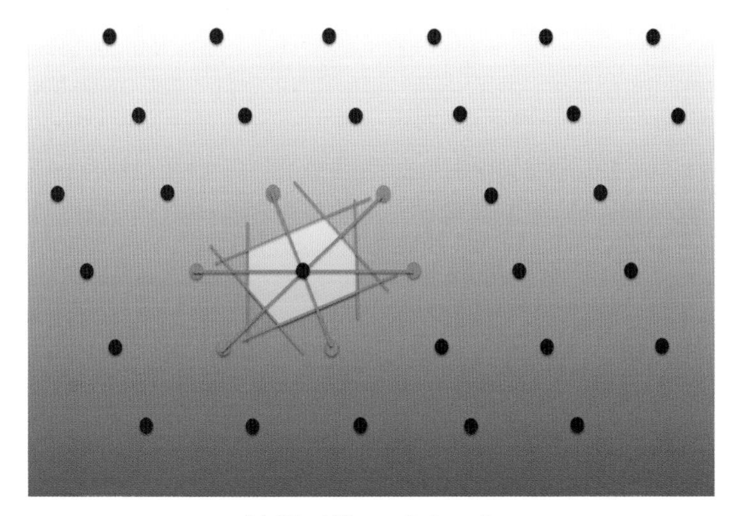

(c) The Wigner-Seitz cell.

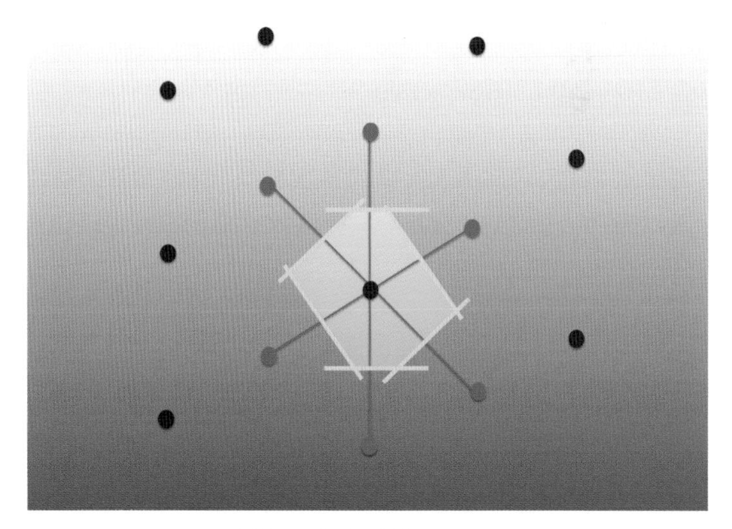

(d) The (first) Brillouin zon.

Figure III.3.3: The real space lattice and the reciprocal wave vector lattice.

dimensional torus R/Λ times the lattice Λ. Free particle quantization gives then a part from the torus which yields the dual or reciprocal lattice Λ^* and a part from the lattice which produces a particular dual torus.

We have illustrated this explicitly for the two-dimensional case in Figure III.3.3. In the Figure (a) we highlighted the so-called periodic *unit cell*, where the symmetry group of Λ is generated by the two basic orange translation vectors. In fact there is an even smaller so-called *fundamental domain* with which the whole plane can be tiled through periodic copying. This domain is highlighted in Figure (c) and obtained as follows. First we start at the origin, and connect it with all neighbouring sites (orange lines), then we draw the perpendicular bisectors (green lines) of the connecting lines. These bisectors then enclose a fundamental periodic (closed) domain called a *Wigner-Seitz cell*. One easily verifies that this cell allows for a space-filling tiling. In figures (a) and (b) we show the construction of the dual lattice, the vectors in the lattices have to satisfy the duality condition:

$$e^{i\mathbf{k_n}\cdot\mathbf{x_i}} = 1 \ , \ \mathbf{k_n} \in \Lambda^* \ , \mathbf{x_j} \in \Lambda \, . \qquad \text{(III.3.1)}$$

The basic translation vectors defining the reciprocal lattice $\mathbf{T_1}$ and $\mathbf{T_2}$ are obtained from the basic translation vectors $\mathbf{t_1}$ and $\mathbf{t_2}$ by the conditions $\mathbf{t_i} \cdot \mathbf{T_j} = 2\pi\delta_{ij}$. The fundamental domain of the dual lattice constructed in Figure (d) is by condensed matter physicists referred to as the (first) Brillouin zone. The 'Brillouin zone' is the 'Wigner-Seitz cell' in wave-vector space.

Electron wavefunctions: bands and gaps. Let us return to the one-dimensional case, and look at the states in the free particle limit as we have depicted in Figure III.3.4. We have plotted the energy as function of the momentum, or the dispersion $E = E(k)$, but we reduced the k-value by some dual lattice vector $2\pi n/a$, as to bring it in the Brillouin zone. In other words we plot $E(k) = E_n(q)$, and that is in fact what is shown on the right-hand side of Figure III.3.1, and in the parametrization given in the lower half of

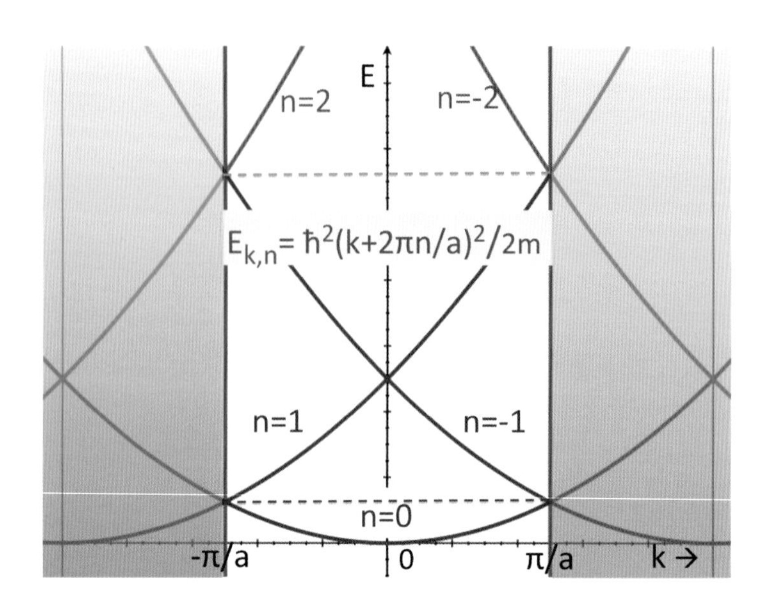

Figure III.3.4: *The Brillouin zone.* We have plotted the energy as function for momentum for free electrons (in one dimension) but have shifted the momentum by an integer times the smallest reciprocal lattice vector $k_1 = 2\pi/a$ as to bring it in the Brillouin zone $-\pi/a < k < \pi/a$, the white colored region. The horizontal axis is the momentum axis, along the vertical axis we have put the electron energy $E = E_n(q)$.

Figure III.3.2. So indeed, the free electrons can have any energy $E_n(q) \leq 0$. Note that in the resulting spectrum the levels fold over at the boundaries $(q = \pm\pi/a)$ and cross in the middle where $q = 0$. If we return to Figure III.3.1 we have argued why by increasing the nuclear potential the continuous spectum will break up, and gaps will open up as depicted in Figure III.3.5, exactly for the special values of q as indicated. Let us now after this introduction move on to the generic spectrum of the quantum electron fluid in an ordinary solid.

Valence and conduction bands. In Figure III.3.6 we give the band structure in the periodic potential landscape of the lattice in which the electrons live. The landscape is characterized by the interatomic distance and the height V_0 of the potential barrier. The electrons fill the bands to a certain maximum level which is called the *Fermi level*,

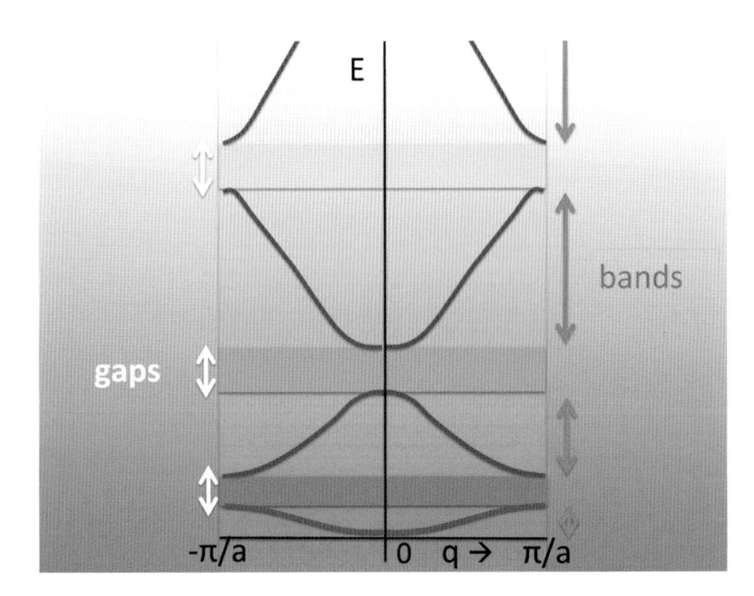

Figure III.3.5: *Gaps open up.* Gaps open up where dispersion curves cross the boundary of the Brillouin zone, or where they intersect. Even though the states will be deformed, the label n of the previous figure remains the label for two successive bands.

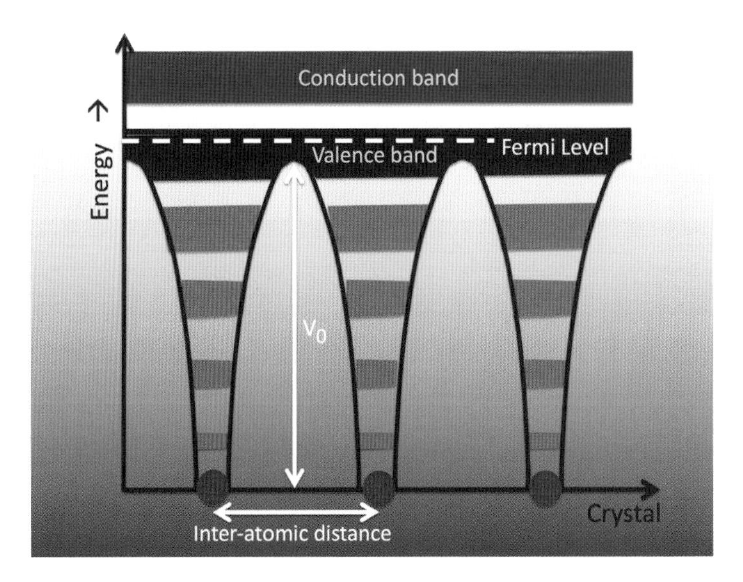

Figure III.3.6: *Electron bands in a crystal.* In a crystal the energy levels are all filled up to the Fermi level (dashed line). The two bands closest to the Fermi level are called the valence and conduction band. The periodic potential is characterized by the interatomic distance and the height of the potential barrier V_0 .

marked by the white dashed line. The two bands closest to the Fermi level are called the *valence band* and the *conduction band* and as we will see the properties of the material will depend strongly on where these bands are located with respect to the Fermi level. The inner electron bands below the valence band consist of pretty much localized states. The allowed states in the 'conduction' bands are not localized but extended, which means that electrons move anywhere in the sample.

Conductors and insulators. How the electrons in the solid collectively behave strongly depends on the position of the *Fermi surface*, which Figure III.3.7 demonstrates. If the Fermi level is in the middle of the valence band, the electrons can move easily because there will be many states available with some more energy, and the material is therefore a *conductor* for electric currents. If the valence band is completely filled and there is not energy enough to enter the conduction band, the electrons cannot move and we are dealing with an *insulator* and we say that the medium has an *energy gap* – is *gapped*. The intermediate case of a *semiconductor* deserves a section of its own.

Semiconductors.

Finally we can imagine that the energy gap between valence and conduction band is narrow, so that not much energy is needed to excite electrons into the next band. This is typically the situation in a *semiconductor*. The image on the right in Figure III.3.7 shows a narrow band gap of a semiconductor at room temperature. The coloring indicates that because of the thermal energy some electronic states at the bottom of the conduction band will be occupied leaving some holes in the valence band. In the next figure we show again the typical energy landscape of what is called an *intrinsic semiconductor*, with the two bands

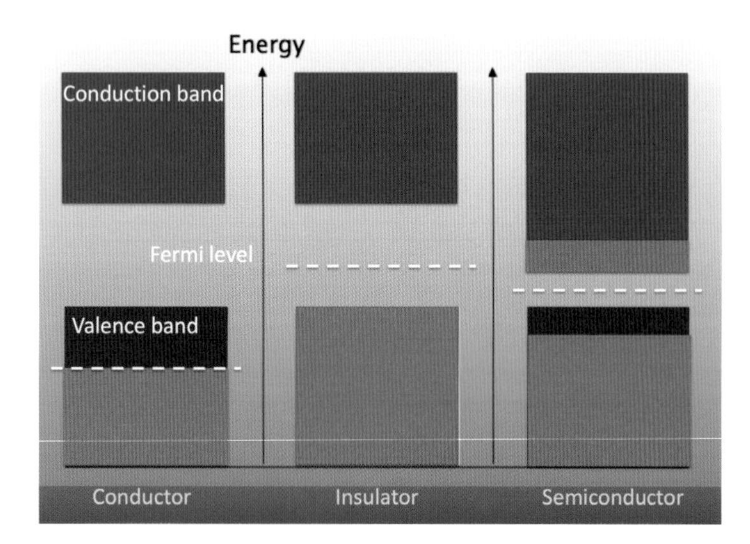

Figure III.3.7: *Energy bands.* The admissible energy levels for the electrons form the *valence* and *conduction* band, where the Fermi level is marked by the dashed white lines. We distinguish a *conductor* (l) where there is basically no gap, an *insulator* (m) where the valence band is filled and there is a big gap, and a *semiconductor* (r) with a narrow gap. The filled states are colored orange and empty states blue.

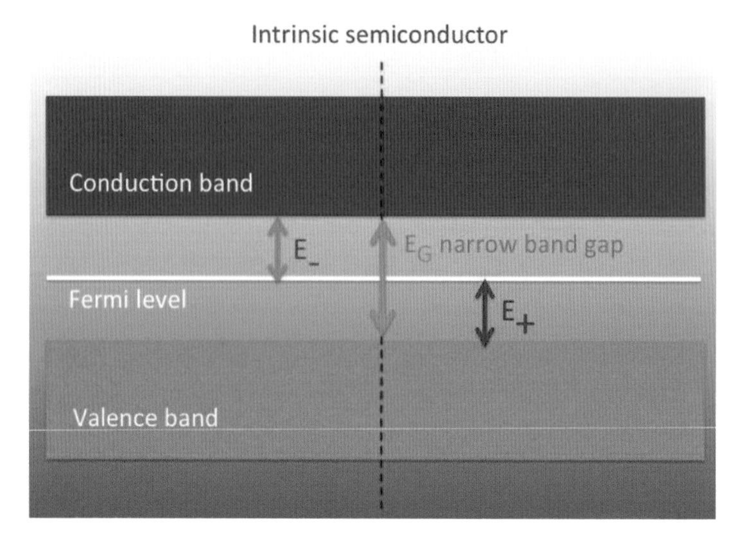

Figure III.3.8: *The intrinsic semiconductor.* The intrinsic semiconductor, is characterized by a narrow gap between valence and conduction band, with the Fermi level exactly in between. The horizontal axis is the space axis, along the vertical axis we have put the electron energy.

and the Fermi level right in between. The electron/hole density in equilibrium is determined by the energy difference between the (conduction/valence) band edge and the Fermi level, which means that as $E_- = E_+ = E_G/2$ the number of charge carriers $n_\pm$ is exponentially suppressed by a Boltzmann factor $\exp(-E_G/2kT)$. But this also implies that its dependence on the energy gap is exponential and that fact is exploited in the idea of doped semiconductors on which all basic semiconductor devices such as transistors are based.

Semiconductors like silicon are at the heart of all modern information storing and processing devices. It is not by accident that the Californian cradle of the information revolution we have witnessed is called 'Silicon Valley'. And it was because of the ever smaller scales at which the semiconductor switches (transistors) could be implemented and exploited that the spectacular large-scale integration of processor and memory chips became possible.

A doped semiconductor. The possibility of *doping*, allows you to somewhat customize the energy landscape in semiconductors. What one does is to replace a certain percentage of the silicon atoms in the lattice by either phosphorus (P) or boron (B) as indicated in Figure III.3.9. In the periodic table phosphorus is the right-hand neighbor of silicon and therefore provides an extra electron, which makes the material somewhat more negatively charged. The effect is to basically lower the band energies with respect to the Fermi level. Substituting with boron has the opposite effect, as boron sits in the column to the left of silicon, and therefore has one valence electron less; the semiconductor will have an excess of positive charges or holes. One may also dope the opposite sides of a semiconductor differently, in which case one gets a *pn-diode* or *pn-junction*, as we have depicted in Figure III.3.10. Now

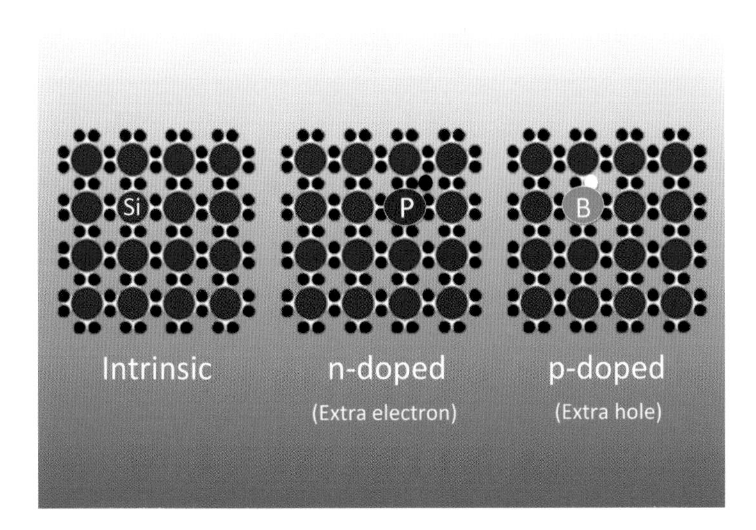

Figure III.3.9: *Doped semiconductor.* We can replace a certain fraction of the silicon atoms in the lattice by either phosphorus (P) or boron (B). The former yields an excess of negative charge carriers (electrons), called *n-doping*, whereas the latter leads to an excess of positive charge carriers (holes), called *p-doping*.

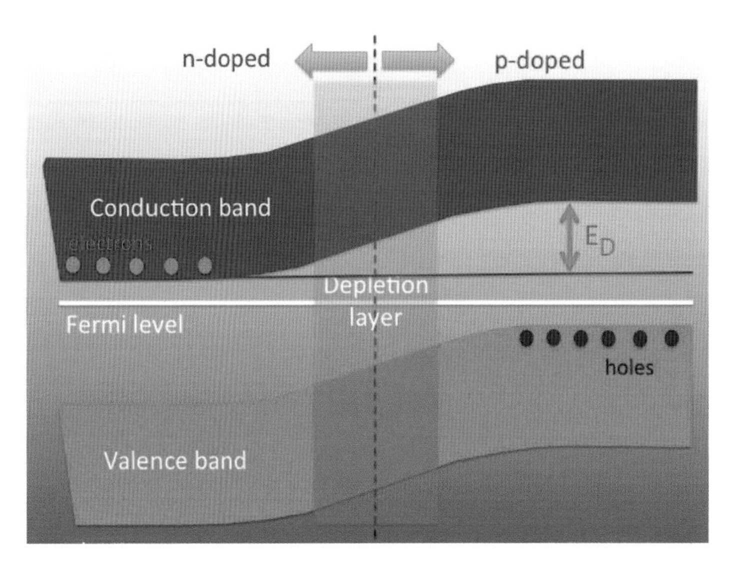

Figure III.3.10: *pn-junction.* By doping a semiconductor we can shift the band structure. With an excess of negative charge carriers (n-doping) we lower the bands, whereas with an excess of positive charge carriers (p-doping) the the bands move up in energy. In the figure you see the band profile of a *np-doped semiconductor* or a *pn-junction*.

in addition to the band gap E_G, a new energy scale E_D is introduced by the doping: on the left side we have many electrons and on the right side only a few, because there is a relative suppression factor $\exp(-E_D/kT)$. For the holes the story is just the opposite, many holes on the right and few on the left. In the middle in the so-called *depletion layer* there are neither free charges nor free holes, it acts as an insulating layer. The Fermi level is the same on both sides, as you can always briefly shortcut the external wires till this equilibrium is established.

Two semiconductor devices. This pn-diode is a simple and useful semiconductor device. Let us briefly indicate two applications without going into much detail.

The photo-voltaic cell. The first possible application is to make a photo-voltaic cell which basically turns solar radiation in the form of photons into electron hole pairs by just exciting electrons from the valence band to the conduction band. This is illustrated in Figure III.3.11, and amounts to creating an opposite charge excess on both sides of the device. In other words creating a voltage difference between the two external plates. Clearly if we couple enough of them in a big array, we can generate high voltages and big currents. And this is a common way to convert solar radiation into electric power. The challenge is to make the efficiency large enough, so light has to be able to enter the semiconductor sufficiently as to maximize the absorption.

The Light Emitting Diode (LED). In Figure III.3.12 we show what happens if we connect the leads to a battery where we introduce a third independent energy scale $E_B = eV_B$. The battery induces an energy (voltage) difference corresponding to E_B between the left and right Fermi levels. These levels split near the depletion layer. One can imagine what happens, the negative lead pushes the electrons

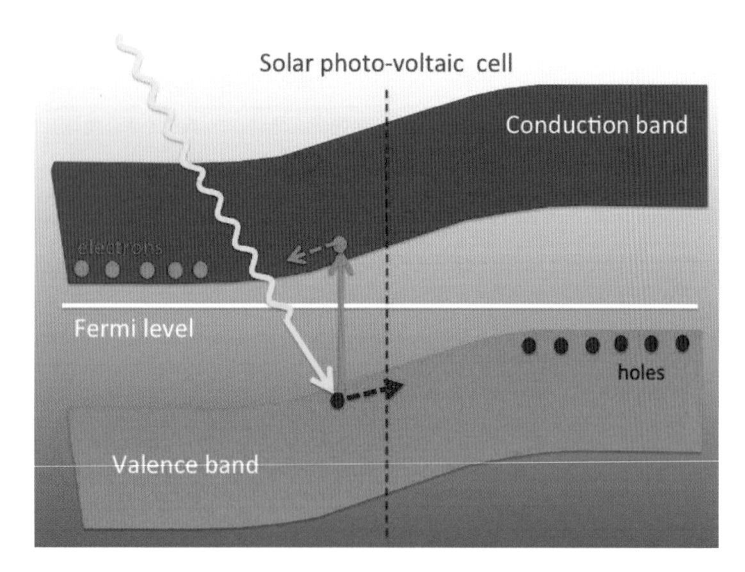

Figure III.3.11: *Photo-voltaic (Solar) cell.* If we have a transparent np-doped semiconductor, light (photons) can be absorbed by the electrons in the valence band and be excited to the conduction band leaving a hole behind. So a voltage will build up over the cell and a current can flow.

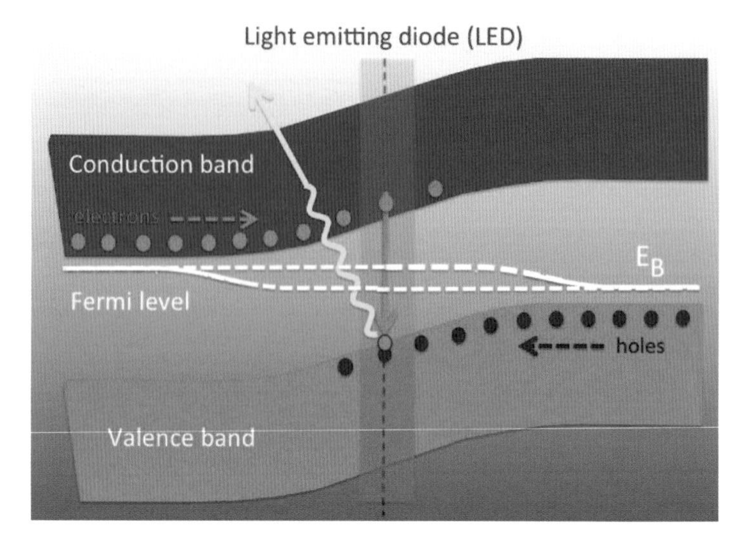

Figure III.3.12: *Light emitting diode (LED).* The LED is more or less the converse of the photo-voltaic cell, in that we now apply a voltage over the semiconductor, which changes the Fermi level on the negative/positive sides. This leads to a recombination of electrons and holes in the center region of the junction producing light.

from the left towards the junction, and similarly the positive lead will push more holes in the system from the right. The effect is that the depletion layer becomes narrower and in fact if the voltage is high enough you will get a current of electrons and holes through the junction. However, as in a stationary state, the relative charge densities between the right and left have to remain exponentially different. What happens is that in the middle region the electrons and holes will recombine and that produces radiation that may be absorbed in the material, but of course it is also possible to implement this in a way that the radiation in the form of photons escapes, and we have a LED. It is a clear advantage that the energy is directly converted into electromagnetic energy, not by heating a wire which in turn starts radiating. Voltages and currents can therefore remain quite low as long as a sufficient percentage of recombined pairs results in visible photons. At present the differences are quite stunning: the LED has a lifespan that is about a factor 50 higher than that of an incandescent bulb, while it costs about a factor 30 more. It is the energy consumption that makes the big difference, because that provides an additional factor of 60. This means that over the lifetime of an LED your yearly electricity bill would be reduced by a few hundred euros/dollars! These numbers also underscore the relative waste in the form of heat that is produced by the old-fashioned light bulb.

Superconductivity

Phonons. It is exciting to go one step deeper into possible scenarios for the collective behavior of the electrons. Looking more closely at the lattice, we know that the nuclei cannot be completely fixed at their positions on the lattice. They are subject to quantum and thermal fluctuations and these lattice fluctuations lead to waves propa-

Figure III.3.13: *Superconductivity.* The discovery of superconductivity, as the measurement of a sudden dramatic drop in resistivity of solid mercury, was made in 1911 in Leiden by Heike Kamerlingh Onnes. It took more then fifty years before a fundamental understanding of this phenomenon was achieved.

gating through the lattice, which are just the familiar sound waves as a matter of fact. In the quantum perspective these waves are considered to be *quasi-particles* which are called *phonons*. So where photons are complementary to light waves, so are these phonons complementary to sound waves, and because sound only propagates through a material medium these quasi-particles are not really fundamental, they are quantized collective excitations of the underlying medium.

Cooper pairs. Now the oscillating nuclei are charged and we should expect that these waves interact again with the electrons. In particle language the phonons will couple to the electrons. And the interesting feature of these interactions is that they lead to an effective attractive force between the electrons. In other words the 'phonons' become the carriers of an attractive force between the electrons. What happens is interesting, close by the electrons are repelled because of their charge, but that repulsion is screened on larger distances and there the at-

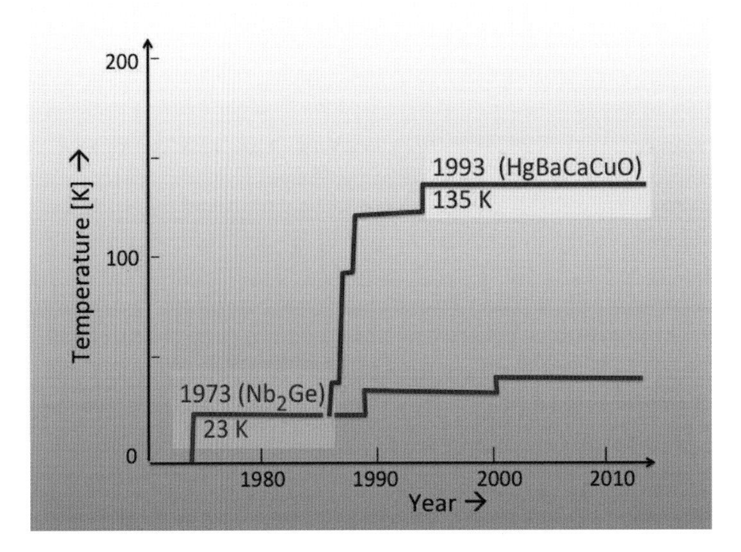

Figure III.3.14: *High temperature superconductivity.* The maximum temperature at which superconductivity takes place has increased dramatically during the last quarter of the 20th century, but appears to have stabilized again. A fundamental understanding of the underlying mechanism, however, is still lacking.

tractive force due to the phonons becomes dominant and creates bound states of electrons, the electrons pair up and form so-called *Cooper pairs*. At low temperatures you may think of the Fermi surface as a sphere in momentum or k-space with well defined radius k_F. A Cooper pair is formed by two electrons at opposite points of the sphere, where furthermore the electrons have spins pointing in opposite directions. In Figure III.3.15 we have indicated the Fermi sphere with two Cooper pairs at the surface, each pair bound through the exchange of a virtual phonon. So we should think of the electron collective no longer as a community of singles but of couples and once more that strongly affects the states that are allowed just as in our earlier societal analogue.

The superconducting ground state. I have already referred to the spin of particles and the Pauli exclusion principle, which decrees that two half-integral spin particles cannot occupy the same state whereas integral spin particles

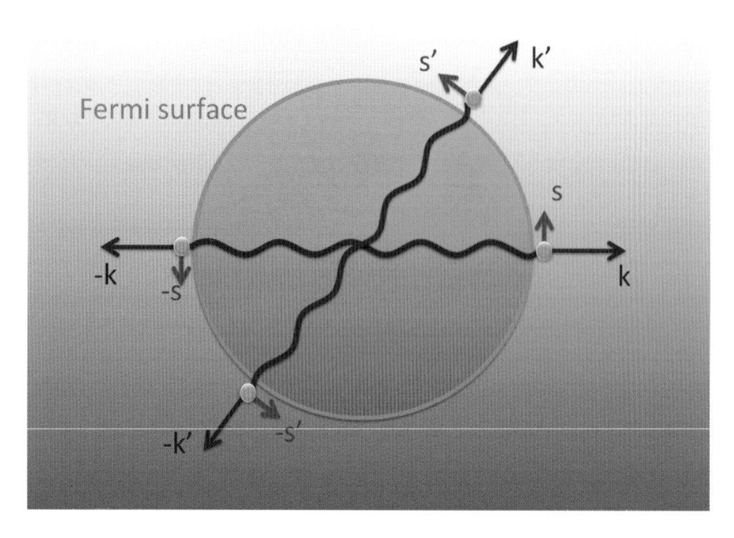

Figure III.3.15: *Cooper pairs.* Cooper pairs are bound states of two widely separated electrons caused by the exchange of virtual phonons. This turns the electron collective effectively into a gas of charged bosons which then condense into the superconducting BCS state.

can. But after the electrons pair up, we are no longer dealing with a collective of spin 1/2 electrons, but with pairs of electrons with opposite spins, which means that the pairs have spin zero. And that has dramatic consequences: whereas the electrons cannot sit in the same state and push each other to ever higher and higher energy states, the charged bosonic pairs all can sit in the same lowest energy state. So you can imagine that there is an enormous energetic advantage for the system of electrons to pair up and all 'condense' in the ground state. Well, it does happen, and we see that for certain conductors, if we cool them down sufficiently, the pairs can form and condense into a surprising new state of matter: the material becomes superconducting. A *superconductor* is a conductor with the miraculous property that it conducts electricity with absolutely *zero* resistance! The most dramatic fact is maybe that this phenomenon is a macroscopic manifestation of quantum theory, *the superconducting state is a macroscopic quantum state.* This is possible because all the Cooper pairs have condensed into a single quantum state.

Bose-Einstein condensates. These kind of condensation effects are a manifestation of Bose-Einstein condensation an effect predicted as early as 1924 by the Indian physicist Satyendra Nath Bose and Albert Einstein. And indeed many other examples have since been found: for example He^4 is a boson and therefore can condense at very low temperature in a state that exhibits the amazing property of *superfluidity.* As we discussed in the previous chapter, there is no viscosity in a superfluid: another one of these quantum miracles which would be inconceivable from a classical point of view. The Bose-Einstein condensates which have been observed in diluted atomic gases, and for which the Americans Eric Cornell, Carl Wieman and Wolfgang Ketterle received the Physics Nobel prize in 2001, are another recent discovery. These condensates are close to the theoretical setting described in the original papers of Bose and Einstein.

Some history. We have made a small *tour d'horizon* to give you a sense of how rich and surprising the macroscopic behavior of a collective of atoms may be, and how intricate the balances of forces are, and to what kind of exotic properties of materials this may lead. It also shows how creative one has to be to get to a detailed physical understanding such exotic properties. It is worth pointing out that superconductivity was discovered by Heike Kamerlingh Onnes in Leiden as early as 1911. He found that the resistance of solid mercury immersed in liquid helium suddenly dropped to zero at a temperature of 4.2 K, as shown in Figure III.3.13. The story goes that he generated a persistent circular current and managed to take it along to Amsterdam to show it to his colleagues over there! Kamerlingh Onnes received the Nobel prize in Physics in 1913 for 'his investigations on the properties of matter at low temperatures which led, *inter alia*, to the production of liquid helium.'

Figure III.3.16: *Magnetic levitation.* A little magnet will be lifted above a superconductor, because of the Meissner effect, which means that magnetic field lines are expelled from a superconducting region. The aura of magic is caused by the boiling liquid nitrogen needed to cool the high-temperature superconductor. (Source: Michigan State University.)

The microscopic mechanism underlying superconductivity remained a complete mystery for a long time. The Russian physicists Lev Landau and Vitaly Ginzburg proposed an effective field theory explaining quite a lot of the phenomenology of the superconductors, but it was not until 1957 that the fundamental quantum mechanism including the pair formation and the precise structure of the superconducting ground state was put forward by the American physicists John Bardeen, Leon Cooper and Robert Schrieffer, who received the Nobel prize for their groundbreaking work in 1972. This splendid theory is known as the BCS theory of superconductivity.

Ever since the 'BCS' breakthrough in the understanding of superconductivity there has been a host of detailed quantum mechanical explanations for the highly surprising ways collectives of atoms may behave and turn into molecular gases, liquids, glasses, liquid crystals, magnets, superconductors or Bose-Einstein condensates, or even assemble into large molecules, all depending on the parameters of the theory. Again, this is the branch of physics which Philip W. Anderson, the celebrated American condensed matter theorist who died in 2020, characterized by the credo 'more is different', referring to the splendid diversity of collective quantum behavior that emerges in macroscopic systems consisting of many interacting constituents. We have emphasized that the differences cannot always be traced back to the differences in the constituent particle types. Though the type of interactions these have is absolutely crucial, the macroscopic phase that is realized may also depend on external parameters, like the temperature, the density, the presence of a magnetic field and so on. To conclude we may say that in trying to understand and predict the splendid diversity of emerging properties, quantum reasoning has become absolutely indispensable.

The Meissner effect. You might wonder what happens if we apply a magnetic field to a superconductor. This is an interesting question to ask because we know that a conductor tends to counteract a change in the magnetic field, which means that currents are generated which are such that they generate a field in the opposite direction. Now you can imagine that because there is no resistance in the superconductor these currents will keep running thereby permanently counteracting the change in magnetic field. The net result is remarkable: magnetic fields cannot penetrate a superconductor! This expulsion of magnetic fields fromn superconducting regions is called the Meissner effect, after the German physicist Walther Meissner who discovered it in 1933.

Here some qualifications have to be made though. The first is that if we keep increasing the magnetic field we end up breaking the pairs and the superconducting phase is destroyed. The second is more interesting, and follows because the electrons (and pairs) have a funny property. It turns out that they cannot detect a specific amount of magnetic flux. What happens in the so-called Type II superconductors is that the magnetic flux can enter the superconductor as long as it is in quantized portions the electron pairs can't see. In other words there is a minimal unit of magnetic flux Φ_0 that is compatible with a condensed charge q and it is given by the simple relation $\Phi_0 = 2\pi\hbar/q$.

In a three-dimensional superconductor these magnetic flux lines that enter the superconductor line up parallel to the direction of the external magnetic field. However the flux lines repel each other and therefore if you increase the strength of the field and look in a plane perpendicular to the field you see that they tend to form a nice triangular lattice. I should point out an additional or better complementary view on this situation. The fact is that in the core of these magnetic filaments the medium becomes a normal conductor again. So in a sense you can say that the magnetic field did not enter the superconductor after all but corresponds to filaments of a normal conductor in the superconductor.

I have all along been emphasizing the use of symmetry arguments. What about the superconducting phase, are they of any use there? The answer is affirmative. Though the argument is somewhat more complex. We all know that electric charge is conserved: you cannot lose an electric charge; it may be transferred from one fundamental particle to another, for example in reactions like proton + electron goes to neutron etc. We have mentioned in previous chapters that this conservation law is a consequence of the internal symmetry called *gauge invariance*.

But if, like in the superconductor, the groundstate is filled with electrically charge particles, then the electric charge is no longer conserved, you can change it by arbitrary multiples of $2e$ without changing the physical situation. The point is that the superconducting state is unusual in that there is no definite number of electrons or pairs in that state. So the story here is that in the superconducting phase charge is no longer conserved because the gauge symmetry is broken. But if a symmetry is broken then we have to ask whether there are not defects that we have to take into account. Yes indeed, the defects are precisely the magnetic vortex lines we have been discussing. The symmetry breaking story once more fits exactly the phenomena observed.

The quantum Hall effect

In the phenomenon of superconductivity we have seen one of the more subtle ways the system of a rigid lattice can interact with the gas of electrons and give rise to a rather surprising form of collective behavior. Are there other examples of interactions electrons may engage in that drastically change their collective behavior? I wouldn't ask you if the answer wasn't yes. A stunning example is the so-called *quantum Hall effect*: it occurs just like superconductivity and superfluidity only at temperatures of a few Kelvins so that its applications have been limited so far. The setting for the quantum Hall effect is a two-dimensional conductor (imagine for example a conducting boundary layer between two insulators) where we apply a strong magnetic field perpendicular to the surface. This situation is depicted in Figure III.3.17(a) .

The physics in this setting is rather counterintuitive. Imagine a little slab of quantum Hall medium and applying a voltage difference V in the x direction. In a normal conductor a current I would start flowing in the x-direction according to Ohm's law decreeing that $I = V/R$ so, inversely proportional to the resistance R. In the quantum Hall medium however, the current starts flowing in the y direction, perpendicular to the applied field! This is even the case in classical physics as Edwin Hall already discovered in 1879. The transversal Hall resistance as a function of the applied magnetic field (with fixed current) is plotted in Figure III.3.17(b). We talk about a transversal or Hall-

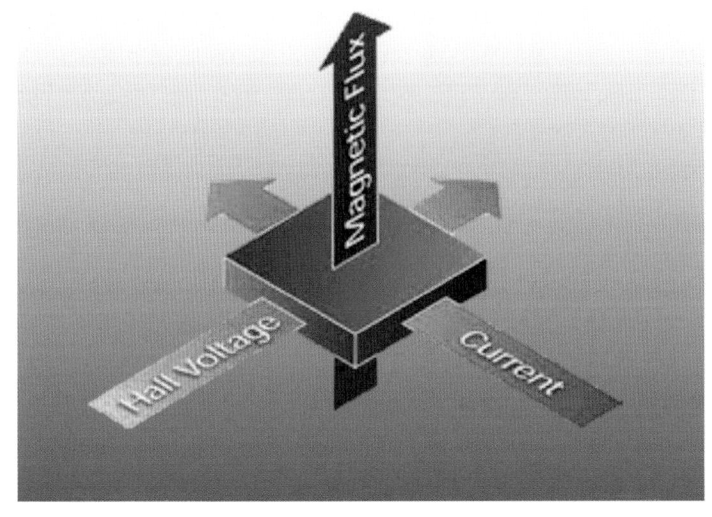

(a) The quantum Hall setup. Driving a current through a planar conductor with a strong magnetic field B orthogonal to the plane yields a transversal potential V_H .

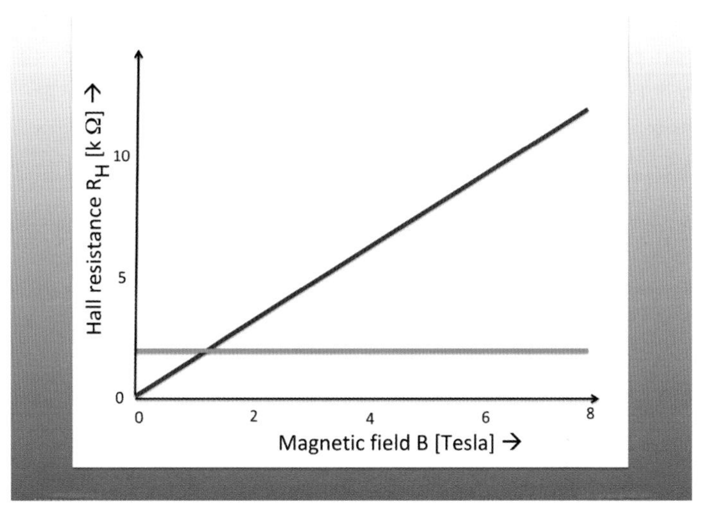

(b) The classical Hall effect shows a linearly rising V_H (blue line) as a function of the applied magnetic field, while keeping the current constant (green line).

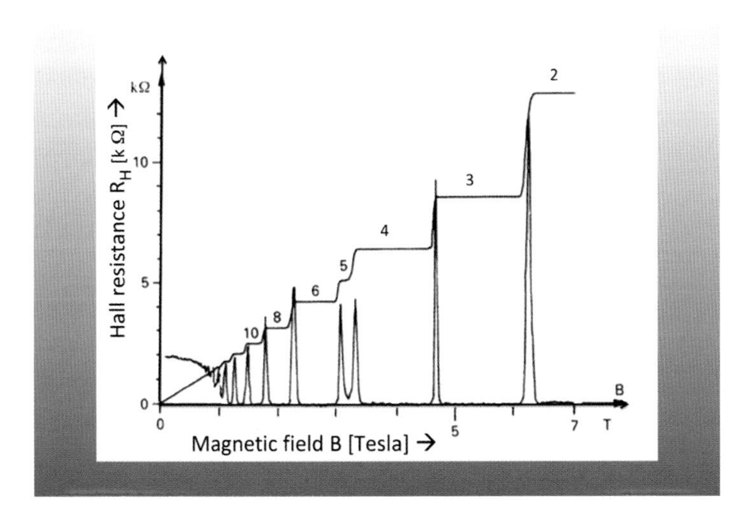

(c) The integer quantum Hall effect showing the plateaus with integer ν values.

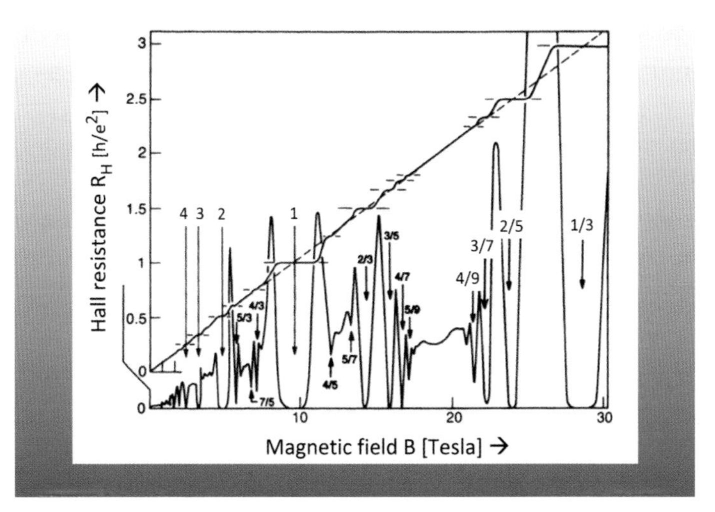

(d) The fractional quantum Hall effect with from right to left the plateau values for $\nu = \frac{1}{3}, \frac{2}{5}, \frac{3}{7}, \frac{4}{9} \ldots$

Figure III.3.17: *From the classical to the quantum Hall effect.*

resistance (ρ), and a Hall-conductivity $\sigma = 1/\rho$.

The integer quantum Hall effect. To consider this system quantum mechanically, there are two things that we ought to understand. The first question is the behavior of a single electron in a magnetic field, and the second is the collective behavior of electrons in this setting. It is beyond the scope of this book to drag you through the beautiful reasoning, but even if we had done so, the phenomenon remains quite puzzling and counterintuitive. Where according to classical physics the transverse conductivity must grow *linear* with the applied field, in reality it does not! If you increase the magnetic field the conductivity remains constant over certain intervals and the value of that conductivity is strictly quantized according to the surprisingly simple relation $\sigma = \nu n e^2/2\pi\hbar$, where ν is the *filling fraction* which is defined as the electron density n_e divided by the magnetic flux density n_B in fundamental flux units ($\Phi_0 2\pi\hbar/e$): in other words $n_B = eB/2\pi\hbar$. We have plotted plateaux in the Hall resistance for the integer effect in Figure III.3.17(c). What you see is that as a function of the applied magnetic field it has plateaus where it stays constant until it jumps to the next plateau (with lower n).

The fractional quantum Hall effect, When you turn up the magnetic field to large values like 30 Tesla, plateaus also show up for fractional values of ν like $\frac{1}{3}, \frac{2}{5}, \frac{3}{7}, \frac{4}{9}, \ldots$, in which case we speak of the *fractional quantum Hall effect* as depicted in Figure III.3.17(d). In the fractional quantum Hall effect we have the unusual situation that the charge carriers in the medium are no longer electrons. Rather they correspond to localized collective excitations of the system which carry *fractional* electric charges, such as $e/3$ or $e/5$ depending on which plateau you are.

So, to put it in more pictorial terms: if I would add an electron to a quantum Hall system it would 'fall apart' in a set of fractional charges as displayed in Figure III.3.18. However, you should not think of these charge carriers as some kind of special 'quark-like' particles that make up an electron.

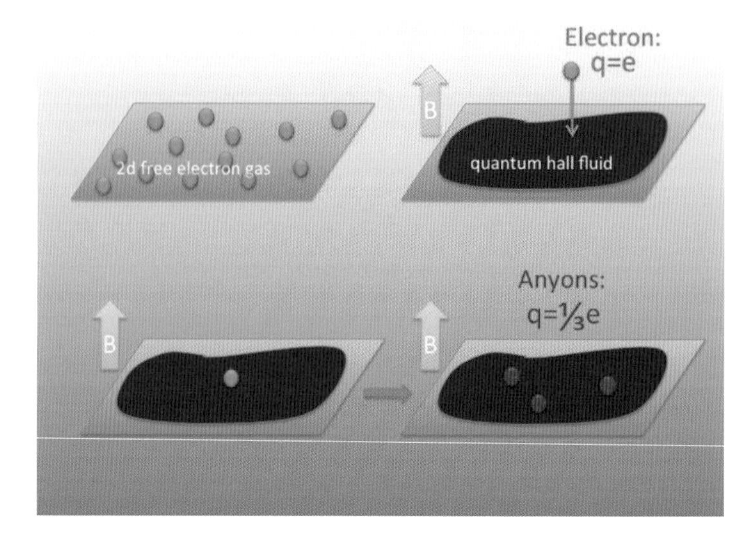

Figure III.3.18: *The quantum Hall fluid.* Putting a 2-dimensional free electron gas near absolute zero in a strong magnetic field one obtains a quantum Hall fluid. Adding a single electron charge to the quantum Hall fluid, the charge will fractionalize into three *anyons* each with charge $e/3$. These anyons are quasiparticles, and are in fact flux-charge composites carrying a exotic spin value $s = q\Phi_0/2\pi = e/3 \cdot \hbar/e = \hbar/3$.

No, these fractional charges are carried by well-localized collective excitations, special modes of the electron field in the presence of the magnetic flux. So, these collective excitations are not only charged, they also carry a magnetic flux quantum along with them. The flux quanta are in that sense the magnetic defects we saw in the type II superconductors and which become particle like in a plane orthogonal to the magnetic flux, but now these flux particles are dressed with a fractional electric charge. Such dually charged excitations that basically can only occur in two dimensions are called *anyons*. We have discussed such flux-charge composites in the section on spin and statistics on page 171 of Chapter II.5, and more specifically the subsection on two-dimensional exotics on page 182. There we showed that such composites may indeed exhibit not just fractional charge, but also fractional spin and statistics properties. For the case where the basic anyonic charge corresponds to $q = e/3$, we demonstrated that the spin of the anyon corresponds to $s = q\Phi_0/2\pi = \hbar/3$.

Quantum Hall systems are of fundamental interest because they represent truly novel states of matter, the existence of which nobody had anticipated. The integer quantum Hall effect was discovered by the German physicist Klaus von Klitzing in 1980, for which he received the Nobel prize in 1985, The more complicated fractional quantum Hall effect, featuring the fractional charge and exotic statistics properties was discovered in the early 1980s and a Nobel prize for theory and experiment was awarded in 1998 to Robert Laughlin, Horst Störmer and Daniel Tsui.

Topological order

Quantum Hall conductors constitute entirely novel states of matter, fundamentally different from the more familiar conducting phases, like ordinary conductors, semi- or superconductors, which are usually referred to as Fermi liquids. From 1980 onwards many phases which exhibit similar unusual behavior have been discovered; these phases which are characterized by certain non-trivial topological interactions are now considered manifestations of a generic property called *topological order*. It concerns phases which are *gapped*, which means that there are no massless degrees of freedom in the system, the relevant degrees of freedom are massive like the anyons, and these have topological long range interactions leading to their non-trivial spin and statistics properties.

Quantum statistics. The term *anyon* was coined by the American physicist Frank Wilczek because these fractionally charged particle also have an exotic type of quantum statistics properties. We have emphasized the essential difference between bosons and fermions, where the latter obey the Pauli exclusion principle saying that no two fermions can sit in exactly the same state whereas bosons can. Another way of saying this is that if we consider a multi-particle state and we interchange two identical type particles then the phase of the state may change. In three or more dimensions, if we repeat the interchange operation, denoted by τ, we are back to the original state, so that implies that $\tau^2 = 1$, which means that the phase change has to equal $\tau \simeq \pm 1$. If we interchange two bosons the state remains unchanged $\tau = 1$ and if we interchange two fermions the state changes sign so $\tau = -1$. We have already pointed out that this difference in statistics (we call it statistics because the rule affects the way the particles can be distributed over the availlable states) accounts for the crucial differences in properties in many body systems. We recall the essential role of the Pauli exclusion principle in understanding the spectrum of atoms with more than one or two electrons.

Braid statistics. The anyons that occur in two-dimensional topologically ordered media satisfy a type of statistics referred to as *braid statistics*, where there is an essential phase difference between interchanging particles clockwise or counterclockwise. So to calculate the state after some time you have to keep track of how often and in what direction the particles have moved around each other. One has to deal with the *braid* of particle world lines in space-time. And to know the state exactly you have to know the braid. A braid is much like a knot, and the theory of knots is a well-studied subject in the topology of three-dimensional manifolds. If we have a particular braid of five differently colored strands, we could connect the corresponding incoming and outgoing strands to obtain a closed knot made of five strands. It is topological because it doesn't matter at what distance the world lines wind around each other and moreover we may move the strands around and deform the knot; but as long as we don't cut the strands the knot remains topologically the same. The knot will be characterized by a number of topological invariants. In terms of the quantum Hall effect this means the way the quantum state changes only depends on who danced around who and in what order. Another way to say this is that the multi-anyon states exhibit long range entanglement.

All possible braids can be composed of elementary moves of moving neighboring pairs around each other. The set of all such intertwining operations forms again a group, and the mathematics of such groups is well understood. In higher dimensions one only can have bosons or fermions, exactly because winding the paths clockwise or anti clockwise is topologically equivalent, while in two dimensions there is in principle an unlimited number of topologically inequivalent windings possible and therefore also for the quantum statistics of states. It is even possible that different particle types exhibit non-trivial mutual statistics properties. This means that the phase of the states may change after moving a particle around another type of particle: in other words applying τ^2 to a pair of particles belonging to different species. In general the multi-anyon states are formally classified as unitary representations of the braid group.

Topological field theory. You may wonder what the theoretical models look like that effectively describe these topologically ordered phases like the quantum Hall fluid. A large and important class of models, but not the only type, are so-called *topological field theories*. In particular the (2+1)-dimensional *Chern-Simons theories*. It is an effective theory, which describes the phenomenology of the topologically ordered phases to a certain extent. And one has to realize that a derivation of this theory from first principles is hard. To give you a flavour of what such theories look like, I show a basic example that is provided by just a (charge q) current $j_\mu =$ coupled to a gauge field A_μ that is described by a $U(1)$ Chern-Simons theory. The equations in relativistic notation are actually quite simple and given by:

$$\frac{\lambda}{2}F_{\mu\nu} = \varepsilon_{\mu\nu\sigma}j^\sigma \quad \Rightarrow \begin{cases} \frac{\lambda}{2}F_{12} = j^0 \to B = \frac{2\rho}{\lambda} \\ \frac{\lambda}{2}\mathbf{E} = \mathbf{j}_\perp \end{cases}, \qquad \text{(III.3.2)}$$

where the parameter λ is the coefficient of the Chern Simons term, which dependent on the setting will be quantized as well. In the quantum Hall effect it is directly linked to the quantized plateaux conductivity. What these equations imply becomes clear if we look at simple situations:

(i) If there is no charge or current, the equations say that there is no field: this is an expression of the fact that there is a gap, and there are no gauge field quanta maybe because they are too heavy to be excited. In other words the pure Chern Simons theory has a 'gauge field' but that field does not describe local field degrees of freedom like photons. It is a purely topological theory, meaning that the only physical *observables* are the path dependent phase factors corresponding to closed loop integrals of the gauge field A_μ.
(ii) If there is a single charge at rest ($j_0 \neq 0$), we see from top equation on the right that the charge gets 'dressed' with a magnetic flux ($F_{12} \neq 0$), or the other way around a given flux quantum may attract charge and thereby creating a dually charged *anyon*. Integrating the charge distribution one obtains the relation between the flux Φ and charge q of the anyon, $\Phi = 2q/\lambda$. This in turn means that if two of those anyons encircle each other one obtains a phase factor $\exp(-iq^2/\lambda)$, which can take all kinds of values.
(iii) the second equation describes the effect of applying a voltage across the sample; the resulting (Hall) current is perpendicular to the electric field. We see that this Chern-Simons term induces exactly the properties we have described before.

Chern-Simons theory. The Chern-Simons theories are playing a fundamental role in modern physics and mathematics. The American mathematical physicist (and outstanding string theorist) Edward Witten from the Institute for Advanced Study in Princeton, recognized its relevance for three dimensional topology and the associated physical phenomena. In 1983 he noted that the Chern Simons action provides an intrinsically three-dimensional definition of knot invariants, and as one is free to choose the gauge group, it defines an infinity of them. For this work he was awarded the Fields medal, the mathematical equivalent of a Nobel prize, in 1990. Secondly, Witten showed that if we look at the theory on spaces with a boundary, the theory can be entirely described by an equivalent (1+1)-dimensional conformal invariant field theory on the boundary which is a striking example of the holographic principle we discussed at the end of Chapter **??** in the context of black holes. Finally, Witten also showed that Einstein's theory of gravity in three space-time dimensions is actually a Chern-Simons theory where the gauge group is the group of local translations and Lorentz transformations. This provides an exciting laboratory to explore the ideas of the holographic principle etc. And as we emphasized in this chapter, topological field theory has bedome an indispensable tool for the description and understanding of a wide variety of topologically ordered phases in condensed matter.

Topological quantum computation. These topological systems can be characterized by certain symmetries which are quite hidden, and an example of what are nowadays called *quantum groups* or *Hopf algebras*. There is a rapidly growing interest in this field of *topologically ordered media* and more recently also materials called *topological insulators*, which exhibit topological order in three dimensions. These media appear to be quite ideal candidates for quantum information storage and processing, exactly because one can change the state by moving particles around each other. Loosely speaking a computation is nothing but a particular complicated braid or knot of a 'register' of anyons in space-time. It is an *intrinsically fault tolerant* way of doing quantum computations because topological moves are insensitive to local perturbations, that is perturbations caused by local interactions and that is all we have been talking about. No surprise therefore that many think of this as a development of great significance. And by many I not only mean scientists, but also security bosses of public organizations and others who have to hide big $ecret$ behind huge numerical keys which were once believed to be unbreakable, but not in the future. Just wait for quantum technologies to come and get them.

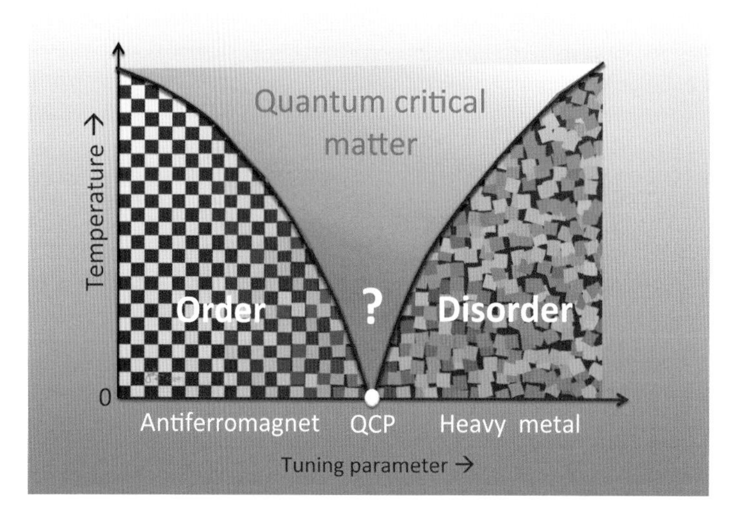

Figure III.3.19: *The quantum critical point.* A quantum critical point separates at zero temperature an ordered (antiferromagnetic) and a disordered phase (a heavy fermion metal). For finite temperature it opens up a region of quantum critical phases, such as what are called 'strange metals.'

Quantum critical points. Figure III.3.19 shows the phase diagram of what is called a *strange metal*, which is characterized by an anomalous quantum critical phase in which the electrical resistivity varies linearly with temperature. This behavior shows up not only at a singular *quantum critical point* (QCP) at zero temperature, but over an extended range of a relevant tuning parameter in the phase diagram. This highly unconventional behavior has defied description within the standard model for metals.

This provides for a new topic that is vigorously pursued at present, and there appear to be a variety of systems that exhibit such a quantum critical point. The general picture that emerges is now that at the quantum critical point, the system can be modelled by an interacting (2+1)-dimensional conformal field theory. This effective theory may, depending on the case, describe emergent Dirac fermions,

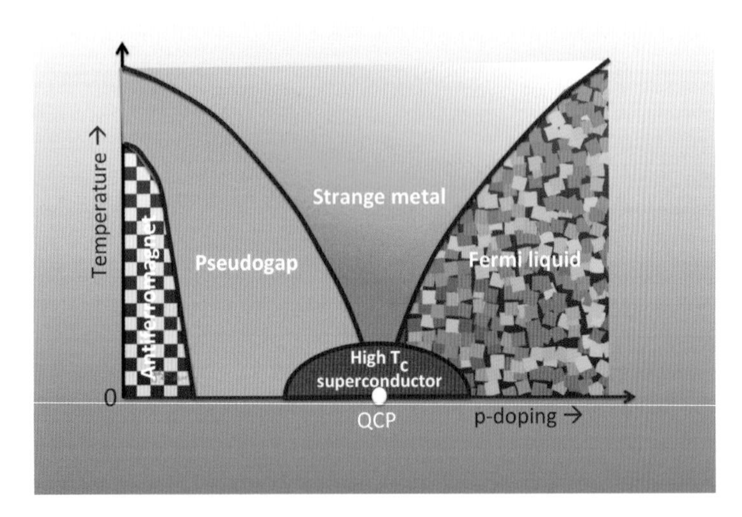

Figure III.3.20: *High* T_C *superconductivity.* The proposed more complicated phase diagram for the *cuprates* exhibiting a high T_C superconducting phase near a quantum critical point (QCP).

scalar (Higgs-like) fields and even emergent $U(1)$ gauge fields. So in a sense many of the previously known models based on principles of gauge invariance, symmetry breaking and so on make a surprising comeback on a totally different stage. But what is most striking is that the original electron degrees of freedom are strongly entangled over large distances, and manifest themselves in vastly different guises. One says that these conformal phases are no longer 'adiabatically' connected to the original Fermi liquid phases. There is no smooth way to connect the two regimes.

What makes the quantum critical point relevant is that the behavior persists away from the critical point. So for example there is a well-accepted view that *high* T_C *superconductivity*, which is effectively realized in the two-dimensional layers of certain materials denoted as *cuprates*, is governed by such a QCP as we have indicated in the phase diagram of Figure III.3.20. So the high temperature superconducting phase would be described by a finite temperature version of the (2+1)-dimensional conformal field theory in question. New insights in these theories, which have been inspired by theories of quantum gravity, like string theory and the AdS-CFT correspondence that we discussed before, definitely look promising in a bid to unravel the mysteries of these strange metals. String theory and hard core condensed matter theory seem strange bed fellows at first sight, but apparently science doesn't know of any taboos in that respect.

Further reading.

On condensed matter physics:

- *Introduction to Solid State Physics*
  Charles Kittel
  Wiley (2004)
- *Solid State Physics*
  Neil W. Ashcroft and N. David Mermin
  Thomson Press (2003)
- *Principles of Condensed Matter Physics*
  P. M. Chaikin and T. C. Lubensky
  Cambridge University Press (1995)
- *Modern Condensed Matter Physics*
  Steven M. Girvin and Kun Yang
  Cambridge University Press (2019)

On superconductivity:

- *Introduction to Superconductivity*
  Michael Tinkham
  Dover Publications (2004)

On topological media:

- *The Quantum Hall Effect*
  Daijiro Yoshioka and D. Yoshioka
  Springer (2010)
- *Introduction to Topological Quantum Computation*
  Jiannis K. Pachos,
  Cambridge University Press, 2012
- *Quantum Phase Transitions*
  Subir Sachdev
  Cambridge University Press (2011)

Chapter III.4

SCALE dependence

In this chapter we explore the notion of scaling. *How does the behavior of physics change if one changes the length or momentum scales?*
We start with some simple geometrical examples of scaling, leading to the notions of scale invariance, self-similarity. and fractals. We move on to discrete maps like conformal mappings used by Escher and dynamical systems like the logistic map.
The next step is to study scaling in physical models, both classical and quantum. This culminates in the notion of renormalization in quantum field theory and the wonderful idea of running coupling constants. We discuss what scaling tells us about the asymptotic behavior of physical theories like the standard model and the possibility of (grand) unification in theories of the fundamental interactions. Finally we point out the profound link between scale (and conformal) invariance and critical behavior

What sets the scale?

When children start building bridges with LEGO they learn what construction engineers know too well: if one simply keeps scaling up the size of a construction it will at a certain point collapse. By simply scaling we mean that we multiply all linear sizes by some given factor. One cannot simply multiply all beam sizes by a factor two to construct a bridge that will span a river twice as wide. The basic reason for this breakdown of scaling was given by Galilei in his discourse on the two world systems, and boils down to the basic observation that the mass of a beam scales as a volume, that is a length cube, while the strength of the beam would only grow with the transverse area meaning a length square. And because the cubic power grows faster than the square, at a certain scale the beam has to break under its own weight.

The question 'what sets the scale' is a vital one, which one had better address before embarking on detailed calculations. In physics the answer is determined by, and expressed in the available dimensionful parameters of the model one employs. Educated guesses are then based on what is called *dimensional analysis* of the parameters that are present in the problem. A given particle mass for example sets a relevant energy scale in a theory in the sense that it separates two regimes defined by energies much smaller and much larger than that mass. One expects that at low energies that mass is so big that the particle will not be excited and therefore will play a negligible role, whereas at high energies the field will effectively behave like a massless field mediating long range interactions, and you expect it to be relevant.

A mass is a dimensionful parameter, and it raises the question what it means to have dimensionless parameters. We have already extensively exploited this principle of dimen-

Figure III.4.1: *The spiralling tail.* This is the spiralling tail of the *panther chameleon* living in Madagascar.

Figure III.4.2: *The spiralling snail house.* This is a beautiful cut of a multi-chamber spiralling house of a snail. The superposed red spiral is a so-called Fibonaci spiral that gives a reasonable approximation.

sional analysis in Chapter I.3, devoted to universal constants, scales and units.[1] At this point one is tempted to claim that a theory with only dimensionless parameters is necessarily invariant under rescaling. In that perspective it furthermore appears that the behavior of a theory at energies much larger than the masses present in the theory will approximate that of some scale invariant model. Interestingly it turns out that this rule of thumb fails in a fundamental way in the quantum domain. This puzzle demands a careful analysis of scale invariance in the quantum domain, a topic that we explore towards the end of this chapter.

We start by showing some relatively easy to envisage geometrical examples of scaling linked to fractals and self-similarity. Next we consider simple dynamical systems where scaling occurs as a function of the parameter in the model. This situation represents a more abstract setting for the property of scaling and (broken) scale invariance. The first is just the *logistic map* an iconic model which exhibits the interesting property of deterministic chaos as the limit of an infinite sequence of period doubling transitions in the space of solutions. Finally we turn to particle dynamics and field theory both from the classical and quantum point of view. The most surprising and also most difficult to understand results concerning scaling are to be found in quantum field theory and generally in many-particle systems. The crucial observation to be made is that scaling can be interpreted as the model following a calculable trajectory in the parameter space of a class of models. And these trajectories may end on certain fixed points where the theory becomes scale invariant. However, depending on the initial conditions the trajectory may also run off to infinity in which case the theory loses its validity and predictive power. This is usually a call for other may be new physics to be taken into account.

[1] In this chapter we will adopt the natural units $\hbar = c = 1$, (except where explicitly indicated otherwise) which means that we can express all dimensional quantities in units of length, denoted as $[x] \sim \ell$, or in units of mass (or energy) denoted by $[\mathrm{mass}] \sim \mathrm{kg}$, which scales as inverse length: $[\mathrm{mass}] = [\mathrm{length}]^{-1} \sim \ell^{-1}$. I will from here on express all quantities in units of length.

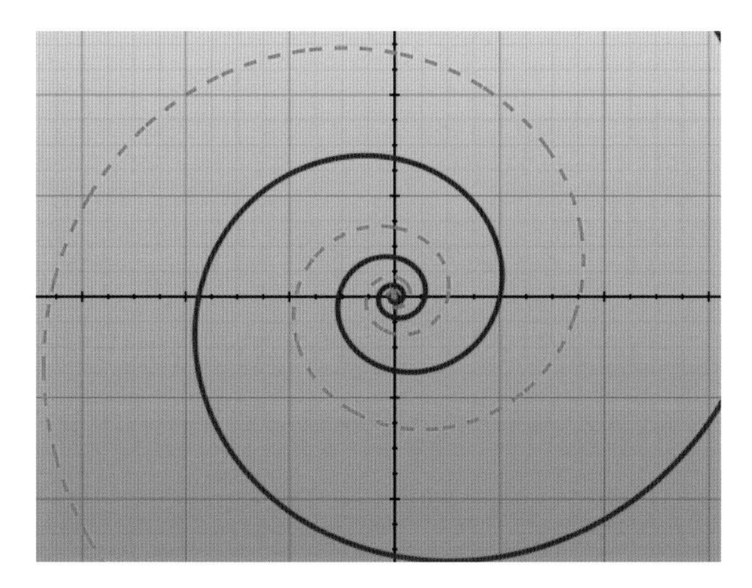

Figure III.4.3: *The logarithmic spiral.* The spiral is given by the equation (III.4.1) corresponding to the red curve. Under a scale transformation $r \to \lambda r$ the spiral is rotated over an angle $\ln \lambda$ corresponding to the blue dashed curve. The curve is therefore strictly invariant only under the discrete set of transformations where $\lambda_n = \exp 2\pi n$.

Scaling in geometry

Self similarity and fractals

Scaling. If we scale an object, we mean to say that under a rescaling of the coordinates it transforms into a larger or smaller conformal object, an object with the same shape but of a different size. If we say that something scales we mean that it has a specific behavior under scale transformations. For example we may have a geometric object like a triangle and ask how it scales when we divide all coordinates by a factor two, evidently it transforms to a triangle 'half the size'. This means that the lengths of the sides become half as long, and therefore that the area becomes one-fourth the original area. If we say that a property scales, we mean that it scales like a length to some power d, and d is then called its *scaling dimension.* So a 'volume' has a scaling dimension three and a 'point' has scaling dimension zero. This definition basically coincides with what is called the *topological dimension* n of the (vector) space $\mathbb{R}^n$, in which the object is naturally embedded.

So, in this section we address the interesting scaling properties are of certain geometric structures and constructions.

Scale invariance. If the object were to be the real line $\mathbb{R}$, then the scale transformation $x \to x/2$ would map the line on itself, and we therefore say that the line as a whole is *scale invariant.* Similarly the spaces $\mathbf{R}^n$ are scale invariant. So in that sense scale transformations are part of the space-time symmetry similar to translations, rotations or Lorentz transformations. However the latter do not change the sizes of things, and therefore leave the space-time metric (which defines the notion of distance and therefore size) invariant. As scale transformations affect the size we expect the metric to change by some overall scale or conformal factor.

The logarithmic spiral. A spiral is a wonderful geometric object that has found many stunning applications in nature as an efficient format for growth. We show two examples in Figures III.4.1 and III.4.2. We recommend reading the beautiful chapter on 'The equiangular spiral' in the famous book *On growth and form* of D'arcy Wentworth Thomson, first published in 1942. The 'equiangular spiral' is just the *logarithmic spiral* depicted in Figure III.4.1, and it is specified by giving the polar angle as a function of the radius:

$$\theta(r) = \ln r\,. \qquad \text{(III.4.1)}$$

Under a scale transformation $r \to \lambda r$ we find that $\theta \to \theta' = \ln \lambda r = \ln r + \ln \lambda\,,$: in other words we get the same curve back but rotated over an angle $\ln \lambda$. So we could say that it is invariant under a combined scale transformation and rotation over an angle of $\ln \lambda$, or we could say that it is strictly invariant under the discrete subset of scale transformations, where $\lambda_n = \exp 2\pi n$.

The Cantor set. The Cantor set can be constructed by iterating a map starting by removing the middle third of the closed unit interval $[01]$: in other words $C_1 : [0,1] \to [0,1/3] \cup [2/3,1]$ and the unit interval is mapped to the disjoint union of two smaller copies of itself. The first few iterations of this map are illustrated in Figure III.4.4. If one keeps iterating indefinitely one obtains a tree that is self similar, in the sense that every subtree is identical to a scaled version of the original tree, and one says that this set is *self-similar*. It is the prototype of a *fractal*, which is a term that refers to its dimensionality.

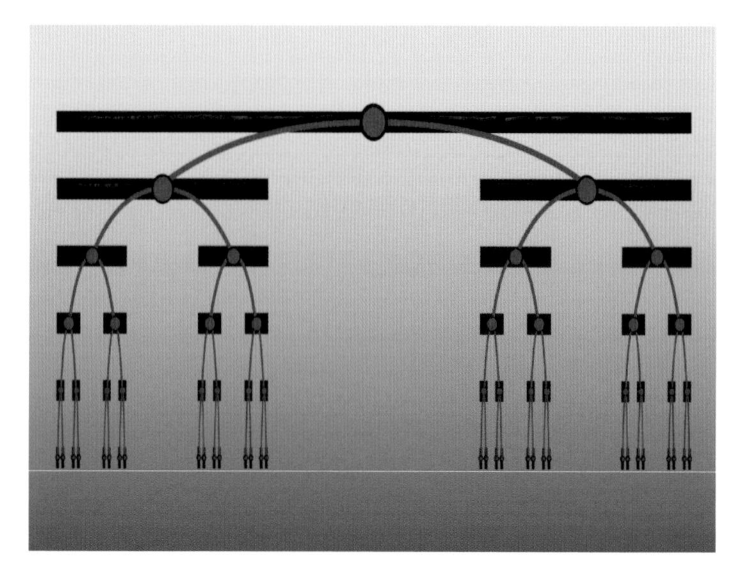

Figure III.4.4: *The Cantor set.* The Cantor set as the result of the infinite iteration of a map where the middle third of the interval is removed starting with the closed unit interval $[0,1]$. The resulting set is the prototype of a *fractal (string)*, clearly displaying the property of *self-similarity*. (Source: Sam Derbyshire)

The Hausdorff dimension. A fundamental property characteristic of the scaling property of a fractal is its non-integer *Hausdorff dimension*, which follows from the map that defines the set. At each step we generate a number of copies which we call m, and a factor s by which it is scaled down. For the Cantor set in the figure we have $m = 2$ and $s = 3$. The Hausdorff dimension is defined as $d = \ln m / \ln s$, and for the Cantor set we get the non-integer value $d = \ln 2 / \ln 3 = 0.631$. It is a fractal indeed. The definition recovers the integer topological dimensions for a line, an area or a volume, as that would amount for example to filling a square with four squares of half the size, indeed yielding $d = \ln 4 / \ln 2 = 2$.

Measure zero. The Cantor set itself is a curious mathematical object: it is an infinite set of boundary points of (length) measure zero. If we start with the unit interval of length 1, then at each step we take out $1/3$ of each subset. So the length that is left over after n iterations is $L_n = (2/3)^n$ which tells us that $L_\infty = 0$, showing that it is indeed a set of measure zero.

The Devil's Staircase, Related to this set is Cantor's function depicted in Figure III.4.5. It is a function that maps the unit interval onto itself, but it is not one-to-one. The function is constant on all regions of the interval that are taken out by the infinite iterative process. This function is also called 'The Devil's Staircase' and satisfies an intriguing functional equation:

$$f(x) = 2f(\frac{x}{3}) \quad x \in [0,1], \tag{III.4.2}$$

that fully captures its scaling behavior. The equation says that if we first cut off the curve at x=1/3 and scale it up horizontally by a factor three, and after that vertically scale it up by a factor two, we get the original function back. This formula encapsulates its scale invariance property An instructive way to think about this function is to look at it as the $n \to \infty$ limit of an iterative approximation scheme defined by:

$$f_n(x) = 2f_{n+1}(\frac{x}{3}),$$

with initial condition $f_0(x) = x$. So indeed, this staircase is develish in that it has an infinite number of steps that in some regions become extremely narrow.

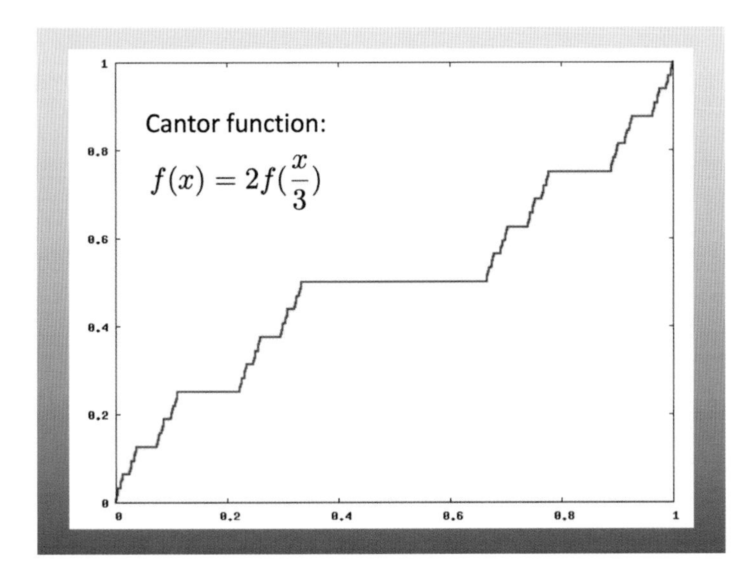

Figure III.4.5: *The Devil's staircase.* An alternative way to represent the Cantor set is as a function from the unit interval $[0, 1]$ onto itself, by Cantor's function, also known as the Devil's Staircase. It is constant on the sub-intervals taken out, and has a constant slope in between. One can guess the scaling property of this function from looking at it: it satisfies the functional equation $f(x) = 2f(x/3)$, which captures the self similarity of the function.

Figure III.4.6: *Sierpinski gasket.* This geometrical structure has fractal properties. It is a self-similar structure. If we take the number of scaling steps to infinity it becomes fractal. If we scale the dimensions by a factor 2, then the length of the yellow curve does not increase by a factor 2 but by a factor 3. This means that the scaling dimension of the gasket would be $d = \ln 3/\ln 2 = 1.58$

The Sierpinski gasket. A slightly a more complicated example is the *Sierpinski triangle* or *gasket* of Figure III.4.6, which is obtained by iterating a discrete map of a shape in to a scaled version of itself. It generates an object which is self-similar by construction. And if we iterate the mapping indefinitely we would end up with a fractal space that would be invariant under a specific set of discrete scale transformations.

The Hausdorff dimension involves again a length downscaling factor s, which for the Sierpinski triangle equals $s = 2$, and a multiplication factor $m = 3$ as is clear from the figure. Therefore the gasket has the *fractal* dimension: $d = \ln 3/\ln 2 = 1.58$.

In the figure we have also drawn a yellow fractal curve and we may apply the same argument, and because for a line segment we have again $s = 2$ and $m = 3$ we find the same value for the fractal dimension, $d = 1.58$, validating our intuition that the dimension of the gasket is more than one and less then two. We may also look at the measure of the objects, the area covered by the purple triangles after k iterations equals $A_n = (\frac{3}{4})^n A_0$, which means that the limiting area would be $A_\infty = 0$, so we find again a set of measure zero. The length of the fractal curve would tend to infinity and its measure is unbounded.

The disc where Escher and Poincaré met

In Figure III.4.7 we depicted a sequence of images that interpolate smoothly between the original Escher art work *Circle Limit II* and its underlying hyperbolic geometry of the disc. This hyperbolic tessellation (or tiling) is composed of

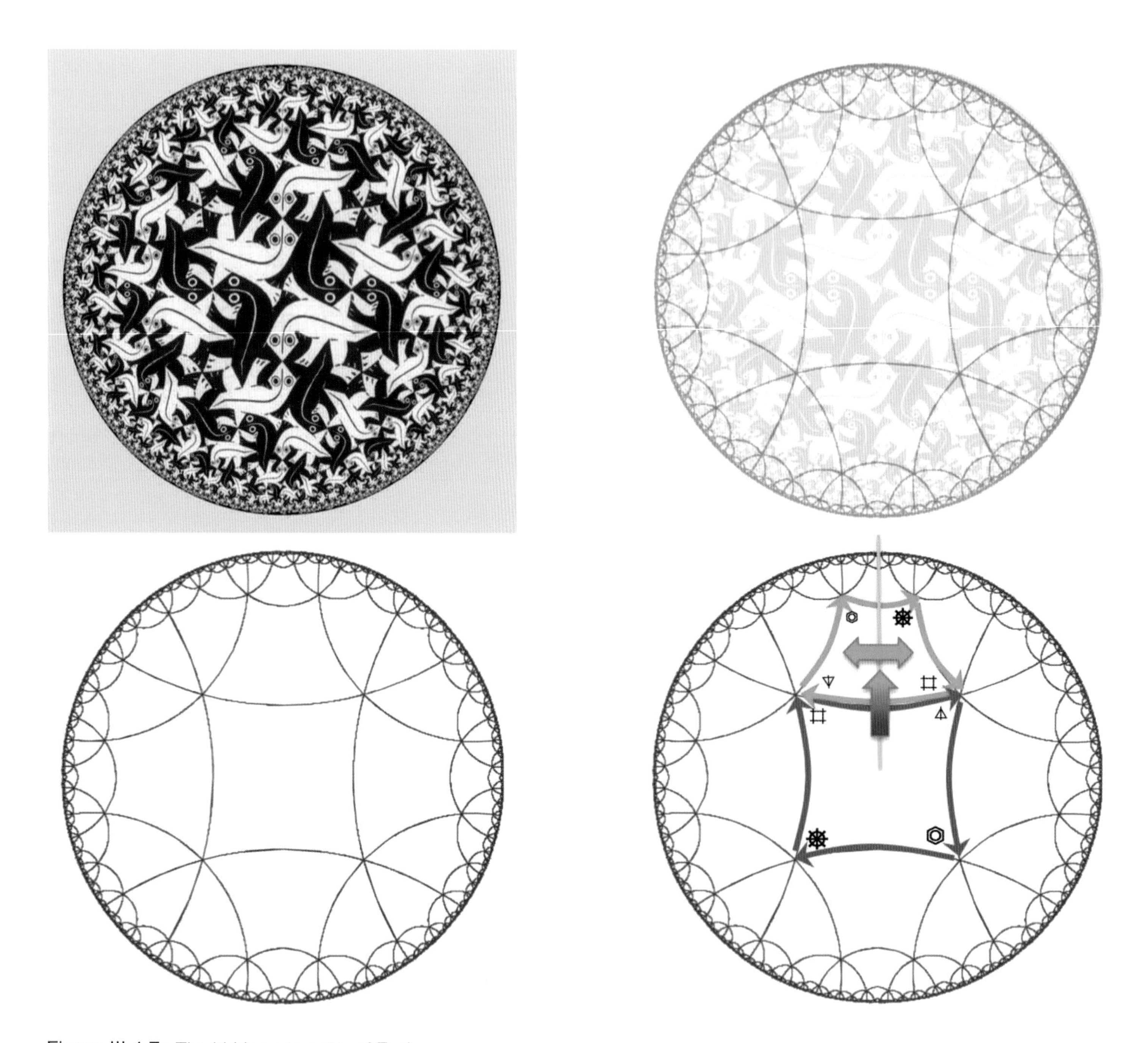

Figure III.4.7: *The hidden geometry of Escher.*

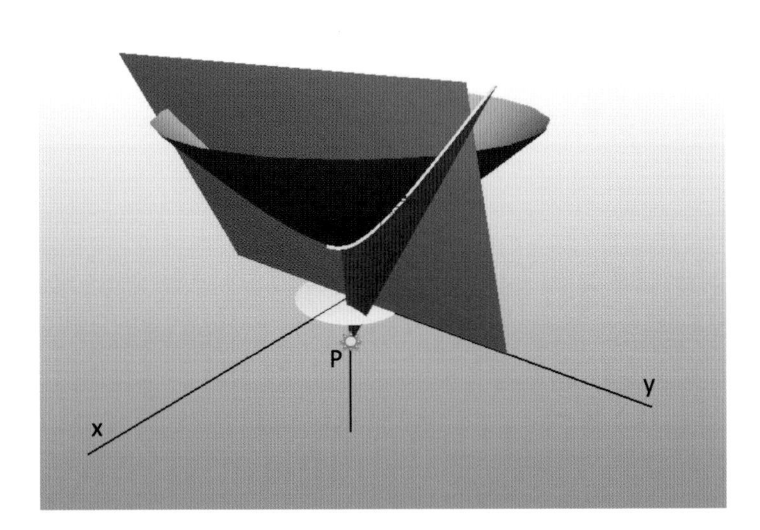

Figure III.4.8: *Poincaré disc.* In the figure we show how to get from the hyperbolic plane in orange with geodesics that are hyperbola like the yellow one. These are obtained by intersecting with a plane through the origin like the green one. The disk obtains by stereo-graphically projecting the hyperbolic plane down to the unit disc in the $z = 0$ plane to the point $P = (0, 0, 1)$.

circular segments that intersect the unit circle orthogonally. Starting with the hyperbolic square at the center one obtains the subsequent segments or vertices by mirroring (inverting) the points in the various circular segments as we indicated in Figure III.4.9. The radial tree connecting the nodes is very similar to the binary tree used to construct the Cantor set as displayed in Figure III.4.4.

The hyperbolic plane. For the hyperbolic plane we may choose the positive $z > 0$ sheet satisfying the equation $x^2 + y^2 - z^2 = 1$. It is the yellow surface in Figure III.4.8. This hyperbolic plane is not so unfamiliar as you might have thought; it is identical to the plane defined by the relativistic energy-momentum vectors p_μ for a particle with unit rest-mass living in a flat two-plus-one–dimensional Minkowski space-time which we discussed in Chapter I.1. You can also view it as the Minkowskian analogue of the unit sphere in three Euclidean dimensions (or rather the Northern hemisphere thereof), which obtains if one switches the sign in front of the z^2 term. The geodesics on the hyperbolic plane correspond to any intersection of the surface with a plane through the origin like the green plane in the figure yielding the yellow hyperbola. These hyperbolas are geodesics to be compared with straight lines on the plane or the great circles on an ordinary spherical surface.

The Poincaré disc. The disc geometry that Escher exploited corresponds to the so-called *Poincaré disc*, which is the stereographic projection of the hyperbolic plane on the unit disc in the flat z=0 plane (light grey in the figure) from the point $P = (0, 0, -1)$. For a given hyperbola one gets a line bundle like the purple surface in the figure, yielding a circular segment that approaches the circle bounding the disc orthogonally as indicated in Figure III.4.7. This bounding circle represents the circle at infinity on the hyperbolic plane. These segments accumulate towards the boundary circle which represents a critical point, or a limit like we described in the previous examples. A wonderful non-Euclidean construction indeed.

The Escher tilings. That fractal geometry of hyperbolic tessellation of the disc clearly exhibits how the basic 'amphibian' gets rescaled and rotated if one approaches the boundary, and indeed the number of them tends to infinity near the boundary. The different hyperbolic tilings can be denoted by a pair of integers $\{n, k\}$, called a Schäfli pair, where n is the number of edges of the basic polygon ($n = 4$ in this case), and k is the number of edges that meet at a vertex ($k = 6$) under equal angles, equaling $360/k$ degrees. Clearly the n angles of the polygon add up to $360\,n/k$ degrees, and if this sum is less than 360°, then we are dealing with a regular tiling of the hyperbolic plane. Note that in Chapter III.2 in the section on crystal structures we discussed the tilings by regular polygons of the plane, where indeed the condition $k = n$ could only be satisfied for $k = 3$, 4, and 6.

Maurits Escher himself was not a mathematician, but his

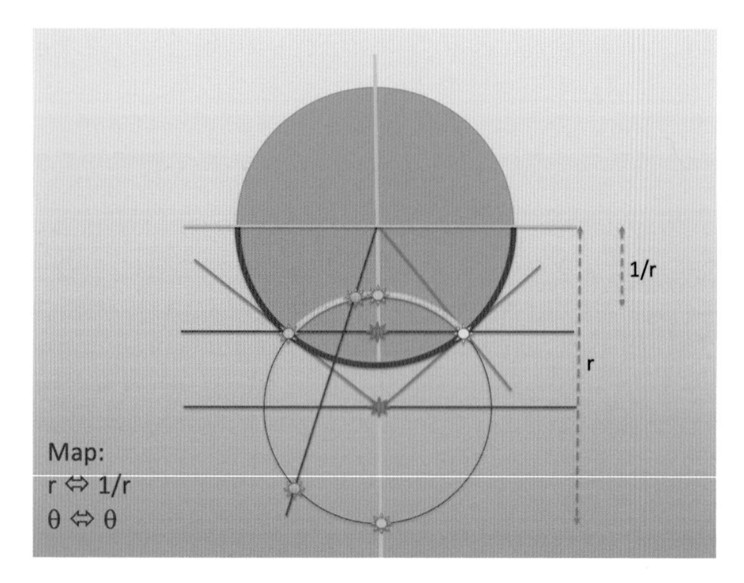

Figure III.4.9: *Inversion map.* This map defines for any point (r, θ) outside the unit circle bounding the disc a mirror point $(1/r, \theta)$.. If a circle crosses the disc, points on the inner and outer segments connected by a radial line through the center are mapped onto each other. The Escher disk combines this mirroring in ever smaller circles with mirroring in a symmetry axis through the center of the disc, as is indicated in the last picture of the previous figure.

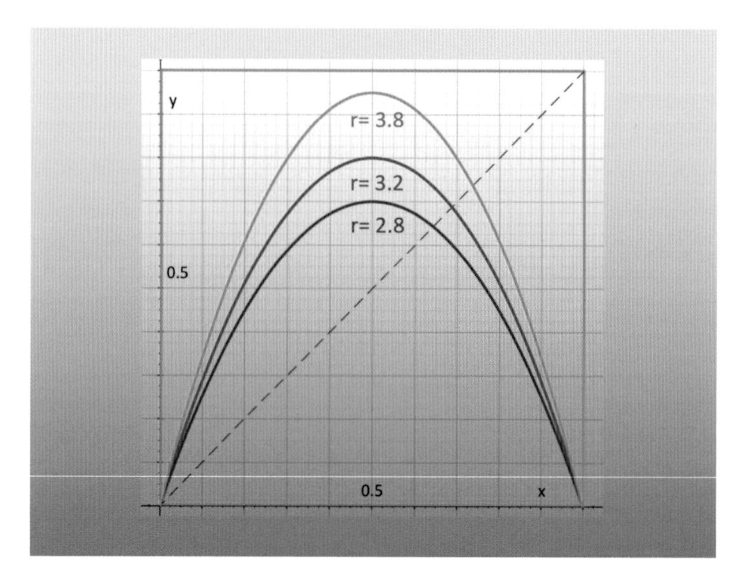

Figure III.4.10: *Logistic map.* This iterative map defines a discrete dynamical system on the unit interval $(0 \leqslant x \leqslant 1)$ and is given by $x_{n+1} = f(x_n) = r\, x_n(x_n - 1)$.

work - not surprisingly - attracted much attention from mathematicians. This started at the International Congress of Mathematicians in Amsterdam in 1954, where one of the organisers, N.G. de Bruijn, had arranged for an exhibition of Escher's work in the *Stedelijk Museum*.[2] In particular the British mathematician H.S.M. Coxeter had many exchanges with Escher on the mathematical meaning and interpretations of his work. It is clear that the interactions fascinated and inspired Escher, but it is also clear that he kept doing the mathematics in 'his own way:'

> My great enthusiasm for this sort of picture and my tenacity in pursuing the study will perhaps lead to a satisfactory solution in the end. ... it seems to be very difficult for Coxeter to write intelligibly to a layman. Finally, no matter how difficult it is, I feel all the more satisfaction from solving a problem like this in my own bumbling fashion.
>
> Escher in a letter to his son George

Escher used the term *coxeteering* for his incredibly imaginative and creative explorations of the hyperbolic disc and its tessalations in a series of prints he called *Circle Limits*.

Scaling in dynamical systems

The systems we have been looking at so far have been completely geometric where the scaling patterns were quite obvious from the start, but now we want to explore the domain of dynamical systems where scaling behavior can be more hidden but highly non-trivial. We start with the *lo-*

[2] For the mathematics of Escher's work I refer to the book edited by H. F. M. Coxeter, M. Emmer, R. Penrose and M. L. Teuber (M.C. Escher: Art and Science) and an article by Doris Schattschneider (Notices of the AMS, Volume 57, Number 6, 2010).

k	cycle(2^k)	r_k
1	2	3
2	4	3.449490
3	8	3.544090
4	16	3.564407
5	32	3.568750
6	64	3.56969
7	128	3.56989
8	256	3.569934
9	512	3.569943
10	1024	3.5699451
11	2048	3.569945557
∞	accumulation point	3.569945672

Table III.4.1: The bifurcation sequence.

gistic map which is a (discrete) dynamical system which exhibits scaling behavior in its parameter space $\{r\}$.

The logistic map

The logistic map is a canonical example of a system which displays what is called *deterministic chaos*. It is an iterative map of the unit interval $(0 \leq x \leq 1)$ onto itself, where each iteration corresponds to a time step. The map is quadratic and given by

$$x_{n+1} = f(x_n) = r\,x_n(x_n - 1) \quad (n = 1, 2, 3, \ldots)\,. \qquad \text{(III.4.3)}$$

It is plotted in Figure III.4.10 for three different values of the parameter r. This is one of the most well-studied equations in mathematical physics with a vast literature dedicated to its remarkable properties.

In Figure III.4.11 we have in the left column depicted the orbits corresponding to the first fifty iterations of the map with initial value $x_0 = 0.2$, for three values of r. What we see is that with increasing values of r the behavior of the orbit for $n \gg 1$ changes drastically.

For small r it starts with a fixed point, then we get into a region where the orbit becomes a 2-cycle, after which one obtains ever smaller regions where the period doubles to some 2^k–cycle. In the second column the same orbits are represented as a *cobweb diagram* where the successive steps are obtained by mirroring the outcome of the n–th iteration in the line $y = x$ to obtain the input for the $(n+1)$–th iteration. In these diagrams the limit cycle behavior is very clear. In the right column we have depicted the so-called *bifurcation diagram*, which shows what the cycles are as a function of r and at what values the period doubling occurs. For increasing r the points r_k, where the period doubles occurs and the 2^k-cycle starts, accumulate at some critical point $r_\infty = 3.56995\ldots$, where a transition to chaotic behavior occurs.

The bifurcation diagram of Figure III.4.12 suggest that there is some form of self-similarity present in this system and it was Mitchell J. Feigenbaum who in 1978 extracted two fundamental constants from the system that characterize the scale invariance of the system near the critical point r_∞.

The first Feigenbaum constant is given by the limiting behavior of the following sequence (see figure):

$$\lim_{k\to\infty} \frac{r_k - r_{k-1}}{r_{k+1} - r_k} = \lim_{k\to\infty} \frac{d_k}{d_{k+1}} = \delta = 4.6692\ldots\,. \qquad \text{(III.4.4)}$$

This number δ is universal in that it does not depend on the details of the map as long as it has quadratic behavior near the maximum and vanishes at the endpoints of the interval, and it turns out that this constant governs the asymptotic behavior of all period doubling sequences. One might rephrase the above equation by saying that for large $k \gg 1$ the interval $d^*_k = r_\infty - r_k$ converges like a geometric series $d^*_k \simeq C\delta^{-k}$.

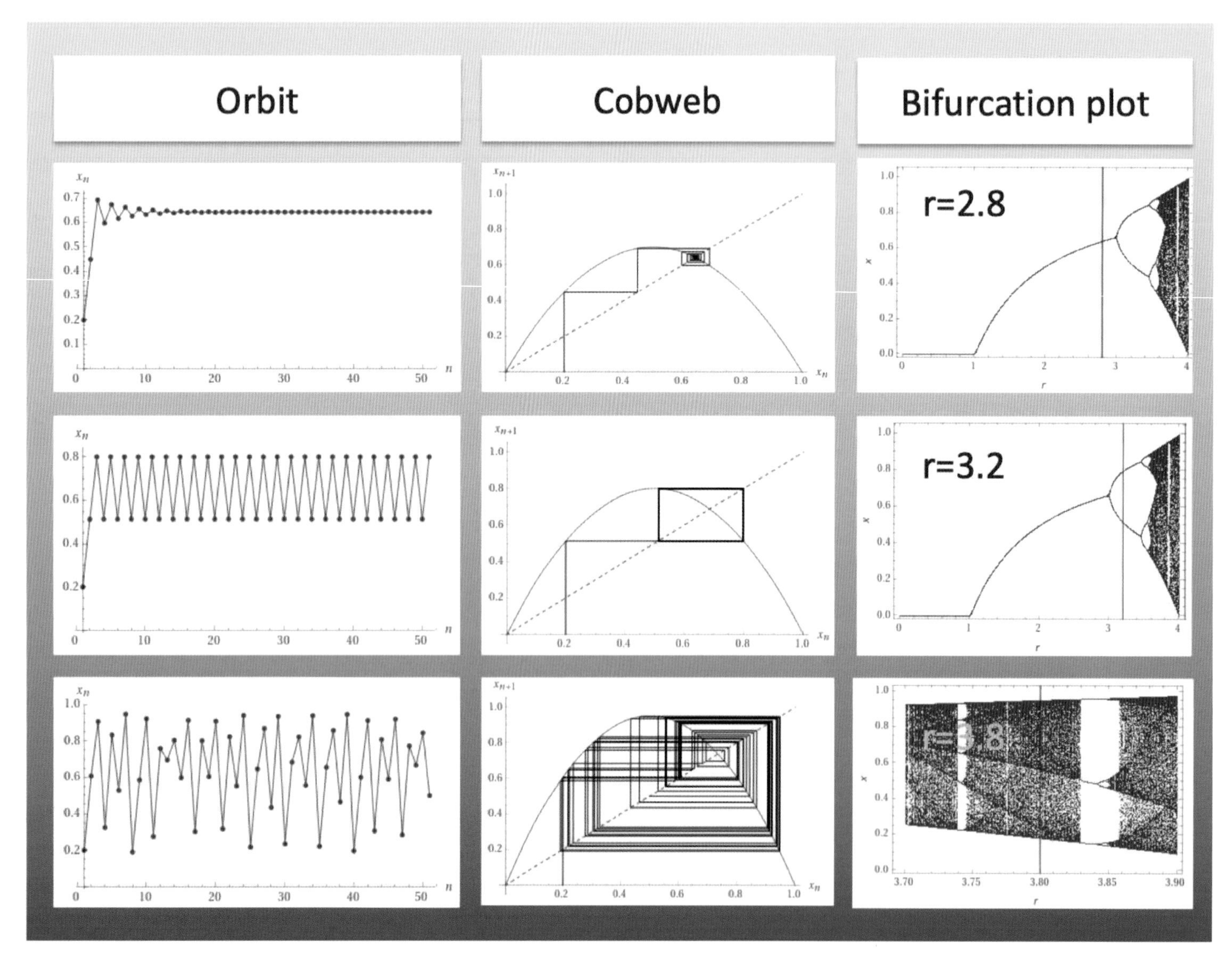

Figure III.4.11: *Logistic map orbits.* We show orbits starting at $x = 0.2$ for different three different r values ($r = 2.8, 3.2$ and 3.8) in the first column. In the second column the same orbits are given as 'cobwebs.' In the final column we marked the corresponding r values in the bifurcation diagram.

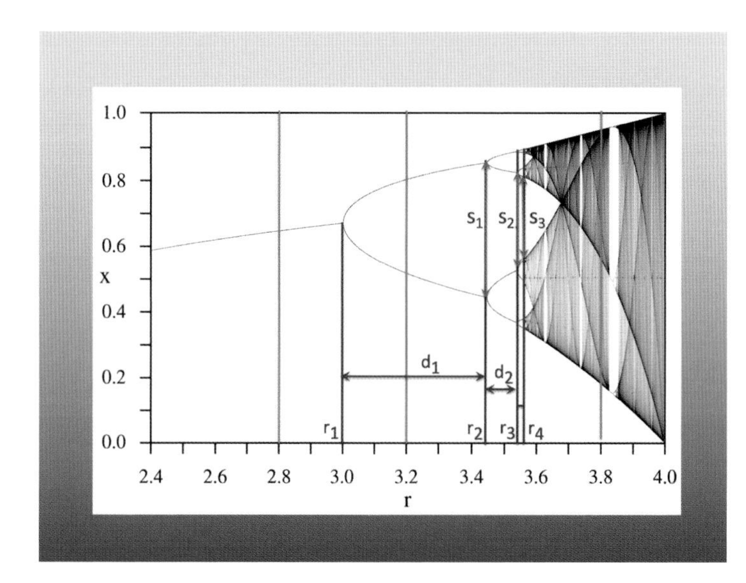

Figure III.4.12: *Bifurcation diagram.* This diagram gives the x values in the subsequent 2^k limit cycles as a function of the r parameter of the logistic map. The limiting behavior does not depend on the initial value x_0, and forms therefore a *global attractor.* Starting at small r the sequence of points r_k where the doubling to a 2^k-cycle starts accumulates at some point $r_\infty = 3.56995...$, after which a highly unpredictable limiting behavior sets in, which is called *deterministic chaos.*

There is a second universal constant that can be extracted from the diagram. It is determined by the limiting behavior of the sequence of separations s_k, where s_k is the separation in x between the two adjacent central values of the 2^k-cycle at $r = r_{k+1}$, as we have indicated in the figure. For large k one finds that $s_{k+1} = s_k/\alpha$ where $\alpha = 2.5029\ldots$.

The essential scaling property of the limiting behavior of the period doubling sequence is expressed by a scaling function $g(x)$, which would be the solution of a functional[3] equation analogous to equation (III.4.2) for the devil's stair-

[3] A *function* $f(x)$ is a mapping from a space $\mathcal{X}$ of the variable to some space of function values, like the real line $\mathbb{R}$ or the complex plane $\mathbb{C}$. Formally a *functional* is a 'function of a function' and corresponds to a map from a space or a certain class of functions $\mathcal{F}$ to a space of values like $\mathbb{R}$ or $\mathbb{C}$.

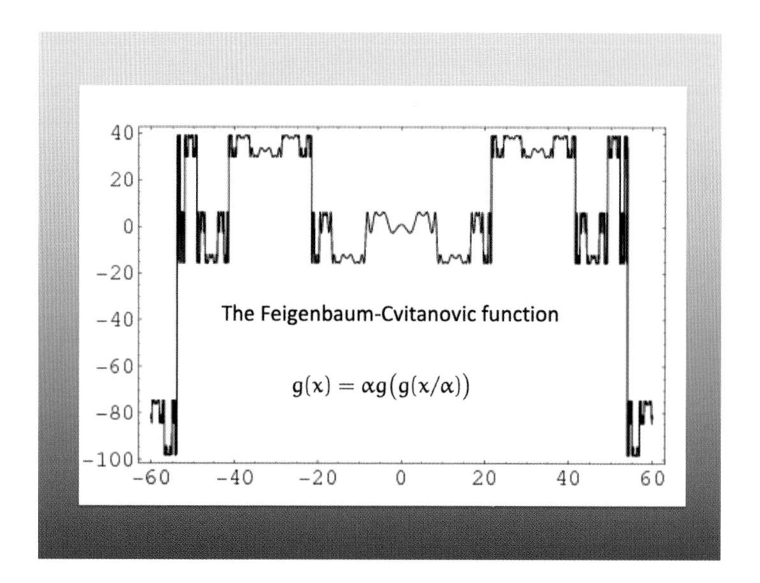

Figure III.4.13: *Feigenbaum-Cvitanovic function.* The F-C function can be compared with Cantor's staircase function. It captures the strange attractor of the logistic map. The function satisfies the F-C functional equation $g(x) = \alpha g(g(x/\alpha))$.

case. The equation for the period doubling sequence is called the Feigenbaum-Cvitanovic equation:

$$g(x) = \alpha g(g(x/\alpha)), \qquad \text{(III.4.5)}$$

with boundary condition $g(0) = 1$. There is a unique solution to this equation that fixes both the value of α and the function $g(x)$ which you should think of as specifying the attractor at the accumulation point (the set of 2^k points in the limit $k \to \infty$). The F-C function is plotted in Figure III.4.13, and could have been called the 'devil's castle' because the embattlements contain ever smaller self-similar versions of the castle. A stunning architectural masterpiece obviously. A remarkable property of this equation and thus its solution is that it is independent of the precise form of the logistic map f, and it is in that sense that the parameter alpha is *universal* over the class of functions $\{f\}$.

Scaling in quantum theory

Quantum mechanics

In earlier chapters we have argued that (continuous) space-time symmetries lead to conserved quantities, and that in quantum theory these conserved quantities are represented by certain operator expressions that act on the Hilbert space. These operators are expressed as functions of the basic degrees of freedom. So, in the quantum mechanics of a particle the basic operators are X and P, corresponding to the classical phase space coordinates x and p. And from these one can construct the operators for other dynamical variables like the energy or angular momentum. The operators work on the Hilbert space of wave functions. In quantum field theory the basic operators are the fields themselves and their conjugate momentum fields and these work on the multi-particle Hilbert space.

Operators that represent space-time symmetries. In a quantum system symmetry operators commute with the Hamiltonian, and therefore transform states that have the same energy among each other: in other words, states that are degenerate. We recall that for the case of the hydrogen atom, the energy levels are labeled by the principal quantum number n, and for any n we have an n^2 degenerate set of states. This set consists of representations of the rotation group $SO(3)$ labeled by the angular momentum eigenvalues l, with $l = 0, \ldots, n-1$. At a given energy level n the total degeneracy can be understood if one adds the Runge-Lenz vector, to be thought of as a vector of symmetry operators to the symmetry algebra. This is a dynamical symmetry which follows from the particular form of the Coulomb (or Newton) potential and is not related to an underlying space-time symmetry. Inclusion of this vector extends the symmetry algebra from $so(3)$ to $so(4)$, as we discussed in connection with Figure II.6.3 in Chapter II.6.

Let us now turn to the expression for the operator Λ that generates scale transformations on a one-particle Hilbert space. We do so after we have recalled how it worked for the case of translations.

The case of translations generated by momentum. In previous chapters we discussed how in quantum theory the momentum operator P acting on a wave function is represented as the Hermitean differential operator $P = -id/dx$ $(\hbar = 1)$. This operator generates 'translations' meaning to say that if we act with a finite transformation on any function

$$T(a)f(x) \equiv e^{iaP}f(x) = f(x+a),$$

then the argument of the function is shifted by an amount a. The momentum operator has a continuous set of eigenfunctions $f_k(x) \simeq e^{ikx}$ because:

$$P\, f_k(x) = kf_k(x).$$

These functions are periodic and the expansion of an arbitrary function in this basis of eigenfunctions amounts to a Fourier decomposition of that function. Needless to say that the only translation invariant function is the constant function, corresponding to $k = 0$. Finally we recall that translational invariance of a system implied that the momentum operator would commute with the Hamiltonian, and henceforth momentum would be conserved.

The scaling operator Λ and its eigenfunctions. Now we ask the same questions about scale invariance: what is the operator representing scale transformations on functions, and what are its eigenfunctions, and finally, what does it mean to say that a system is scale invariant? The scale operator is $\Lambda(x) \equiv x\dfrac{d}{dx}$ and its eigenfunctions are quite simple to derive:

$$\begin{aligned} &x\frac{d}{dx}\, g_d(x) = d\, g_d(x) \\ &\qquad \Rightarrow \frac{dg_d}{g_d} = \frac{d}{x} \Rightarrow \ln g_d = d \ln x = \ln x^d . \end{aligned} \tag{III.4.6}$$

So again there is a continuum of eigenfunctions which are just powers of x : $g_d(x) \sim x^d$ for any d. The eigenvalue d is called the scaling dimension. Under a finite scaling transformation $S(\alpha)$ we would get:

$$S(\alpha)g_d(x) \equiv e^{\alpha x(d/dx)}g_d(x) = e^{\alpha d}g_d(x).$$

This expression gains transparency and elegance if we take the parameter logarithmic:

$$S(\ln\lambda)g_d(x) = e^{d\ln\lambda}g_d(x) = \lambda^d g_d(x) = g_d(\lambda x).$$

Power laws. This gives an alternative way to define a *scaling function* in general; it is any function $h(x)$ that satisfies the scaling law:

$$h(\lambda x) = \lambda^d h(x), \tag{III.4.7}$$

for any λ, where the power d is defined as the scaling dimension of the function. Indeed the scaling functions are the eigenfunctions of the scaling operator and are just single powers of their argument. A scale invariant function is the eigenfunction with $d = 0$, again meaning any constant function.

We just saw that making the scale transformation $S(\ln\lambda)$ on an eigenfunction effectively multiplies the argument of that function with λ. This is a special property in the sense that it multiplies the argument and not the function. Thus, if I apply the operator to an arbitrary linear combination of eigenfunctions, I get exactly the same combination back with scaled argument. In other words if we think of an arbitrary function that can formally be expanded in a power series, then what the scale transformation S does is just to scale the argument of that arbitrary function. This is to be expected because it is the defining property of a scaling transformation on any function, but it does not imply that any arbitrary function is a scaling function, as it will in general not satisfy the scaling property (III.4.7).

The symmetry algebra including scaling. To further discuss scaling properties it is useful to study its commutation relations with other elementary operators forming the dynamical Lie algebra. For example from

$$\begin{aligned} [\Lambda, X] &= \frac{i}{\hbar}[XP, X] = \frac{i}{\hbar}(XPX - XXP) = \frac{i}{\hbar}X[P, X] = X \\ [\Lambda, P] &= \frac{i}{\hbar}[XP, P] = \frac{i}{\hbar}(XPP - PXP) = \frac{i}{\hbar}[X, P]P = -P \end{aligned} \tag{III.4.8}$$

It gives the operator back multiplied by its naive scaling dimension, which is the dimension of the operator in units of length. Note that the angular momentum operator has scaling dimension zero as it involves products of X and P components; this is also consistent with its quantization in integer multiples of $\hbar$ which at this point is dimensionless as it has units $Js \sim \ell^0$.

The calculation we just did shows that we can extend the combined Lorentz and translation symmetry, denoted as the *Poincaré group*, with the scale transformations. Including the scale transformations we also need to include the so-called *inversion operator* I with $I : \mathbf{x} \to \mathbf{x}/x^2$. Adding these two operators to the dynamical operator algebra, one ends up with a closed Lie algebra with fifteen generators, which is referred to as the *conformal algebra* which for four-dimensional Minkowski space is the algebra $so(4,2)$. This algebra corresponds (is isomorphic) to the 'rotations' in a six-dimensional 'space' with four space and two time dimensions.

So far we have mainly discussed mathematical features of scaling functions and operators. Let us now return to the physics of scale invariance. We do this at various levels of increasing complexity starting with simple classical systems and moving up to applications of scaling in quantum (field) theory.

Scaling properties of some Hamiltonians. Having the scale operator it is interesting to see what one can learn about the scaling properties of some Hamiltonians and other operators.

To keep it simple we look at a particle with Hamiltonian $H = U + V$ or Lagrangian $L = U - V$, where kinetic term $U = P^2/2M$ and for the potential we choose a simple power, $V = a_k x^k$. Now for consistency we must have that $[H] = [U] = [V] = \ell^{-1}$. This implies that indeed $[U] = [M]^{-1} \cdot 2[P] = \ell^{-1}$, as expected. For the potential term we find that $[V] = [a_k] \cdot \ell^k = \ell^{-1}$, from which we conclude that $[a_k] = \ell^{-1-k}$, so this simple power counting yields the dimensionality of the parameters or coupling constants.

We see that the kinetic and potential terms will in general scale differently under scale transformations of the coordinates. Just transforming coordinates and keeping the parameters fixed we get that:

$$x \to x' = \lambda x \Rightarrow H \to H' = \frac{1}{\lambda} H(\lambda) = \frac{p^2}{\lambda^2 M} + a_k \lambda^k x^k .$$

This expression leads us to conclude that under a rescaling of the coordinates the Hamiltonian is mapped into a similar Hamiltonian $H(\lambda)$, with different, scale dependent, parameters: $M' = M(\lambda) = \lambda M$ and $a_k' = a_k(\lambda) = \lambda^{k+1} a_k$.

Let us look at some simple cases:

1. The harmonic oscillator.
The potential is given by $V(x) = \frac{1}{2} K x^2$, and corresponds to the case $k = 2$. The spectrum is depicted in Figure II.5.14 on page 162 of Part II. It is equally spaced, with energy levels $E_n = \omega(n + \frac{1}{2})$ where the frequency ω is given by $\omega = \sqrt{K/M}$. The frequency is the only physically relevant parameter and we see that its scale dependence is : $\omega(\lambda) = \sqrt{K(\lambda)/M(\lambda)} = \lambda\omega$. The spectrum apparently scales linearly with λ.

The concept that we want to emphasize is the fact that under scaling the theory changes. If we define the theory as a point in the space of parameters, then under rescaling the theory will trace out a trajectory in that space. In the example at hand, the parameter space is a plane with coordinates M and K. With $M(\lambda) = \lambda M$ and $K(\lambda) = \lambda^3 K$, we see that we can eliminate the λ, to obtain a function $K(\lambda) = (K/M^3) M(\lambda)^3$. We have depicted one such trajectory for a particular initial condition $K(1) = K$ and $M(1) = M$ in Figure III.4.14.

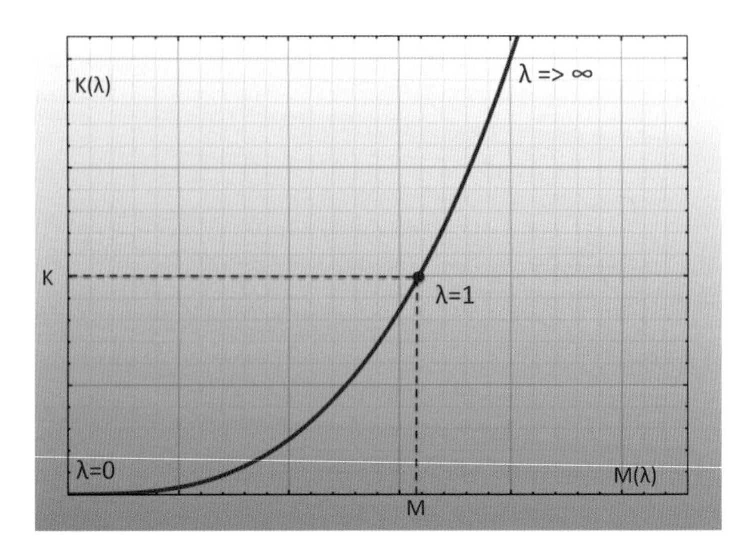

Figure III.4.14: *Scaling trajectory of harmonic oscillator.* Scaling the coordinate by a factor λ in the harmonic oscillator Hamiltonian is equivalent to a trajectory of the parameters $M(\lambda)$ and $K(\lambda)$ through parameter space.

What we learn from this graph is not earth-shattering, just that for large values of λ, the potential term starts to dominate so that the system will get locked into the ground state. On the other hand if $\lambda \to 0$ the kinetic term dominates and the hamiltonian approaches that of a free particle, where the energy gap tends to zero. So at short distances the theory has a fixed point where the theory is free, a primitive precursor of the notion of what is called 'asymptotic freedom'. This is not so surprising, because it is what we could have concluded directly from the linear λ dependence of $\omega(\lambda)$, which implies that the energy gap tends to zero.

2. The hydrogen atom.

The part of the Hamiltonian that is of interest here is the radial part because when we scale the coordinates we rescale the r variable and not the angular variables θ and φ. This reflects the fact that the angular derivatives of the Hamiltonian are all contained in the the term $\mathbf{L}^2/2Mr^2$, where the angular momentum operator $\mathbf{L} = \mathbf{X} \times \mathbf{P}$. In view of the relations (III.4.8) the scaling dimension of $\mathbf{L}$ is $d_L = 0$, and thus, as stated before, the angular momentum is scale invariant. So, we are left with the 'radial' Hamiltonian, which is very similar to the one given in equation (I.4.1) we discussed in Chapter I.4, it takes the form:

$$H = \frac{p_r^2}{2M} + \frac{l(l+1)}{2Mr^2} - \frac{e^2}{4\pi r},$$

where l is the angular momentum label, and $l(l+1)$ is the eigenvalue of the operator $\mathbf{L}^2$. Doing the scaling exercise as before we find that $M(\lambda) = \lambda M$ and, interestingly, that the charge does *not* rescale $e(\lambda) = e$. Let us look what that implies for the spectrum in this case, the discrete bound state energy levels are labeled by the principal quantum number n, and are given by:

$$E_n = \frac{E_1}{n^2} \quad \text{with} \quad E_1 = M\left(\frac{e^2}{4\pi}\right)^2.$$

We conclude that the levels simply scale like $E_n(\lambda) = \lambda E_n$, confirming our naive expectations.

On the one-particle level the quantum analysis of scaling properties does not lead to surprising new insights. It merely confirms the behavior you would expect on the basis of naive dimensional analysis. As we will see in the remaining sections of this chapter it is in quantum field theory that interesting complications arise.

Quantum field theory

In this subsection we turn to the question what scaling means in quantum field theory. We will look at this problem from a rather general and abstract point of view, avoiding as many technicalities as possible. In later sections we give more details about how these results can be obtained.

The fundamental question is again to understand how parameters of the model change depending on the scale at which one looks at the system. And as the quantum uncertainty relations imply an inverse relation between spatial scale (wavelength) and momentum or energy, we expect to learn something about the energy dependence of the phenomena the theory describes. By exploiting arguments like the ones we used in the previous subsection we may even probe the domain of validity of certain theories.

Actions and Lagrangians. In general a theory can be defined by its energy function or Hamiltonian H, or its action S. As mentioned before, in relativistic systems and field theories, one prefers the action because it is a manifestly Lorentz invariant quantity, while the energy is not as it is a component of the energy-momentum four vector.

The action can be written as a functional of the field, a space-time integral over a *Lagrange density* $\mathcal{L}$, which is an expression in the fields and their derivatives. We write:

$$S = \int \mathcal{L}\, d^4x, \qquad \text{(III.4.9)}$$

and in units where $\hbar = c = 1$ the action is a dimensionless quantity. At this point the difference between the quantum and classical expression resides completely in the interpretation of the fields. Classical fields are just scalar, or vector, or spinor valued functions on coordinate space. Quantum fields are very different types of objects: they are operator valued and work on some multi-particle Hilbert space as we discussed in Chapters I.4 and II.5.

Three examples. In the remaining sections of this chapter we will refer to the three different examples of Lagrangian densities we introduce next.

- *The ϕ^4 model.* The first action is about the simplest non-trivial field theory one can think of and it owes its popularity exactly to the fact that it is often used to demonstrate the intricacies of quantum field theory. It is a theory of a real scalar field $\phi(x^\mu)$ with a quartic self-interaction. The action of this so-called 'ϕ-fourth theory' is defined by the relativistic Lagrangian density $\mathcal{L}$:

$$\mathcal{L}(\phi, \partial_\mu\phi) = \frac{1}{2}(\partial_\mu\phi)^2 + \frac{1}{2}m^2\phi^2 + \frac{\lambda_4}{4!}\phi^4 . \qquad \text{(III.4.10)}$$

The classical field ϕ is just an arbitrary function which may be expanded in an orthonormal set of basis functions, for example energy momentum eigenstates or planes waves $\{\phi(k)\}$:

$$\phi(x) \sim \int \phi(k)\, e^{-ik\cdot x}\, d^4k .$$

In Chapter II.5 we pointed out that in quantum field theory the fields are operators acting on a multi-particle Hilbert space and can create or annihilate particles in any given energy momentum state labeled by k^μ. with $k^2 = m^2$ (m = rest mass). The first two terms of the Lagrangian are often denoted as $\mathcal{L}_0$, and being quadratic in the fields, they make up the free field theory. The last term denoted by $\mathcal{L}_{int}$ describes the self-interactions of the field with coupling strengh λ_4.

- *The toy model.* Of course a field theory can be defined in any number of space-time dimensions, and formally nothing forbids us, for pedagogical reasons, to restrict ourselves to a theory with only a time dimension. Then the field becomes just like a time-dependent position coordinate $\phi(t) \sim x(t)$. We may even go one step further, as we will do here, and consider a *zero-dimensional* field theory. 'That is not much of a theory', you might complain, and your point is well taken. Zero-dimensional means there is no space and no time, so the 'field' has just a single constant mode (like the zero-energy mode of the theory above), so the 'field' is just a real or complex variable. It is very much a toy model that we only introduce to illustrate at a very basic level what the effect of quantum corrections in a field theory look like.

Our toy model only has two real modes: a light mode with 'mass' m denoted by φ, and a heavy mode with 'mass' $M >> m$ denoted by χ and is defined by a simple polynomial action:

$$S(\varphi, \chi) = \frac{m^2}{2}\varphi^2 + \frac{M^2}{2}\chi^2 + \frac{\lambda}{4}\varphi^2\chi^2 . \qquad \text{(III.4.11)}$$

This action has no derivatives; the terms quadratic in the fields represent the free modes and the quartic term describes the interaction between the two modes. This very rudimentary theory will in the next section be used to illustrate certain structural (diagrammatic) aspects of perturbation theory and Feynman rules.

- *Quantum Electrodynamics* The third example is the Lagrangian for QED, the theory we discussed already in Chapter I.4 and in the section on gauge invariance in Chapter II.6 ,

$$\mathcal{L} = -\frac{1}{4}F_{\mu\nu}F^{\mu\nu} + \bar{\psi}(i\partial\!\!\!/ + m\mathbf{1} + eA\!\!\!/)\psi . \qquad \text{(III.4.12)}$$

Let us make some observations about this Lagrangian:
(i) It is a compact expression of which each part is manifestly Lorentz and gauge invariant.
(ii) Besides the Maxwell field describing the photon, and the Dirac field describing the electrons and positrons, the action contains two parameters: the electron/positron mass m and the coupling constant corresponding to the electron charge e.
(iii) The first three terms are quadratic in the fields and represent the free part of the action. The first term gives rise to the free photon propagator, while the second and third correspond to the free electron/positron propagator. In the Feynman diagrammatic language these propagators correspond to the wiggly and straight lines that were shown in Figure I.4.28 in Chapter I.4, while the final interaction term corresponds to the interaction vertex diagram of Figure I.4.29. They are also shown in Figure III.4.19.

The naive scaling dimensions of fields. To be able to discuss the scaling properties we first determine the naive

Field	Dimension	Coupling	Dimension
$\phi(x)$	-1	m	-1
		λ_n	$4-n$
$A_\mu(x)$	-1	e	0
$\Psi(x)$	$-\frac{3}{2}$		

Table III.4.2: *Scaling dimensions in 4-dimensional space-time.* We have listed the naive 'power counting' scaling dimensions in units of length of some fields and coupling constants. The self-couplings λ_n refer to terms in the energy density of the type $\lambda_n \phi^n$. Note that the quartic coupling for scalar field is dimensionless: $[\lambda_4] = \ell^0$.

scaling dimensions of the fields, which are obtained by applying dimensional analysis. A good starting point is the action which in the system with $\hbar = c = 1$ has dimension zero: $[S] \sim \ell^0$, and the Lagrangian therefore has units $[\mathcal{L}] \sim \ell^{-4}$. From the quadratic terms in the Lagrangian of the scalar field given by equation (III.4.16) we learn that the dimension of the field has to be $[\phi] \sim \ell^{-1}$. Consequently the quartic self-coupling of the $\lambda\phi^4$ term λ has to be dimensionless. For the Maxwell field the Lagrangian $[\mathcal{L}] \sim F^2 \sim (\partial A)^2$ and as $[\mathcal{L}] \sim \ell^{-4}$ we conclude that the gauge potential, like the scalar field, scales like $[A] \sim \ell^{-1}$. From the mass term for the Dirac field $\sim m\overline{\psi}\psi$ we obtain that $[\psi] \sim \ell^{-3/2}$. And from the interaction term $e\not{A}\overline{\psi}\psi$ we subsequently verify that the coupling constant e is dimensionless. We summarize the naive scaling dimensions in units of length, of the various fields and coupling constants in the Table III.4.2.

Scaling in classical field theory. Assigning these scaling dimensions to the fields allows us to discuss the scale invariance of classical field theories. To find out we make a scale transformation of the coordinates $x \to \lambda x$. The fields being space-time dependent will transform accordingly, like $\varphi(x) \to \varphi(\lambda x) = \lambda^d \varphi(x)$. Note that the parameters *do not* transform under this coordinate transformation. After the transformation of the coordinates and fields we see that most terms in the action are invariant, and only the mass terms change in the sense that $m \to m' = \lambda m$. The net effect is that after the transformation you get the same theory back but with a different mass parameter. This argument shows that already at the classical level rescaling corresponds to the theory moving through parameter space. A further message is that in classical theories the mass terms break scale invariance. Massless theories like the Maxwell theory are therefore scale invariant. In fact these results also hold for the classical approximation of the quantum theory, where we think of the field excitations as particle states but where we ignore the typical quantum corrections as will become clear shortly. In the quantum domain we have to take into account the inverse relation between length scales (wavelength) and momentum or energy scales. This implies that if we scale the theory by large λ we effectively take the low energy, long wave length limit which means that the mass is relatively large and in the limit would become the dominant term. In that regime we cannot excite particle modes and there is no dynamics left. If we take the opposite $\lambda \to 0$ limit, then we study the theory in the high-energy regime where the mass effectively plays no role! And at this level of the discussion we would be tempted to conclude that theories become scale invariant in the high-energy limit. However, this conclusion turns out to be premature because taking the quantum corrections into account we will see that these break this naively expected scale invariance.

Quantum complications. To make sensible predictions in quantum field theory that can be compared with experiment, the calculations which are perturbative in nature, require a *renormalization program* to be executed.[4] It is

[4] I must admit that this sounds like the theory is 'abnormal' and has

exactly this renormalization program, which involves cutting off certain momentum integrals that is responsible for the scaling violations. These violations lead to *anomalous scaling dimensions* for the parameters and fields.

We will try to elucidate some of the outstanding features of that program. One we have mentioned already is that rescaling the theory is the same as effectively rescaling the parameters in the model. What one finds is that potentially at every successive step in the quantum approximation new interaction terms may appear in what is called the *effective action*. In other words, conceivable terms that had zero coefficient in the classical theory one starts with, may become non-zero. And the behavior of the theory under rescaling depends on to what extent these extra terms are relevant at the scale one is interested in. The strong requirement of *renormalizability* means that only a finite number of scale dependent renormalizations of parameters and fields is needed to render the calculations finite to any order. This implies that systematic quantum calculations can be made which lead to unambiguous predictions for physical observables to arbitrary precision.

The Euclidean path integral

As we pointed out in the subsection on statistical mechanics in Chapter I.1, there is a interesting analogy between the statistical description of multi-particle classical physics and quantum physics, in spite of all their fundamental differences. This is not too surprising because after all, a field has an infinite number of modes that represents an infinite number of local degrees of freedom and we learned that quantum field theory defines a Hilbert space with states that can have any number of particles in it.

to go to a camp to be 'renormalized,' through a process of 'ideological purification,' in order to adapt it to the 'new normal'. This terminology of course started with *normalizing* wave functions and distributions, just meaning imposing a norm, saying nothing about wavefunctions being normal or not.

In classical statistical physics we can derive the thermodynamic properties from the partition function, Z which is the sum or integral over the phase space Γ of the system, weighted by the Boltzmann factor,

$$Z = \int \exp(-H/kT)\, d\Gamma\,,$$

where $H = H(\Gamma)$ is the Hamiltonian of the system, the integral of the energy density over all of space. An important quantity is then the (Helmholtz) free energy F defined as $F = -kT \ln Z$. What we showed in Chapter I.1 was that the *free energy* was equal $F = U - TS$. And we worked through the example of the ideal gas in the section on page 53. One thing is obvious, the (classical) statistical physics underlying thermodynamics becomes racing a dead horse if the temperature is zero, because there is no thermodynamics as everything is stuck in its lowest state. But that is different in the quantum domain.

The analogy. Quantum field theory is basically a theory at zero temperature, though of course a temperature can be introduced in addition. But what makes quantum field theory at zero temperature already interesting is that there are always quantum fluctuations present in the system. This is an unavoidable consequence of the uncertainty principle. Indeed, the role of thermal fluctuations is taken up by the quantum fluctuations, and instead of the temperature the external parameters are typically Planck's constant and possibly some coupling constants. In some sense you could argue that Planck's constant takes the place of Boltzmann's constant and the external parameter that plays the role of temperature is a fundamental coupling strength appearing in the theory. And indeed whereas the free energy governs the classical phase diagram depending on the thermodynamic variables like P, V, T and S, that role is now played by the masses and coupling constants. Therefore one may expect different quantum phases and phase transitions to occur in different regions of parameter space even at zero temperature.

Statistical Physics		Quantum Field Theory	
Phase space	Γ	Field	ϕ
Energy function	$H(\Gamma)$	Euclidean Action	$S[\phi]$
Partition function	$Z = \int e^{-H(\Gamma)/kT}\, d\Gamma$	Path integral	$Z = \int e^{-S[\phi]/\hbar}[d\phi]$
Free energy	$F = -kT \ln Z$	Effective action	$S_{eff} = -\hbar \ln Z$

Table III.4.3: *Correspondence between the fundamental concepts of (classical) statistical physics and quantum field theory.*

The path integral. This fascinating analogy between classical statistical physics and quantum field theory becomes much more tangible once we introduce the *Euclidean path integral* as a tool to do calculations in quantum field theory. In quantum theory we define the (Euclidean) path integral or *quantum partition function*, as a weighted sum over the *classical* configuration space, where each configuration is weighted by the exponential of its classical action:

$$Z \equiv \int e^{-S[\phi]/\hbar}[d\phi]\,. \tag{III.4.13}$$

So indeed, the path integral approach to quantum theory does away with wave functions and in fact with Hilbert space, but shows that the same information on quantum amplitudes can be extracted from the corresponding classical expressions, and averaged over all paths or classical field configurations that match the required boundary conditions. Of course this integration over infinite-dimensional spaces is not simple and to properly define it one encounters a lot of mathematical pittfalls. It requires defining a proper integration measure $[d\Phi]$ for the 'space of field configurations.' But even having a suitable measure, calculating the integral exactly, is too much to hope for, and the best one has been able to do in general is to develop a systematic approximation scheme by expanding the expressions in a power series in $\hbar$ and the coupling constants, using Feynman diagrams and rules. These calculations are notoriously subtle and require a rather unusual arsenal of skills. I will avoid all these highly relevant technicalities here, but nevertheless continue the overall narrative, plainly quoting the results along the way if we need them. And this way I hope to be able to convey the central ideas and discuss what they mean. I refer interested readers to the final section of this chapter where we go a step further in explaining the perturbative approach and consider some specific quantum processes in more detail.

In the comparison with statistical physics the temperature parameter is replaced by some coupling constant times $\hbar$, and S is now the classical(!) (Euclidean) action which is equal to the Lagrangian density integrated over all of Euclidean space-time. The integral involves 'imaginary time', which means that we set $t \to i\tau$, so that the flat Minkowski space-time just becomes 4-dimensional Euclidean space with $x_4 = \tau$. The idea is that in Euclidean space the mathematical manipulations are much simpler and in particular more convergent than in Minkowski space. But the price one has to pay is that after the calculation is finished one has to 'rotate' back to Minkowski space-time in order to interpret the results.

The effective action. The analogue of a free energy is then the so-called *effective action* S_{eff}. :

$$S_{eff} \equiv \hbar \ln Z \tag{III.4.14}$$

And as in the definition of Z we have summed or integrated over all field variables, the effective action only depends on the parameters of the theory. This function or its derivatives could become discontinuous, signalling what we have earlier called quantum phase transitions. A strong way to express this analogy is to say that quantum theory in d spatial dimensions is just statistical mechanics in $(d+1)$ dimensions, where the Euclidean action of the d-dimensional space become a 'would be' $(d+1)$-dimensional Hamiltonian. An example of this was provided by the $d = 2$ Ising model (discussed in the section on magnetic order in Chapter III.2), where one encounters a quantum phase transition at zero temperature at some critical value of the external magnetic field. It has been shown that the characteristics of that transition indeed correspond to the $d = 3$ classical Ising model.

In Table III.4.3 we have summarized the correspondences between statistical physics and quantum field theory. And it should be said that this Feynman *path integral* approach to quantum theory is in many ways complementary to the operator, Hilbert space approach, and has led to many new and valuable insights into the quantum world. It has become an indispensible tool in our modeling and understanding of physical reality.

Scaling and renormalization

In this section we discuss scaling properties in a generic way, following the renormalization group approach of Kenneth Wilson using the language of the Euclidean path integral and the effective action as introduced in the previous section. We apply the formalism to the ϕ—fourth model. Wilson received the Physics Nobel prize for his work in 1982.

The Wilson approach to renormalization.
The starting point is to define the theory with *momentum cut-off* Λ:

$$Z = \int [D\phi]_\Lambda \exp\left(-\int \mathcal{L}_0 \, d^4x\right), \tag{III.4.15}$$

with the ϕ—fourth bare Lagrangian density:

$$\mathcal{L}(\phi, \partial_\mu \phi) = \frac{1}{2}(\partial_\mu \phi)^2 + \frac{1}{2} m^2 \phi^2 + \frac{\lambda_4}{4!}\phi^4 . \tag{III.4.16}$$

The integration is over all space-time field configurations and has a measure with some momentum cut-off:

$$[D\phi]_\Lambda = \prod_{|k|<\Lambda} d\phi(k) . \tag{III.4.17}$$

You can think of it in the following way. Any field configuration can be expended in a complete set of energy-momentum eigenfunctions,

$$\phi(x) = \sum_k a_k \, \phi_k(x).$$

Integrating over the field configurations basically means that you integrate over the space of expansion coefficients, so the measure is then simply:

$$[D\phi]_\Lambda = \prod_{|k|<\Lambda} da_k ,$$

where the integral is only performed over the a_k with $k < \Lambda$. The importance of the cut-off is that all integrals are calculable in principle but the results may depend on the cut-off.

Integrating out high momentum modes. We continue by splitting the field modes depending on their momentum by defining:

$$\phi = \phi^{<} + \phi^{>} \quad \text{with} \quad \phi^{>} = \begin{cases} \phi(k) \text{ for } b\Lambda < k < \Lambda \\ 0 \text{ otherwise.} \end{cases} \tag{III.4.18}$$

Now we have to expand out the Lagrangian and split it in the part that depends only on $\phi^{<}$ that has the same form as $\mathcal{L}$ and the part that depends on both $\phi^{<}$ and $\phi^{>}$ and their derivatives. The path integral then becomes a product of two factors. The idea is to perform the integral over the $\phi^{>}(k)$ components in the second factor.

The effective Lagrangian. The theory obtained after integration over these high momentum modes is an effective theory for the field ϕ but now with a cut-off $b\Lambda$:

$$Z = \int [D\phi]_{b\Lambda} \exp\left(-\int \mathcal{L}_{\text{eff}}\, d^4x\right),$$

where the effective Lagrangian $\mathcal{L}_{\text{eff}}$ will be equal to $\mathcal{L}$ plus an infinite number of correction terms in increasing powers of the coupling constant λ_4 and the field ϕ and its derivatives. The calculation of this expansion is a complicated matter and will not concern us here because the qualitative features we want to address can be discussed without. The philosophy is similar to a calculation we will do in the toy model in the final section, in that by integrating out a high-mass variable χ we obtain an effective Lagrangian which can be thought of as an infinite power series in the remaining low-mass variable ϕ. In the toy model this can be done explicitly, and therefore gives you a good idea. In the situation here we deal with fields and their derivatives, that all depend on space-time coordinates. The expansion becomes similar to the toy model diagrammatically, but the loop diagrams now involve integrations over the loop momenta in the high momentum range.

Why am I telling you all this, where are we? So far we have mapped a rather simple field theory with a cut-off Λ on a much more complicated theory with cut-off $b\Lambda$. What is that good for? To see that we return to the scaling properties of the terms in the effective Lagrangian, and apply dimensional analysis to the new interaction parameters introduced by integrating out the high momentum modes. Let us write,

$$\mathcal{L}_{\text{eff}} = \mathcal{L}_0 + \text{correction terms},$$

where $\mathcal{L}_0$ only contains the quadratic terms describing the original free field theory. The correction terms in principle contain all powers of the field ϕ and their derivatives. This is somewhat disturbing as we now have to deal with an extremely complicated effective description, but we are not done yet.

The effective theory has a momentum cut-off $b\Lambda$, and it is this theory we want to rescale. We do so by rescaling the momentum by $k \to k/b$ and the coordinates by $x \to bx$. This rescaling of the coordinates brings out certain powers of b in front of the terms in the effective Lagrangian. And because $b < 1$ we are going to smaller spatial and larger momentum scales. As the Lagrangian has dimension ℓ^{-4} and $[\phi] \sim \ell^{-1}$, one finds that the coupling constants $g_{m,n}$ for a term with a power of the field m and the number of derivatives equal n has to scale with a power of the scaling factor b given by:

$$g_{n,m} \to b^{n(d/2-1)+m-d} g_{m,n}\,.$$

This expression is consistent with the values we assigned before, for example the ϕ^4 coupling $\lambda_4 = g_{4,0}$ in a space-time dimension $d = 4$ yields indeed a power equal zero, confirming that λ_4 is dimensionless. Now we want to distinguish three possible cases for the scale dependence of the couplings in the effective Lagrangian:

- power > 0: the term is *irrelevant*
- power $= 0$: the term is *marginal*
- power < 0: the term is *relevant*.

At this point we should mention that also extra terms of the type that were already present in $\mathcal{L}_0$ will be generated and these terms are absorbed into the new renormalized fields and parameters. In the case at hand $\phi \to \phi'$, $m \to m'$ and $\lambda_4 \to \lambda_4'$, so that indeed $\mathcal{L}_0$ in the next iteration looks the same but with renormalized fields and parameters. If we imagine iterating this procedure, repeating the rescaling after integrating out the highest momentum modes, we get a sequence of maps of the coupling constants, and it is this sequence of maps that we refer to as the *renormalization group trajectory*. What we arrive at is a flow of the model in the space coupling constants. The important point of distinguishing the various terms is that the irrelevant ones get suppressed by powers of b, while the relevant ones have inverse powers and will grow. For the marginal operators one has to make higher order calculations to determine which way they will go. The upshot is that the renormalization group action maps out a trajectory of the given theory in the space of coupling constants, in other words, in the space of theories. In the next section we will discuss the *renormalization group equations* that determine the trajectories and go through some relevant examples.

Note that the question whether interaction terms are relevant, irrelevant or marginal depends strongly on the space-time dimension d. One can easily check that the ϕ^4 term is marginal for $d = 4$ but it becomes relevant if $d < 4$. For $d = 2$ one finds that all powers of the field become relevant, because the exponent becomes -2 for all of them. A mass term scales as expected like b^{2-d} and is therefore relevant for all $d > 2$.

The asymptotic behavior of the theory one considers now depends on where these trajectories go. They may move towards a fixed point that could be either zero or nonzero, or trajectories could run off to infinity , which means that the theory looses its meaning and becomes inadequate to describe the physics. The irrelevant terms go to zero as they are suppressed by the increasing powers of the cutoff.

So most of the scary looking terms that appeared after integrating over high momentum modes disappear again because of the rescalings, and because of their irrelevance. This brings us back to the question of scale invariance. If the couplings in a theory go to a fixed point, then the theory defined by that fixed point is by definition scale invariant!

We note that the ϕ^4 theory in four space-time dimensions has what is called 'trivial' fixed point where the parameters m^2 and λ_4 are both zero, and $\mathcal{L}^{(\prime)} = (\partial_\mu \phi)^2$. This theory is in fact invariant under the conformal group as we have mentioned before. It has been shown that the ϕ^4 theory for $d = 3$ has a non-trivial fixed point, The so-called Fisher–Wilson fixed point.

The statement is that theories that have only relevant and marginal terms are called *renormalizable*. It is in those theories that it is possible to take the cut-off Λ to infinity sending the irrelevant terms to zero. The effect of all the quantum perturbations can then be absorbed in sensible redefinitions of field and parameters.

The importance of the Wilson's renormalization group perspective is that it a priori assumes that there is a real physical cut-off and that the physics at lower energy may show some dependence on it. This typically is the case in applications in condensed matter and you had better take it into account. There is no need to send the cut-off to infinity, because it is really there. On the other hand it used to be somewhat of a mystery if not a miracle why the fundamental theories like the Standard Model are all renormalizable (from the start). And one wondered why Nature was so judicious in its choice. Just to please physicists so they could do meaningful perturbative calculations? The Wilson approach makes clear that renormalizability is exactly what survives in a natural way. Those are the terms that basically survive in the renormalisation group flow. Quite arbitrary theories may well flow towards a scale invariant fixed point that lies inside a subspace of relevant renormalizable theories, which do not need to be scale invariant! The Wilsonian perspective we have outlined leads to the conclusion that the renormalizable models are universal in that they describe the asymptotic behavior of large classes of other models. ■ ■

The quantum bank. Whether you study the stars, write poems, or are world champion armwrestler, in the end we all have to deal with banks. You need a loan or a mortgage and you get immersed in a labyrinth of options: this one looks even more advantageous then the other. Ultimately it always boils down to interest rates, and those rates are calculated based on a mysterious mixture of facts and fictions concerning the certainties of your present and the uncertainties of your future. But one thing remains true under all circumstances: borrowing money costs money! And you are happy because you are spending money you don't have!

Now back to quantum, In the realms of quantum theory the currency is energy rather than dollars. Yet there is also a bank, which is basically the vacuum itself. We know that because of the Heisenberg uncertainty relations, a quantum marble cannot be at rest at the bottom of the bowl, it has to jiggle around a bit. There is no certainty ever in the quantum world. This may work to the advantage of the participants in the sense that there are always quantum fluctuations even in the ground state and even at zero temperature. Quantum reality is such that there is always some energy around. And the idea of the cooperative quantum bank is that it provides very cheap energy loans, but they come with some unusual restrictions. The slogan is, you can borrow as much as you want but only for a very short period.

Whereas the money banks usually have very high interest rates for ultra short-term loans, the quantum bank's energy loans work exactly the opposite way. As long as you $\Delta E x \Delta t \leq \frac{\hbar}{2}$ you are doing fine. So if I am a photon and play it big, I can borrow energy so that I can produce for example an electron-positron pair to impress my fellow photons as long as the loan is very short term. But now the catch is that because the overall energy has to be conserved, the quantum bank insists that you return your energy before the Federal Reserve gets wind of it. And this is what certain real-life Quants in real banks don't seem to understand. There is a moment of reckoning: you speculate yourself into heaven, but you have to be back home with two legs on the ground in time! In other words the quantum world makes sure that the pair just created annihilates back into the vacuum and the photon continues its journey, as if nothing ever happened to it. You would think. But no it isn't as simple as that. The photon carries its creative banking experiences with it and they effectively change its behavior.

It reminds me of my good old student days at Delft University, when I was cycling home late at night along the beautiful 'Oude Delft' canal from the lab, or was it a party? Suddenly I got pulled over by the police. Trouble! Probably a costly ticket because I had no lights on my bike. And while the officer was searching for his ticket book in the car, I shoved my old bike in the canal. Bloop...gone! When the police officer returned and started to make a solemn declaration about 'your bike sir appears to be missing some appropriate lighting'....I interrupted him and asked what bike he was talking about. 'But I thought that ...' 'Yes, may be you thought, but look ...' This caused some consternation. Indeed, here were powerful fluctuations at work that the officer on duty apparently had no working knowledge of! □

Running coupling constants

As we have seen, quantum theory and in particular quantum field theory has come up with a surprising answer to questions about the spatial or momentum scale dependence of the coupling parameters in a given theory. Though the road to the result is highly technical and the arguments may at first appear to be quite opaque, what results is clearcut and strikingly simple.

The renormalization program yields equations that govern the behavior of the parameters of the theory as a function of scale. These are differential equations that remind you of an ordinary dynamical system, say a set of interacting Newtonian particles. Now you have to imagine that these equations describe the 'motion' of a given theory in parameter space, not as a function of time but as a function of scale! And that's where the term 'running coupling constants' comes from. It is kind of mind boggling to think of a given theory 'running' in the space of theories. Yet that is what happens and moreover, it teaches us about the limiting or asymptotic behavior of such theories. This may be in the high momentum (ultraviolet) or the low momentum (infrared) limit, depending on the problem one is interested in.

The first and maybe simplest equation of this type – called the Gellman-Low equation – was written down for QED. Later the general renormalization group approach which we described, culminated in the so-called Callan-Symanzik equations for the scaling behavior of any composite local operators of the type we encountered in the expansions. These *renormalization group equations* govern the flow of points in the space of (renomalized) coupling constants which we will denote by $\mathcal{W}$. Let us consider the simple case of a single coupling constant g. The theory has a momentum cut-off Λ, and the equation involves the renormalized coupling which we denote by $\bar{g}$, which depends on the momentum scale through its logarithm only, $\bar{g} = \bar{g}(\log \bar{p})$, where we choose $\bar{p}$ to be the dimensionless momentum variable $\bar{p} \equiv p/\Lambda$. The renormalization group equation has the simple form:

$$\frac{d\bar{g}}{d \log \bar{p}} = \beta(\bar{g})\,. \qquad \text{(III.4.19)}$$

This equation just says that the rate of change of the coupling $\bar{g}$ equals a function $\beta(\bar{g})$, not surprisingly called the *beta-function*. This function depends on $\log \bar{p}$, but only through the coupling constant $\bar{g}$. In that sense you can think of it as a *functional equation* for $\bar{g}$ as a function $\log \bar{p}$, in the spirit of equation (III.4.5).

Let us assume that at some large distance (small momentum) this coupling is small, then we may look at β for small $\bar{g}$ and develop it there as a power series like:

$$\beta(\bar{g}) = a\bar{g} + b\bar{g}^2 + \cdots\,, \qquad \text{(III.4.20)}$$

and for small $\bar{g}$ the successive terms will become ever smaller and we can safely truncate the series. Now given the quantum field theory the coefficients $a, b, \cdots$ can be calculated using perturbation theory. This approach allows us to deduce important general features of the theory. It is important though to note that because the beta function is mostly calculated perturbatively, it follows that the results obtained can only be trusted in the domain where the perturbation theory holds, in other words, where the expansion parameters are small. Of course the rare cases where models can be solved exactly serve as ideal testing grounds for the tools we are describing here.

Mechanical analogues

Let me point out a mechanical analogy that should be familiar and thus helpful. It refers back to our discussion on dynamical systems on page 11 of the section on Newtonian mechanics in Chapter I.1. If we think of a complicated theory with many parameters, we will have a system of coupled equations but all with the same first derivative with respect to $\log \bar{p}$ on the left-hand side. Using $\log \bar{p}$ instead of $\bar{p}$ makes the equations particularly simple, the only thing you have to keep in mind is that $\log \bar{p}$ grows monotonically with $\bar{p}$, so if $\log \bar{p}$ becomes large then $\bar{p}$ does also, but for $\bar{p}$ going to zero $\log \bar{p}$ goes to minus infinity. In this sense we may think of $\log \bar{p}$ as some kind of 'time' variable t. Then the equation just describes the motion of a point in the (coupling constant) space $\mathcal{W}$ of the system.

Stated differently, as the point represents a particular theory, its motion describes a trajectory in a space of theories! The left-hand side is the 'velocity' or rate of change which depends – through the expression on the right-hand side – on where you are in the coupling constant space. So the equation defines a vector or flow field over $\mathcal{W}$, in a similar way that Newton's dynamical equations for a particle define a flow over the phase space, as we discussed in Chapter I.1. The equation governs the trajectories completely once the initial conditions for $\bar{g}(t)$ at some $t = t_0$ are given, just like Newton's equations do after you give the initial positions and velocities of a bunch of interacting point particles. These dynamical systems are usually nonlinear, and also in the case at hand the dynamical system is nonlinear as we see from the expansion in equation (III.4.20). As we remarked in Chapter I.1, it allows us to search for universal behavior, because the system may for large values of time, or high momentum ($t = \ln \bar{p}$), end up in some fixed point or limit cycle and may for long time scales exhibit universal behavior.

It is amusing to see how we manage to address deep questions in the realm of Quantum Field Theory because we have been able to map the problem onto a rather simple Newtonian dynamical system. Indeed, from equation (III.4.19) one sees that for the points where the β-function vanishes the 'velocity' is zero, so these points correspond to stationary points. This translates into the statement that that theory becomes invariant under further rescaling. It

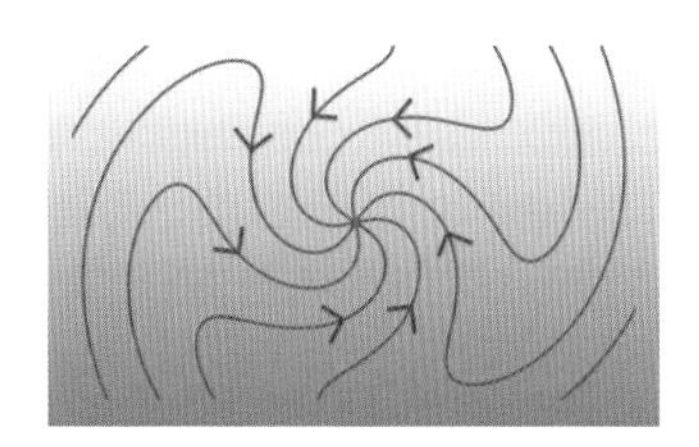

(a) Stable fixed point

(b) Landscape near a stable fixed point

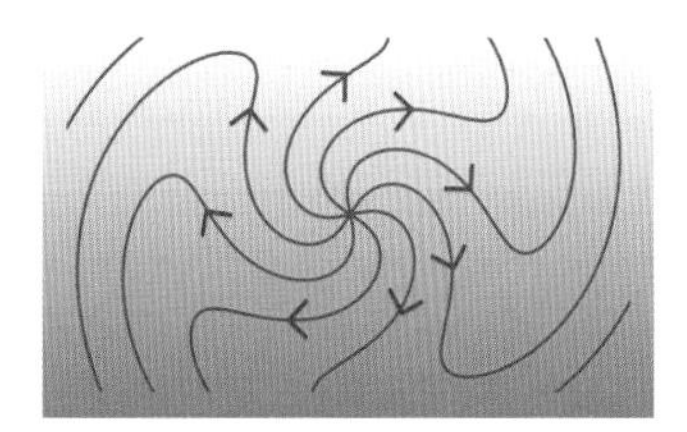

(c) An unstable fixed point

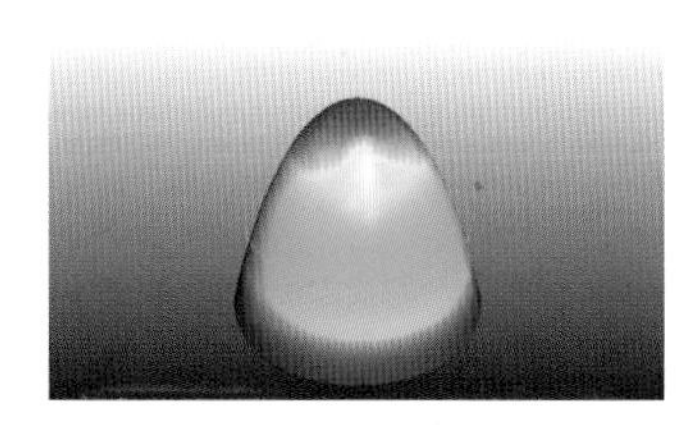

(d) Landscape near an unstable fixed point point

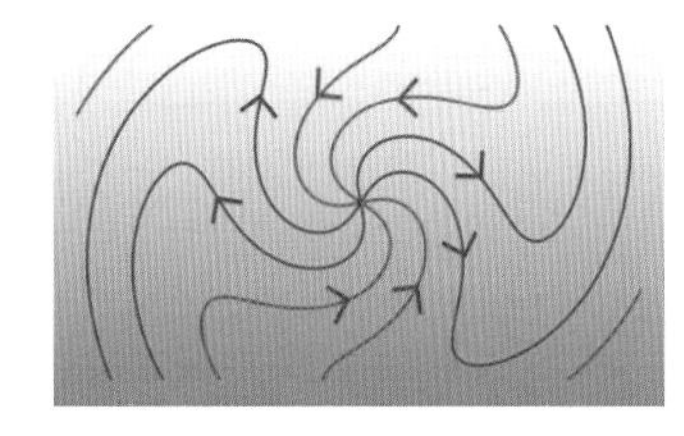

(e) A saddle point.

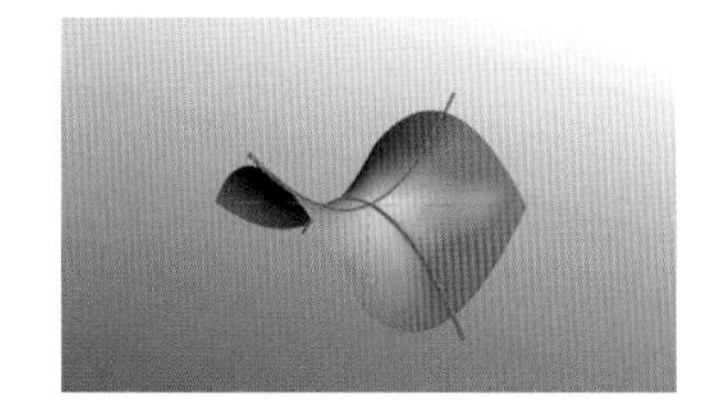

(f) Landscape near a saddle point

Figure III.4.15: *Fixed points.* The three types of fixed points one may encounter in a two-dimensional parameter space. In (f) we see that lines of steepest descent and steepest ascent are perpendicular.

is a theory which is called ultraviolet (high momentum) stable, because it has ended up in in some scale invariant fixed point. Note that this analysis allows for theories that are quite different initially to end up in the same ultra violet fixed point. They belong to the same universality class.

For a single coupling we have only one dimension and it is straight forward to see what is possible for small coupling, where we only take along a few terms in the expansion (III.4.20). For example the system may move to a sta-

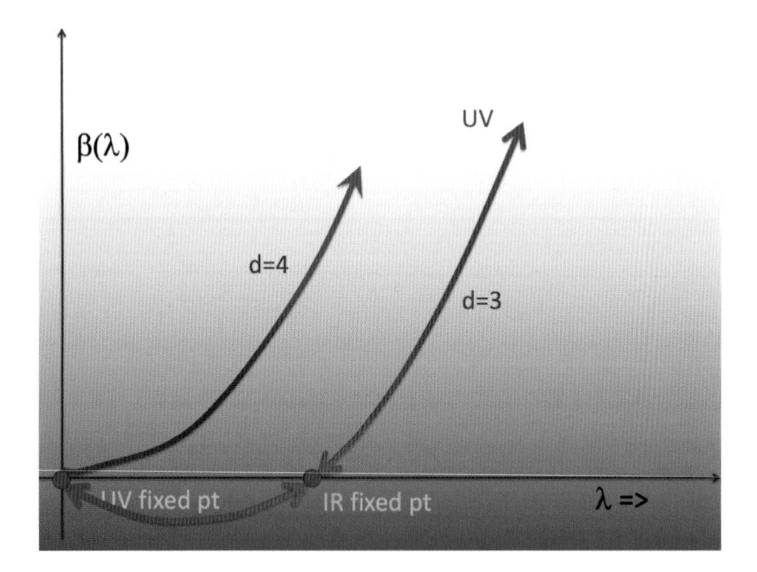

Figure III.4.16: *Beta functions of the ϕ^4 theory in 3 and 4 dimensions.* Depending on the starting value of λ_i we have sketched the asymptotic behavior of the coupling constant $\lambda = \lambda(\log p)$. In the infrared region (decreasing $\log p$) there is a non-trivial IR fixed point for $\lambda = \lambda_0$ for $d < 4$. In the ultraviolet limit (increasing $\log p$) we find for $\lambda_i < \lambda_0$ a trivial fixed point ($\lambda = 0$) where the theory behaves like a free theory with zero coupling. For $\lambda_i > \lambda_0$ the coupling keeps increasing, at least for as long as the expansion makes sense.

ble fixed point where it would stay for ever after, or we may have an unstable fixed point and the system would move away from it under any small perturbation.

If we think of a two-dimensional parameter space, such stationary points can in general only have three generic types of behavior: either the point is attractive, or repulsive, or it is a saddle point. This is illustrated in Figure III.4.15. In two or more dimensions one also could imagine the possibilities of limit cycles, or more exotic attractors where the system could display even chaotic behavior. But generic features of these renormalization group equations appear to exclude that. Nature saves us the humbling demise that our theories would get lost in chaotic asymptotics. Coping with quantum uncertainties is enough of a challenge!

The scalar ϕ^4 theory. Let us now turn to an explicit example. What do the renormalization group equations look like for the scalar model we have been discussing? It has two parameters, $\bar{m}^2$ and $\bar{\lambda}_4$, and therefore two equations with two beta functions. To lowest non-trivial order these read as follows:

$$\frac{d\,\bar{\lambda}_4}{d\log\bar{p}} = \beta_\lambda(\bar{\lambda}_4) = -(4-d)\bar{\lambda}_4 + \frac{3\bar{\lambda}_4^2}{16\pi^2}\,, \qquad \text{(III.4.21)}$$

$$\frac{d\bar{m}^2}{d\log\bar{p}} = \beta_m(\bar{\lambda}_4) = [-2+\gamma_m(\bar{\lambda}_4)]\bar{m}^2\,. \qquad \text{(III.4.22)}$$

Let us make some observations with respect to these equations:

(i) The constant term on the right-hand side of the equations gives the naive scaling dimensions, namely 0 and -2 respectively.

(ii) The other terms are radiative corrections to the numbers, and are supposed to be small. The anomalous term $\gamma_m(\bar{\lambda}_4)$ vanishes if $\bar{\lambda}_4 = 0$.

(iii) As all corrections take the form of a power series in $\bar{\lambda}_4$ only, it is the $\bar{\lambda}_4$ equation that drives the dynamics. So, let us then start with the first equation. In four or more dimensions the beta function is positive and the coupling will therefore keep growing until it becomes so large that the perturbation series breaks down in that successive terms are no longer decreasing. What happens in the strong coupling regime in that case cannot be answered through this analysis, because the series diverges the approximation scheme becomes invalid. One would have to resort to strong coupling approximations meaning numerical lattice simulations. The conclusion appears to be that there is no fixed point at larger values of the coupling, which means that the theory deteriorates into the quartic term, not a physically interesting or meaningful result.

(iv) In Figure III.4.16 we depicted the beta function $\beta_\lambda(\bar{\lambda}_4)$ for $d = 3$ and $d = 4$. Where the blue direction is the direction of increasing momentum (ultraviolet), while the red arrows point in the decreasing momentum (infrared). We see that for $d < 4$ the beta function has two zeros, mean-

ing that there are two fixed points: one at zero and one larger than zero at some value λ^*. The new point is an infrared stable fixed point.
(v) If we let d approach 4 from below we see that the two fixed points merge at the trivial fixed point $\bar{\lambda}_4 = 0$ which corresponds to the free field theory.
(vi) Finally the renormalization equation for the mass parameter has on the right-hand side the constant -2 which just reflects the naive scaling we have discussed already. If we scale up the theory one expects the mass term to become less and less relevant. while in the trivial fixed point it is the one and only relevant parameter. The precise form of the solution is:

$$\bar{m}^2 \simeq \left(\frac{m}{\Lambda}\right)^2 \left(\frac{\Lambda}{p^2}\right)^{2+\gamma}. \tag{III.4.23}$$

If in less than four dimensions the system sits in the nontrivial Fisher-Wilson infrared fixed point, we get the anomalous correction to the naive scaling law corresponding to $\gamma(\lambda^*)$. This correction plays a role in the $d = 3$ statistical physics of magnetic materials. It has no effect on the ultraviolet behavior of the theory.

Gauge couplings

The following picture emerges: the constant a in the expansion of the beta function (III.4.20) has a generic structure:

$$a = d - n, \tag{III.4.24}$$

where d is the physical space-time dimension and n is some critical dimension, critical because the scaling behavior of the theory depends critically on whether d is smaller or larger than n. If $d < n$ then $a < 0$ and the growth rate of g is negative and g will decrease with growing momentum, or what amounts to the same, with decreasing distances. In this case the coupling constant will go to zero, its like no interactions are left at small distances. And as the linear approximation will get better and better with decreasing g, the prediction that this theory behaves as a theory of free particles at small distances is reliable and consistent.

If however $d > n$ the situation looks pretty bad because now the coupling grows bigger at smaller distances and the approximation breaks down and we would need the complete β function.

Now there is still the 'in between' possibility with $d = n$, and it turns out to be of considerable interest in the situations that nature faces us with. In that case we have to turn to the next term in the series with coefficient b. If we only keep the b term the solution becomes:

$$g(p) = \frac{c}{1 - bc \log p}, \tag{III.4.25}$$

with c some positive constant. Again we may look at what happens for when b is positive, respectively negative. The different behaviors are plotted in Figure III.4.17 and interestingly we encounter both cases in realistic particle theories.

Quantum electrodynamics. The case with positive b corresponds to pure *quantum electrodynamics (QED)*, the theory of photons, electrons and positrons. From the blue curve we see that g becomes very small for small values of $\log p$, that is large distances. We recall that the expansion parameter in QED is the fine structure constant $\alpha = e^2/4\pi\epsilon_0\hbar c \simeq 1/137$. This corresponds to the familiar regime where charges are free and have weak electric interactions, and perturbation theory can be trusted, and allows for calculations of exceptional precision. The decrease of the coupling at larger distances reflects the situation that the quantum fluctuations tend to screen the 'bare' or 'naked' charge. This effect is called *vacuum polarization* because due to the quantum uncertainties the quantum fluctuations in the fields result in the excitation of virtual electron-positron pairs and these screen the 'bare' charge. Vacuum polarization is discussed in more detail in the following section on page 123.

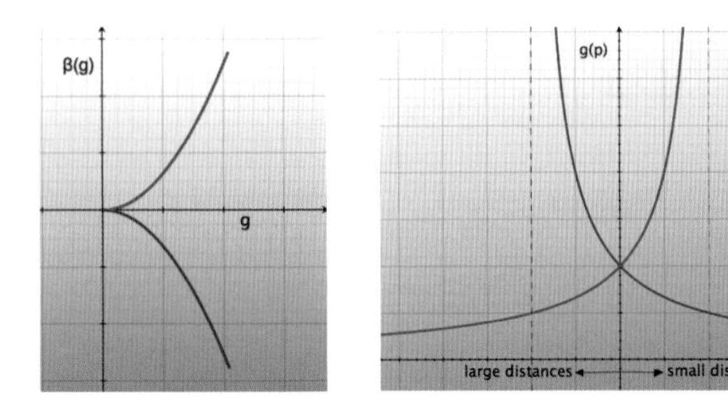

Figure III.4.17: *Running coupling constants.* On the left a plot of the bèta function $\beta(g)$ of equation (III.4.20) for positive (blue) and negative (purple) sign of the constant b. On the right we plotted the solutions for $g(\ln p)$ of equation (III.4.25), showing the dependence of the coupling strength on the logarithm of the momentum. The blue curve goes to infinity for a finite value of $\log p$ at the so-called Landau singularity. The purple curve corresponds to negative b, the coupling tends to zero for small distances which is called *asymptotic freedom.*

For increasing momenta the coupling becomes infinite for some finite momentum scale, which taken literally would suggest that the naked charge would be infinite. This singular behavior is called a *Landau pole*, and the presence of such a pole indicates that the theory becomes untenable past a certain scale and has to break down somehow. In general it is true that a coupling growing large is a strong signal that the theory is no longer to be trusted past that point. This is not a disaster but just a whistleblower announcing that the model is losing its validity and presumably some new physics has to enter the conversation to allow us to escape the singularity.

This illustrates again a notion that I have mentioned before, namely that theories are not right or wrong per se, but rather have a limited domain of validity. In the present context a large coupling usually means that the physical system will enter another regime for which the theoretical picture one started off with becomes inadequate. Renormalization in that sense helps theories to predict their own demise. How nice to have theories which know about their own limitations. For the case at hand the resolution came much later when it was discovered that at small scales it made no sense to look at the electromagnetic interactions separately. The remedy was to combine the electromagnetic and the weak nuclear interactions into a single unified 'electroweak' theory which turned out to behave extremely well also for extremely small distances as we have been able to verify in the *Large Hadron Collider* (LHC) at the European accelerator centre CERN in Geneva. In fact the word 'large' here implies precisely 'large momenta', and this collider smashes particles into each other with very high energies, and that means that they can come very, very close to each other. The LHC was specially built to investigate what happens to the interactions at very small distances.

Quantum chromodynamics. Let us now look at the purple curve in the figure corresponding to negative values of b. It shows that the coupling goes to zero with increasing $\log p$ or at smaller distances. Therefore the theory ends up describing non-interacting – free – particles for large momenta. This behavior under scaling is realized in *Quantum Chromodynamics (QCQ)*, the theory for the strong nuclear force. We see that the 'strong' interactions between quarks, paradoxically enough becomes extremely weak at small distances. This remarkable behavior of the strong interactions is called *asymptotic freedom.* For a long time it was thought that the problem of the strong nuclear forces could never be solved along the lines of quantum field theory, but this picture changed drastically after 'asymptotic freedom' was discovered and the strong interactions were tamed because they turned out to be the manifestation of a well-behaved weakly coupled theory at small distance scales. This totally different asymptotic behavior of QED and QCD, is of course due to the self-interacting nature of the gluons. Those self-interactions distinguish the non-abelian from the abelian theories. For the discovery of asymptotic freedom the physics Nobel prize 2004 was awarded to David Gross, David Politzer and Frank Wilczek.

From the purple curve we also see that going towards small momenta the coupling grows 'without limit' at some finite value of $\log p$. This behavior is sometimes called *infrared slavery* because the particle would become extremely strongly coupled. The physical interpretation of an increasing coupling constant is that at a scale where the coupling becomes of order unity, the perturbative predictions lose their reliability, and one expects other physics and non-perturbative effects to come into play. For QCD there are two fundamental phenomena that are linked to this. The first is the formation of the quark-antiquark condensate that causes *chiral symmetry breaking* as we discussed in Chapter II.6 on symmetry breaking on page 207. This symmetry breaking lead to the interpretation of the three pion particles ($\pi^{\pm}$ and π_0) as the 'massless' Goldstone degrees of freedom associated with the breaking. The second non-perturbative phenomenon manifest at that scale is the confinement of quarks. As mentioned before the collective of quarks reorganizes itself into tightly bound composites called *hadrons* made up of either three quarks (called *baryons*) or form a quark an anti-quark pair (called *mesons*). The protons and neutrons are the nuclear particles from which all familiar forms of matter are build, and these are baryons. The pions however belong to the group of the mesons. What this means is that at scales where the becomes large the perturbative approach breaks down and the behavior of the theory is no longer what one would expect from the its weak coupling behavior. At that point it is important to switch to a different effective theory that is formulated directly in terms of the hadrons. In the case of QCD this turns out to be a *nonlinear sigma model* that we will not further dwell on.

Grand unification: where strong joins weak

The idea of renormalization and running coupling constants led to a powerful insight into the possibility of unifying the different types of interactions into a single framework often

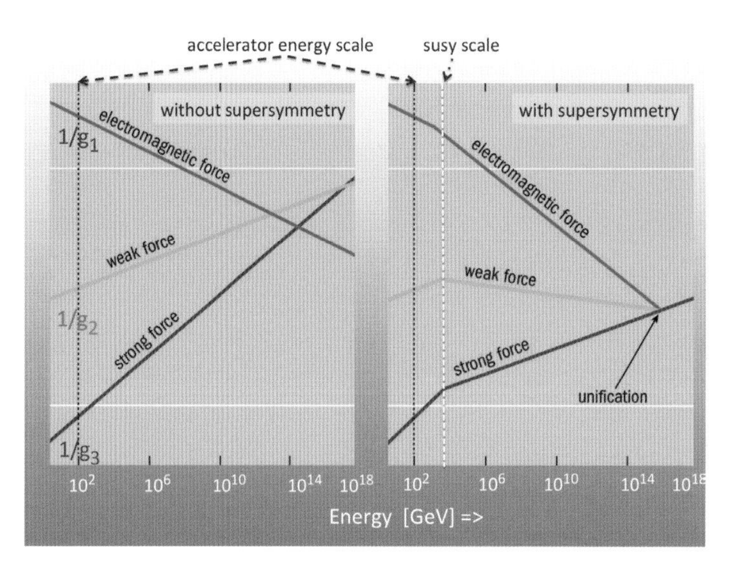

Figure III.4.18: *Unifications.* The subsequent unifications of fundamental interactions suggested by the running coupling strength of the various forces meeting at ever higher energy scales. Experiments at the Large Hadron Collider at CERN in Geneva go up to about 10^3 GeV.

referred to as a *Grand Unified Theory* or GUT. We have already alluded to the fact that the problem of the ill-defined electromagnetic coupling at small distances was resolved by the unification of the electromagnetic and the weak interactions. On the other hand we mentioned the strong nuclear force which turned to become weak at short distances. As we explained in Chapter I.4, these three interactions are now described in a single combined theory called the *Standard Model*. This theory has so far successfully survived extensive testing through many different types of experiments, and appears to be able to predict and explain all the data that are available at present.

To give you an impression of what could be a successful next step up the quantum ladder of unification you should look at Figure III.4.18. The picture gives the expectation of how the grand unification could be achieved. Experiments go up to a level 500 GeV so we have witnessed the electroweak unification and we see the strong coupling coming down. Applying the renormalization techniques and scaling arguments we discussed before to the Standard Model, one may calculate the trajectories of the various coupling constants (assuming that no new physics shows up at other intermediate scales) to substantially higher energy scales and indeed it is suggestive to anticipate a further unification at the GUT scale of around 10^{15} GeV. In fact if we extend the Standard Model to its minimal supersymmetric extension, the resulting trajectories for the three couplings of the model really intersect at a single point near 10^{15} Gev as is shown on the right-hand side of Figure III.4.18. Then the extra (susy) scale of the breaking of supersymmetry has to be introduced because we haven't observed any superpartners of the ordinary particles at low energies. Even more speculative would be the unification with gravity at the Planck scale 10^{19} GeV. Such are the grand vistas and holy grails of modern high-energy physics.

Phase transitions

In the previous sections we have seen that in many body systems described by statistical mechanics or quantum field theory, we may by changing the external parameters being the temperature or some coupling constants have the theory end up in a fixed point of the renormalization group equations. In points where the $beta$-function vanishes the theory is scale invariant. We have seen an ultraviolet fixed point in QCD and an infrared fixed point in the ϕ-fourth theory in three dimensions.

In most of physics this remarkable property of scale invariance is the hallmark of a so-called *critical point* where the system exhibits critical behavior. The behavior around such fixed points, may exhibit fluctuations on all scales, but these can be understood because of the self-similar nature of their spectrum. The correlations display a power law behavior .

The power laws that characterize the critical behavior have universal properties which only depend on the dimensions and nature of the critical point. Many models which may be much more complicated for example having quite a few parameters at the start may move into a universal fixed points where their behavior is described by a much simpler model with fewer parameters. In many lower-dimensional cases the critical models can be solved exactly, which provides important insights about the phase structure of large classes of models, think for example of the Ising model. These ideas where initially developed in statistical physics by Michael Fisher and Leo Kadanoff, and as mentioned in the context of quantum field theory carried further by Kenneth Wilson who received the Nobel prize for his work in 1982.

And it is indeed by the *renormalization group* approach that theorists have on the one hand been able to come up with many interesting and successful explanations, and on the other have been able to construct representative models for a myriad of physical phenomena. They could solve these simplified models exactly and therefore could provide calculable models for a vast range of critical phenomena.

So to conclude, we have shown that one may think of a space of coupling constants where a given theory is characterized by some point in that space where the couplings take particular values. Now there is a set of coupled renormalization group equations for this set which determines a flow of the point through this space that may or or may not end up in some fixed point. In a fixed point the system's behavior becomes scale invariant, and as such it exhibits some characteristic universal behavior of the theory. The renormalization group equations define flow lines in the space of parameters and starting at a given point in the space the theory follows the flow line to some fixed point. Clearly many different theories can end up in the same type of fixed point and that is what we mean by universal critical behavior see Figure III.4.15(a).

On the calculation of quantum corrections

Renormalization is a scheme that guarantees a peaceful coexistence with infinities.

Perturbation theory 

What do we mean if we say we have a quantum field theory like QED or the standard model, or a theory of pions, or of superconductivity? The casual term 'The theory' usually refers to a number of inclusions or formal steps starting from three ingredients:
(i) an *action* (or Hamiltonian), which allows us to derive a set of
(ii) *Feynman rules* describing the propagators (two point (correlation) functions) for the particles in the theory, and also the interaction vertices;
(iii) If we are interested in a particular physical quantum process, we can usually *not* calculate the probability amplitude for that process exactly. It is however possible to make a systematic perturbative approximation, by making a diagrammatic expansion for the quantum amplitude of any process in increasing powers of the relevant coupling constant(s) and in powers of $\hbar$.
Such an approximation scheme is only reliable if the expansion parameter is sufficiently small. This procedure, called *perturbation theory*, is schematically depicted in Figure III.4.19.

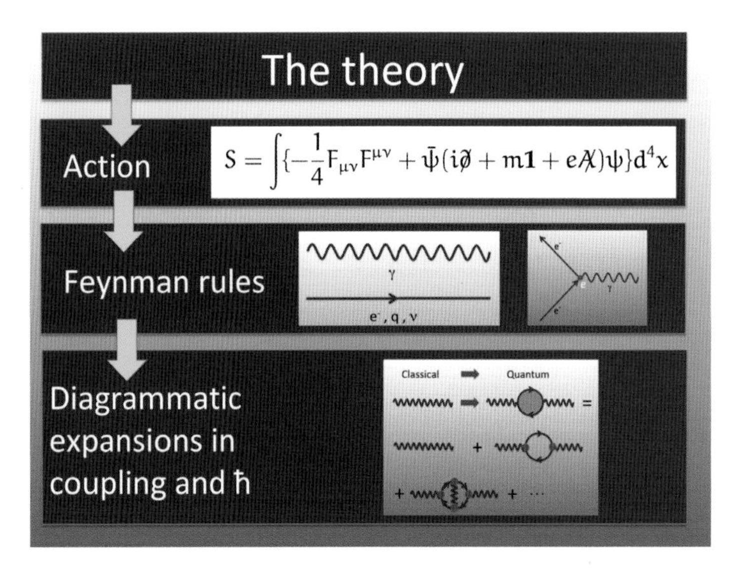

Figure III.4.19: *The perturbative approach.* A theory (like QED) is defined by its classical action, giving the functional form of the theory in terms of the particles (fields) and their interactions. From the action one derives the set of Feynman rules that allow for a systematic diagrammatic expansion of any physical process, This is a series expansion in increasing powers of the coupling(s) and the Planck constant $\hbar$.

The toy model as tutorial in the language of diagrams. Let us take a very simple toy model to illustrate the quant-essential difference between classical and quantum reasoning.[5] The model concerns a drastic simplification and only serves to illustrate certain generic properties of quantum corrections. We are not about to really calculate anything realistic because it turns out that those calculations are quite complicated, and it is where a lot of bright students spend a considerable amount of time on. But luckily we are not the part of the workforce we are just curious tourists! We just want to stare in awe at the statue and need not make one ourselves; we love to eat a sausage but rather not go through how they are made! We are here to see how others did the work!

The toy model is a field theory in zero-dimensional spacetime, where we consider two real valued fields φ and χ. You could say we are studying a system with two modes. The action function has only mass terms and an interaction term (there are no space or time derivatives) and looks therefore almost trivial:

$$S(\varphi,\chi) = \frac{m^2}{2}\varphi^2 + \frac{M^2}{2}\chi^2 + \frac{\lambda}{4}\varphi^2\chi^2, \qquad \text{(III.4.26)}$$

and let us assume that $M \gg m$. You might wonder, what if

[5] I encountered this model in a set of lecture notes on 'Applications of QFT to Geometry' by Dr Andy Neitze of Princeton University.

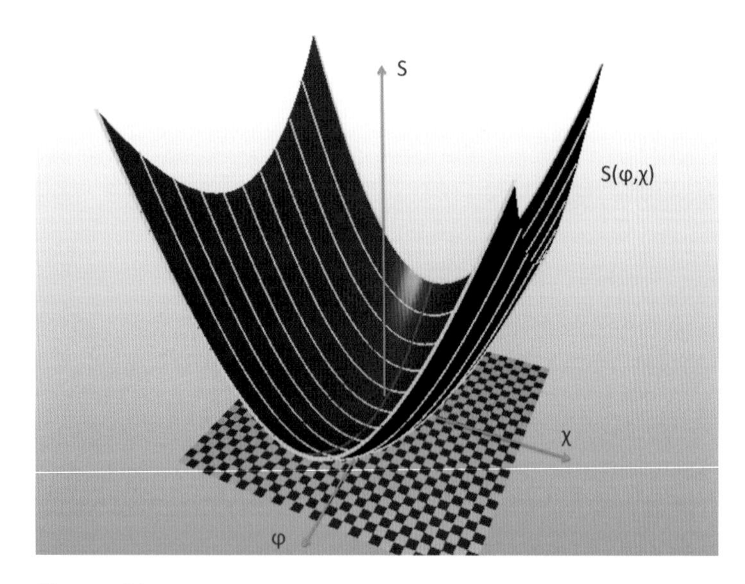

Figure III.4.20: *Action of toy model.* The surface corresponds to the classical action $S(\varphi, \chi)$ as a function of the variables φ and χ.

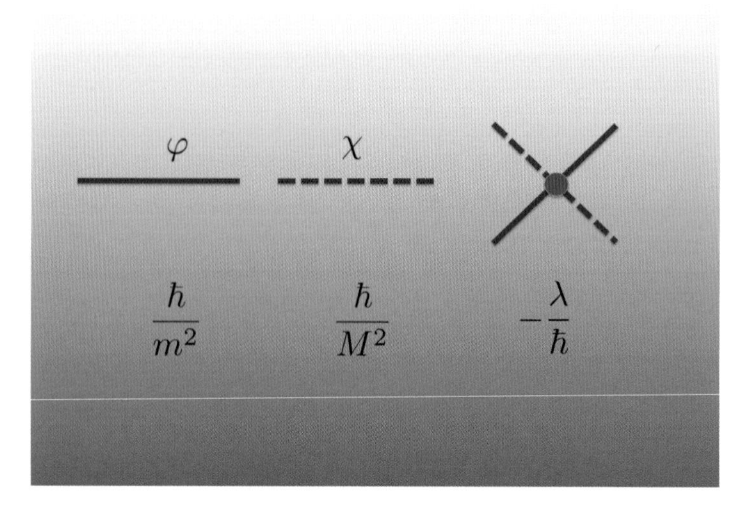

Figure III.4.21: *Feynman rules for toy model.* The Feynman rules are derived from the action and give the functional for the various terms in the action.

anything we can learn from a model in which such a drastic amputation of reality has taken place. In a sense you are correct: the fields are just real variables, and the quantum aspect as we will see is kind of restricted to the $\hbar$ which we stick in. So in the end we integrate a function, and expand the result, and yes the structure one obtains looks very much like the things we encounter in field theory. This is a pedagogical workout, illuminating and even fun. Let us therefore respectfully execute some 'standard calculations' imagining that we are dealing with a real field theory and see what it delivers and also what not.

The three terms in the action correspond to the three Feynman rules (the elementary diagrams) that we give in Figure III.4.21. The free part yields the two 'propagators,' and the quartic term yields the interaction term with coupling strength equal λ.

Effective actions. Let us consider the most trivial process imaginable namely where the in and out state are both empty. Classically if nothing goes in and nothing goes out then there is a unit probability that nothing happens in between.

What we have is a very heavy mode and a very light mode that interact with each other. What you have classically is that it costs a lot of energy to excite the heavy χ mode and that it is easy to excite the light φ mode. So for energies well below M only the light mode will be present and we can forget about the heavy χ mode altogether. But if we do a quantum calculation we should allow for virtual manifestations of the heavy mode, and we have to integrate over all possible values that field may take. We say that we 'integrate out' the heavy mode. And this in turn will drastically change the resulting effective theory for the light mode. It will change three things: (i) it will change the mass of the light mode, (ii) it will change the strength of the interaction term and (iii) it will generate an infinite number of new self-interactions for the light mode. These are quantum effects that affect the low energy behavior of the theory. And these are precisely the generic aspects we like to illustrate with this tiny toy model. We can integrate over the the χ

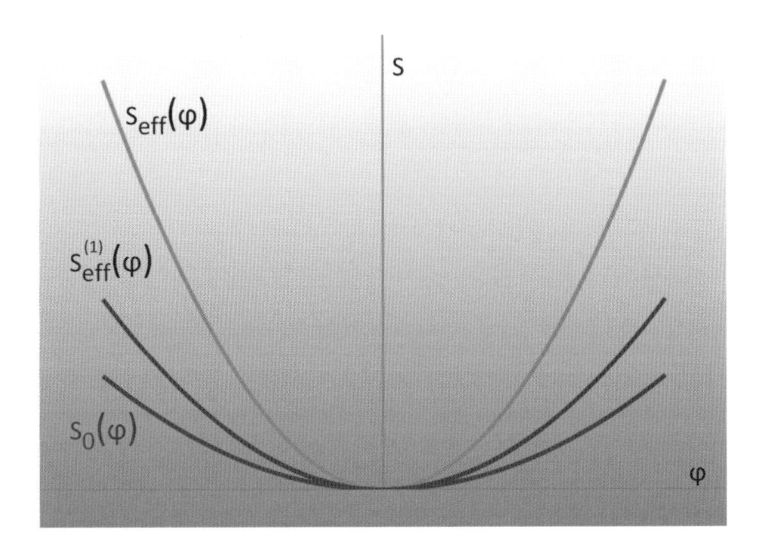

Figure III.4.22: *Effective action for* φ *field.* The graphs correspond to, (i) the classical action $S_0(\varphi) \equiv (\varphi, 0)$ (blue curve), (ii) the effective action $S^{(1)}_{eff}$ including the lowest order corrections in χ (dark purple curve), and (iii) the complete effective action where the χ field has been integrated out exactly (light purple cuve).

,

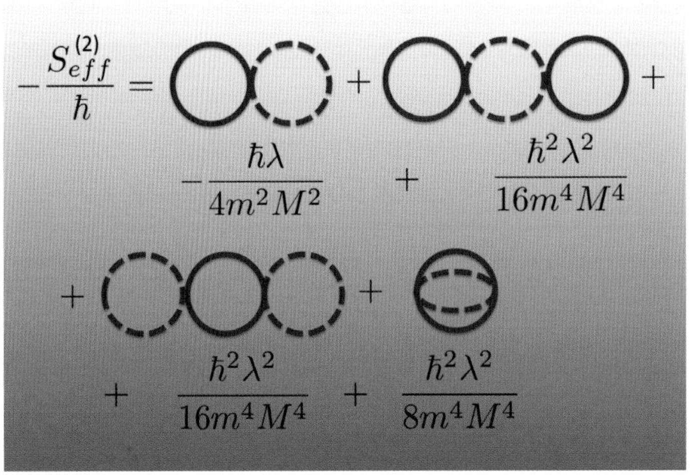

field variable and extract an effective action $S_{eff}(\varphi)$ for the φ field through the defining relation:

$$e^{-S_{eff}(\varphi)/\hbar} = \int e^{-S(\varphi,\chi)/\hbar}\, d\chi\,. \qquad \text{(III.4.27)}$$

Is this very complicated you may ask? The answer is: if you have real space-time dependent fields it is quite involved, but in our little kindergarten theory, there are no evil agents that could spoil our curiosity. As you know the action function is just quadratic in ϕ as well as χ which means that the complicated looking formula involves just one Gaussian integral over χ:

$$\int_{-\infty}^{+\infty} e^{-a\chi^2}\, d\chi = \sqrt{\frac{\pi}{a}} = e^{-\frac{1}{2}\ln\frac{a}{\pi}}\,. \qquad \text{(III.4.28)}$$

In our integral we have that $a = (M^2 + \lambda\varphi^2/2)\hbar$ and we obtain for the integral $\left(\frac{2\pi\hbar}{M^2+\lambda\varphi^2/2}\right)^{\frac{1}{2}}$. So the effective

$$-\frac{S^{(2)}_{eff}}{\hbar} = \quad + \quad +$$
$$-\frac{\hbar\lambda}{4m^2M^2} \quad + \quad \frac{\hbar^2\lambda^2}{16m^4M^4}$$
$$+ \quad + $$
$$+ \quad \frac{\hbar^2\lambda^2}{16m^4M^4} \quad + \quad \frac{\hbar^2\lambda^2}{8m^4M^4}$$

Figure III.4.23: *Effective action expansion.* The diagrammatic expansion of the effective action for the toy model of equation (III.4.26), and the expression for the terms up to order λ^2 and $\hbar^2$.

action for the φ field becomes:

$$S_{eff}(\varphi) = \frac{m^2}{2}\varphi^2 + \frac{\hbar}{2}\ln(1 + \frac{\lambda\varphi^2}{2M^2}) + \frac{\hbar}{2}\ln\frac{M^2}{2\pi\hbar}$$

This logarithm $\ln(1+b)$ can for small b be expanded in a power series $\ln(1+b) = b - \frac{1}{2}b^2 + \frac{1}{3}b^3 + \ldots$.

Now on a quantum level we are supposed to draw all possible vacuum to vacuum diagrams: these are diagrams without incoming or outgoing lines. Are such diagrams possible? Well, yes, of course! We have drawn the first few diagrams in Figure III.4.23, where we listed them in powers of the coupling constant λ and included all diagrams up to second order. Applying the Feynman rules given in Figure III.4.21, we can in principle write the amplitudes but we are in particular interested in the coefficients of the successive terms and the powers in terms of the fields. After some algebra you get a result for the sum that is not too

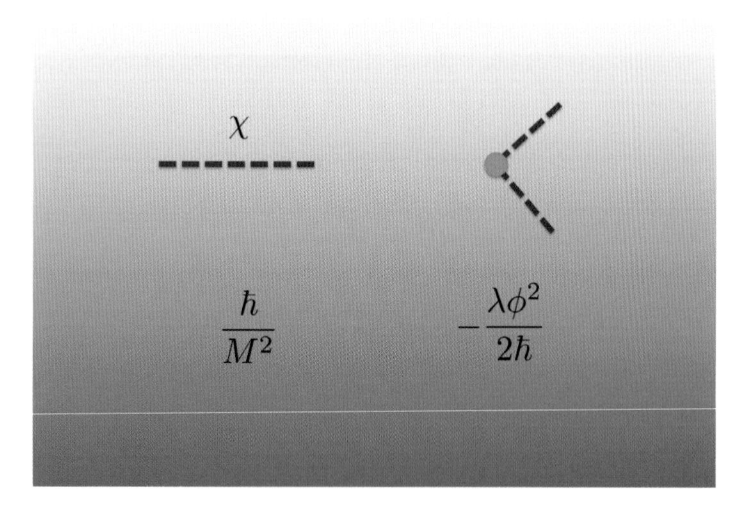

Figure III.4.24: *Effective Feynman rules for toy model.* These are the effective Feynman rules for the χ field if we treat the φ field as an external source corresponding to the green dot.

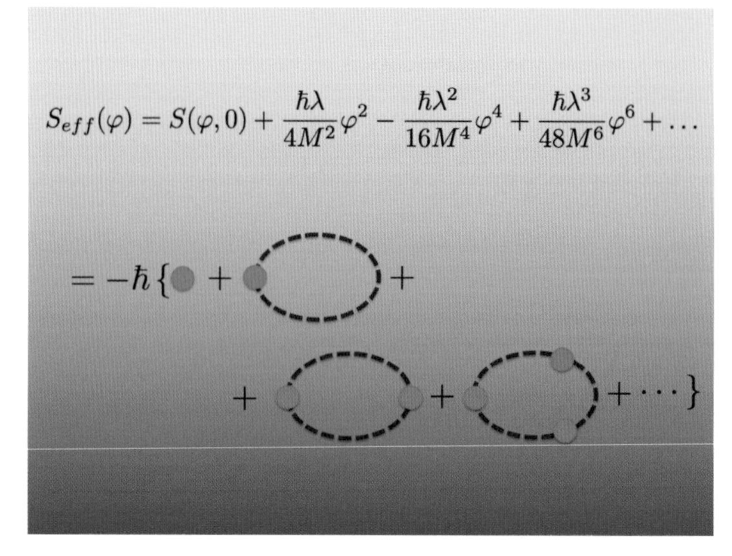

Figure III.4.25: *Effective action for φ field* This is the effective action for the φ field if we integrate out the high mass χ field. All diagrams have one loop and thus one power of $\hbar$, and they all contribute to the lowest order quantum corrections. The power of the coupling parameter $\lambda/2M^2$ is given by the number of propagators in each diagram.

surprising either:

$$S_{\text{eff}}(\varphi) = S(\varphi, 0) + \frac{\hbar\lambda}{4M^2}\varphi^2 - \frac{\hbar\lambda^2}{16M^4}\varphi^4 + \frac{\hbar\lambda^3}{48M^6}\varphi^6 + \ldots \tag{III.4.29}$$

This is an expression worth contemplating, because it exhibits many structural features of what quantum corrections on classical physics look like. We make the following observations:

(i) First of all note that the correction have a factor $\hbar$ so they vanish in the classical limit, in the classical limit the presence of the χ field decouples and it does not affect the effective φ theory.

(ii) The second remarkable fact is that summing over all χ contributions, which is what integrating the field out means, generates self interactions of order n with an effective coupling constant $\lambda_n \sim \hbar(\lambda/M^2)^n$. Most important is the lowest order term quadratic in φ: in other words it will shift the mass to $m^2_{\text{eff}} = m + \frac{\hbar\lambda}{2M^2}$. The take home message is, that quantum corrections may introduce novel interaction terms that were not there on a classical level.

(iii) One might also derive effective Feynman diagrams for the φ field where the higher order terms are represented as new couplings λ_{2n} labeling the strength of the vertices with $2n$ external lines. This is depicted in Figure III.4.26.

(iv) A fundamental question that remains at this point is whether the effective quantum theory can produce interaction terms that violate the symmetries (and therefore conservation laws) of classical theory. We see an example in the toy model above. The effective potential for the φ field has positive coefficients for the φ^2 and φ^6 terms but a negative coefficient for the φ^4 term, which means that the potential will have local minima at for $\varphi = 0$ but also for $\varphi \neq 0$. It would correspond to a metastable state where the mirror symmetry $\varphi \to -\varphi$ is violated. We briefly return to this question shortly when we talk about anomalies.■ ■

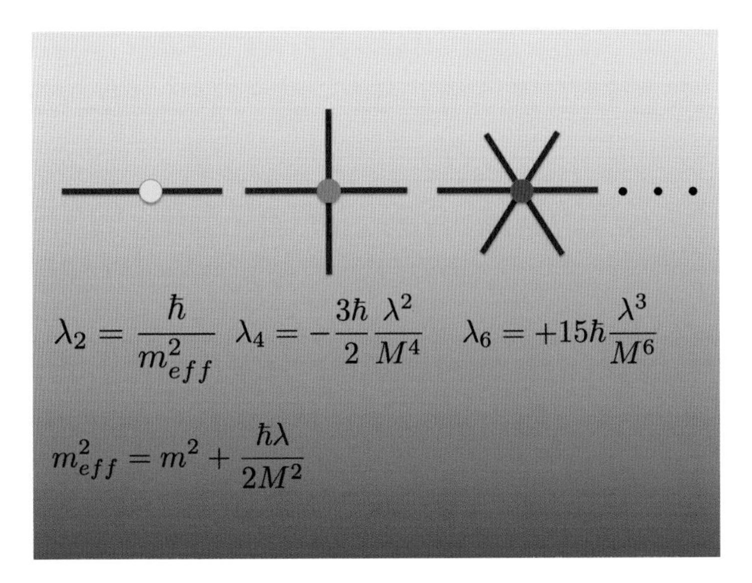

Figure III.4.26: *Effective Feynman rules.* The Feynman rules for the effective action for the φ field. The terms are defined as $\frac{1}{2n!}\lambda_{2n}\varphi^{2n}$ and yield the diagrams as shown.

Quantum fluctuations in QED

We pointed out before that we may specify a theory by postulating a set of fields representing the basic constituents and their interactions by giving the coupled equations they have to satisfy or equivalently by giving an energy or action function(al) in terms of them including the interactions. Such a model is characterized by its particular functional form which contains a number of parameters like coupling strengths and masses. These parameters are just the coefficients of the various terms in the action. Of course there are also the universal parameters such as the velocity of light and Planck's constant, which are hidden as we have 'set' them equal to one.

Now you would think that the parameters are directly determined by making measurements of them. Here we have to be careful because the story is not so simple.

In quantum theories even in the most idealized situations one has to deal with the effect of *quantum fluctuations*, because such fluctuations are an inevitable ingredient as a consequence of the uncertainty relations between position and momentum and time end energy. The size of the energy fluctuations grows inversely proportional with the spatial scale one chooses to look at. So, the theory describes also what the fluctuations are in these quantities and if one goes to smaller distances or higher momenta the effect of these fluctuations is that they will lead to significant differences between the *bare values* of the parameters that I wrote down in the equations and those that would effectively be observed. The parameters are indeed external but they are in fact corrected by the quantum processes described by the theory.

To make a consistent comparison with experimental results one should first calculate, then include these 'quantum' corrections and then choose the bare parameters in such a way that the observed data match the calculated parameters *including* the corrections. It's like buying a box of chocolates, since there may be a significant difference between the weight of the box as a whole and the net weight of the chocolates, as the wrapping may be surprisingly elaborate. The lore is that the more exquisite the chocolates the more elaborate the wrapping. Reality is similarly hidden from us by an elaborate quantum wrapping.

The calculations of these corrections turn out to be quite involved. What we like to do here is not so much doing such calculations as outlining the structure of what they involve. And what all that has to do with the scale dependence of the theory. Briefly stated: if one naively calculates these quantum corrections using the diagrammatic approach of Feynman, one finds that the calculations diverge, that they give infinite answers. This is not so much an indication that things are wrong, but rather that they are more subtle than you would naively expect. And Nature is subtle for sure.

What happens is that if one calculates the effect of certain quantum degrees of freedom these cause infinite changes in the effective parameters of the theory and that would render the theory useless, except when these divergencies can be 'subtracted' in a meaningful and consistent way that allows for a set of uniquely defined finite parameters after all. This procedure for dealing in a physically sensible way with these unwanted infinities is called *renormalization* which in turn can be understood in a more general approach called the *renomalization group.*

What one learns is that the renormalization procedure imposes serious constraints on the set of couplings or interaction terms one starts off with. Theories satisfying these constraints are called renormalizable and you will not be surprised to hear that the Standard Model of elementary particles and their interactions is a renormalizable gauge theory. However, Einstein's theory of general relativity is not renormalizable in the above sense, and the construction of a quantum theory of gravity is still best described as 'work in progress.'

Renormalization. Renormalization amounts to systematically extracting the finite quantum corrections to the parameters of the bare (classical) theory. It involves a rather technical two-step procedure to handle the infinities that pop up in the calculations of quantum corrections to masses and other coupling constants. The first part is *regularization* of the divergent expressions. This can be done in many different ways, but the simplest conceivable is to just introduce a cut-off in momentum space. This means that we simply ignore the contributions of very high momentum fluctuations. The second part is to introduce a *subtraction* depending on the cutoff, which renders the calculated amplitudes finite. The subtraction involves the introduction of *counter terms* in the action, and once these have been introduced one can take the limit of the cut-off to infinity. The dependence on the cut-off has disappeared and one is left with a finite physically meaningful result

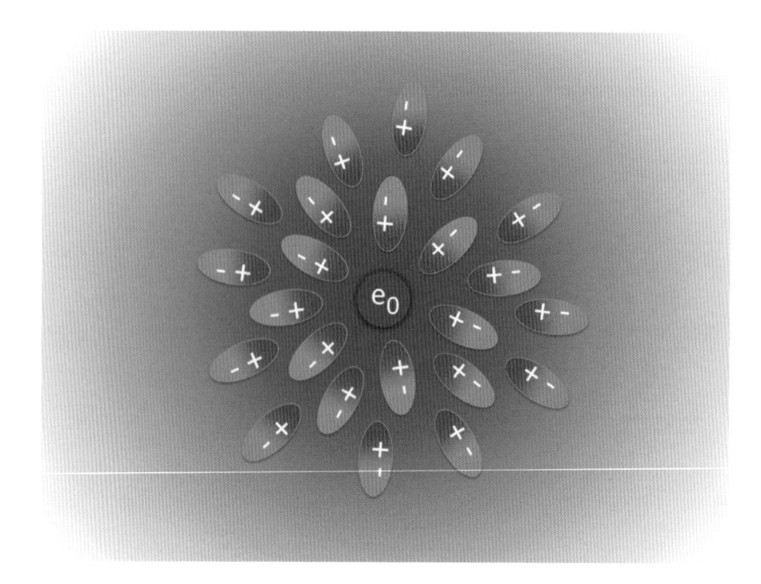

Figure III.4.27: *Virtual electron-positron pairs.* Vacuum fluctuations in the electromagnetic field give rise to a cloud of virtual electron-positron pairs that effectively screen the 'bare' charge, and make the effective charge distance or momentum dependent.

In practice the contribution of the quantum fluctuations depends on two things: (i) a momentum cut-off Λ which indicates that one only takes into account fluctuations larger then a certain spatial scale $d \gtrsim 1/\Lambda$, and (ii) on how accurate one calculates the effect of the fluctuations on the parameter values of interest. The calculated parameter change is encoded in what is called the β function, and this function can be calculated to an increasing degree of accuracy. We have discussed already examples which showed that these technical considerations are crucial in determining in which parameter domains one may expect results that do or do not make sense. In the following paragraphs we will give some remarkable results that will show the analytic power of these methods if it comes to understanding the asymptotic (high-energy) behavior of physical systems and the theories that describe them.

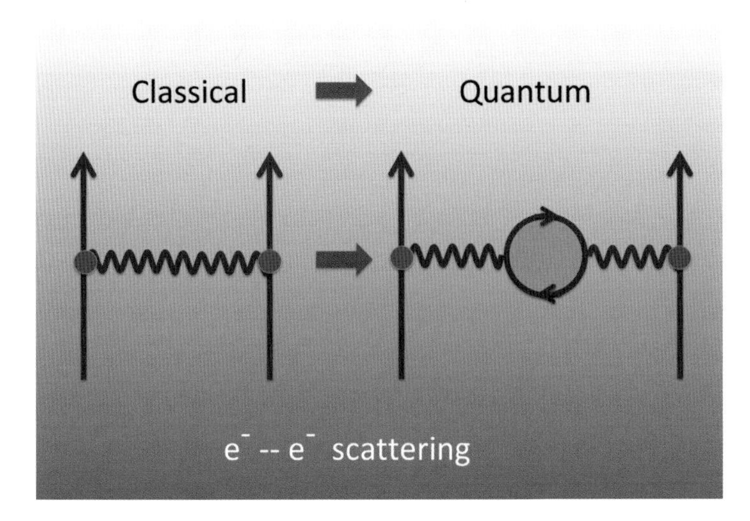

Figure III.4.28: *From classical to quantum process.* The Feynman diagram on the left represents two electrons that scatter of each other by exchanging a single photon. This diagram yields the classical result. On the right we give the quantum process where we have 'dressed' the photon propagator with a 'blob' which means that all quantum corrections have been included.

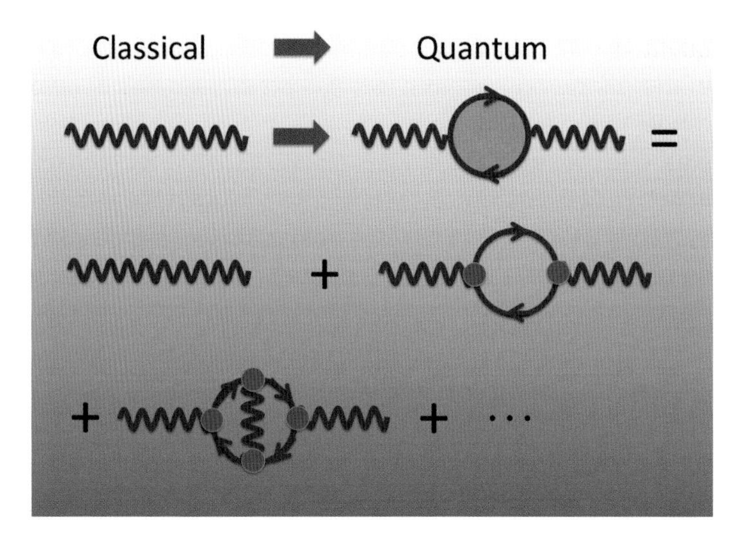

Figure III.4.29: *Quantum corrections.* Corrections due to virtual processes to the photon propagator. The blob has a systematic expansion in terms of ever more complex diagrams. Two blue dots lead to a factor $\alpha = e^2/4\pi\hbar c \simeq 1/137$ in the contribution of the diagram to the quantum mechanical scattering amplitude. So higher order terms (in α) become smaller and usually we include diagrams up to second order.

A realistic example: Vacuum polarization

We think of force laws like the gravitational law of Newton or the Coulomb law of electrostatics as specifying the strength of a force depending on some charge or mass and depending on some variable like the distance and then there is also an interaction strength, which is a dimension full constant (parameter) to be determined through experiment. That means we have to measure it at some characteristic scale and then assume it is constant not only in time but also in space. Both assumptions may be challenged. It may well be that by going to smaller or larger distances the effective coupling constants if one measures them would change.

Let me indicate why the effective coupling might change by exploiting some of the intuitive notions we have mentioned before. It is clear that if we have a charge for example, the field around this charge will become ever stronger at small distances. The energy density of the field increases and may at a certain distance become so big that it becomes possible by Einstein's $E = mc^2$ law, that charged particle antiparticle pairs are created near the charge. The idea is that the 'empty' space is not empty at all but filled with electron-positron pairs that form a cloud around the charge. This cloud will in fact screen the 'bare' charge of the electron. This means that at a distance further out we see an effective charge that will be smaller than the charge we started off with. Translated in the language of the coupling strength of the charge to the field, we see that it is not constant but depends on the scale at which it is measured. The amount of screening depends on at what distance we look at the charge. We say that the vacuum becomes polarized. As we measure at some distance it is interesting to ask whether we can find out what the bare charge would be, or what the effective charge at other distances would be. The coupling constants may be on the run but where are they going? Is it going to be ever smaller or ever bigger and maybe become infinite? In theories of various sorts describing different types of interactions many different scenarios present themselves including the possibility that bare parameters that were chosen to be zero become non-zero due to these quantum fluctuation effects, which basically amounts to saying that the theory itself acquires new extra parameters that you didn't put in at the start! Under certain circumstances theories are apparently capable to 'improve' upon themselves. One might say that taking this kind of background into account provides insight in the range of validity of the theory one started off with and that is certainly a remarkable conclusion that deserves a closer look.

A divergent diagram. Let us consider the two point function for the photon. In the second line of Figure III.4.29 we have drawn some Feynman diagrams that describe processes that contribute to the propagator or two-point function for the photon. In the first, the wiggly line is just the bare propagator which in momentum space is just given by the expression:

$$S(k) \simeq \frac{1}{k^2}$$

So this describes a mode with momentum of the photon propagating between two space-time points. The second diagram with two interactions where an electron-positron pair is created and subsequently annihilated. It is a so-called *virtual process* because there are no external lines connected to the closed fermionic loop. Now momentum is conserved in the interaction points so overall that means thatbthe the momentum carried by the ingoing photon must be the same as that carried by the outgoing photon, and at the vertex it implies that if the electron created has momentum p, then the positron has to have momentum $k-p$. If we just do the counting of powers of p, the propagator of the electron yields a factor $1/(p-m)$, and the positron a factor $1/(k+p-m)$. The problem arises because we have to sum or integrate all possible amplitudes, which means all possible values of the momentum p going around the loop. so we have to calculate an integral

$$\int \frac{1}{(p-m)(k+p-m)}\, p^3 dp \simeq \Lambda^2$$

For large p the dominant contribution comes from

$$\int p^3/p^2\, dp = \int p\, dp = \infty\,.$$

In other words, the integral behaves badly and is divergent! This is bad news because we know that physical amplitudes and probabilities are finite. What we need is a way to manage the deluge of infinities popping up in our calculations in such a way that physically meaningful results are obtained The infinities have to be artefacts of our calculational methodology otherwise the theory makes no sense.

This leads to the intricate protocol called *renormalization* that we have mentioned before. It refers to the three step procedure, where we first regulate the divergencies, then *subtract* the would be divergencies, which allows to redefine or renormalize the fields and parameters in the theory in a consistent and unique way.

Regularization and renormalization. The first step we take is to in some way *regulate* the divergent integral by introducing a high momentum cut-off, meaning that we limit the momentum range we integrate such that $p \leqslant \Lambda$. Then the leading term will be quadratic in Λ as indicated in the equation above.

Once you have applied such a *regularization* to all the divergent expressions, *renormalization* means that you apply a well-defined procedure to *subtract* the divergent expressions in a consistent way that leaves you with unique finite results for the quantum corrections to any diagram with given external lines. However, there are only a finite number of renomalizations (correction factors) you can implement in a given field theory; you can basically renormalize the fields, the masses and the coupling constants and that's it. So for electrodynamics you could at most accommodate two field, one mass, and one coupling constant renormalization. There are dependencies between them and one is left with three correction factors, Z_1, Z_2 and Z_3 associated with the renormalization of the wave function(s), the charge and the fermion mass respectively. The fact that QED is *renomalizable* means that if you calculate all diagrams for all amplitudes to arbitrary order in the coupling constant, all divergencies that you will ever encounter can be absorbed in those three constants. This is by no means obvious; it means that the theory has to meet certain exquisite requirements We will have more to say about what that means and which generic properties determine whether a theory is renormalizable or not.

Let us reflect for a moment on what the above technical rather magical manipulations have to do with the main subject of this chapter which is 'scaling' and 'scale invariance.' It is quite clear that once you introduce a cut-off or any other way to regularize the theory, then that will break any form of scale invariance, precisely because we explicitly introduce a scale in the theory 'by hand.' And though the results claim to be independent of the particular value of the cut-off, renormalization nevertheless deeply affects the high-energy asymptotic behavior of quantum field theories and in particular spoils the scale invariance one might have expected.

The cut-off and the subtraction point

The role of the cut-off is rather profound. With a bit of common sense one would say: of course there ought to be a cutoff because the theory may not be fit to describe fluctuations in the medium below a certain scale. Think of a fluid which on a macroscopic level is a continuum, but if we go down in scale we know that it is ultimately just a collection of molecules and on that scale the continuum assumption is certainly a bad one. Evidently in such a case it is the interatomic separation in the liquid that sets the scale for the distance cutoff $d \sim 1/\Lambda$. Let us now turn to the all-important question of the accuracy of the β functions, i.e. the functions that describe the scale dependence of the effective parameters in the model. The arguments became rather subtle to a point where even the scientist themselves became utterly surprised by the success of their calculations. What happened? In many cases the difference between the measured quantities and the calculated ones grew ever larger with increasing momentum. And indeed new parameters had to be introduced in the bare energy function. What one did was to just introduced so called counter terms also depending on the cutoff introduced that cancelled the calculated effect and after that let the cutoff go to infinity (or zero), so that the difference ended up being finite and independent of the cutoff. The physicists developed a well defined procedure, or maybe we should call it a calculational trick, called *renormalization* that would lead to predictions free of ambiguities, if and only if after some given order in the approximation scheme of the beta function no new parameters had to be introduced. That means that after a certain point the number of parameters of the theory would stay fixed and finite. Renormalization would then only change those parameters, and that was considered admissible from a physical point of view, though mathematically one was kind of jiggling infinities to fabricate finite numbers that should fit the experimental data.

But as usual the proof was in eating the sausage without advertising too much what went in it. And the results turned out to be splendid and the renormalization methods allowed us to calculate many new physical effects with exceptional precision. For example the pinnacle of such calculations is the high order calculation of the anomalous magnetic moment of the electron which matches experiment up to 11 significant digits! Now that is what one calls hard science!

Figure III.4.30: $g-2$ *diagrams.* Some of the tenth-order diagrams contributing to the calculation of the anomalous magnetic moment of the electron or muon. (Physical Review Letters109.111807, 2012)

In 1987 the experimental measurements (R. S. Van Dyck, Jr., P. B. Schwinberg and H. G. Dehmelt) reached the unbelievable precision:

$$a_e = (g-2)/2 = 1159652188.4(4.3) \times 10^{-12}.$$

The heroic QED calculation to the tenth-order in perturbation theory involving 12,672 diagrams performed by the Japanese team of Aoyama, Hayakawa, Kinoshita, and Nio produced the theoretical value:

$$a_e(\text{theory}) = 1159652181.78(77) \times 10^{?12},$$

which was published in 2012. To give you an idea of what this looks like we present some of the tenth-order diagrams in Figure III.4.30.

Anomalies. If regularization violates the symmetries of the classical action, we produce anomalies. The would-be conserved current is no longer conserved, the divergence of the current is no longer zero but there will be an anomalous source term in the quantum version of that law. So the question is how serious that is. What it means that in the quantum real world we would see processes that violate some naively expected conservation laws. For example there is a famous decay of a neutral pion π_0 into two photons the would be forbidden but actually has been observed, so such anomalous processes do occur.

Now there is one important restriction here, as we have argued, gauge symmetries lead to electric or color charge conservation and it is known that if we break local gauge symmetries, that leads to severe inconsistencies and the theory would become non-renormalizable. So in the first place we have to make sure we have a gauge invariant regulator. However, that may not be enough, and one has to make sure to adjust the particle content of the theory such that the contributions of the different particle species to the anomaly cancell. This has indeed led to the constraint of the *family structure* of the Standard Model. If the particles appear in what we called 'families' than the cancellation of all gauge anomalies is guaranteed.

As a matter of fact here again it is the gravitational interaction which is after all a gauge theory which has a gravitational anomaly, which makes the 'naive' perturbative quantization of Einstein's general theory of relativity a well-established night mare! In fact it is exactly why an anomaly free gravity theory pops up in string theory. It turns out that the gravitational anomalies cancel in ten-dimensional space-time, where strings supposedly live.

Further reading.
On scaling, renormalization and critical phenomena:

- *Fractals*
  John P. Briggs
  Touchstone Books (1992)
- *Quantum Field Theory*
  David Skinner
  Cambridge University (Lecture notes)
- *An Introduction To Quantum Field Theory*
  Michael E. Peskin and Daniel V. Schroeder
  CRC Press (1995)
- *The Theory of Critical Phenomena: An Introduction to the Renormalization Group*
  J.J. Binney, N.J. Dowrick, A.J. Fisher and M.E.J. Newman
  Clarendon Press (1992)
- *Phase Transitions and Renormalization Group*
  Jean Zinn-Justin
  Oxford University Press (2013)

Complementary reading:

- *The Fractal Geometry of Nature*
  Benoit Mandelbrot
  W. H. Freeman and Co. (1982)
- *Fractals: Endlessly Repeated Geometric Figures*
  H. Lauwerier
  Princeton University Press (1991)
- *M.C. Escher: Art and Science*
  H.S.M. Coxeter, M. Emmer, R. Penrose and M.J. Teuber Eds
  North-Holland (1986)
- The Mathematical Side of M.C. Escher
  Doris Schattschneider Article in Notices of the AMS, Volume 57 nr 6 (2010)
- *Scale: The Universal Laws of Growth, Innovation, Sustainability, and the Pace of Life in Organisms, Cities, Economies, and Companies*
  Geoffrey B. West
  Penguin Press (2017)

Nature in search of itself.

Science is a deeply human endeavor, as it requires the unique combination of basic capabilities like curiosity, reason, intuition, creativity and collaboration. It expresses the collective curiosity of mankind and has resulted in the double helix of science and technology that keeps transforming our world over and again. It embodies a cumulative, evolutionary process that continuously creates new options for society while at the same time forcing it to face the severe ethical dilemmas that come along.

All of us have witnessed how science has profoundly affected the human condition and transformed society, and how in many instances it managed to transcend man's painful political, ethnic, and religious differences. As such it is a true cornerstone of civilization. At least as long as we can ensure that it does not fall prey to all kinds of abuse by dark forces bent on power and financial or political gain only.

If knowledge is our destiny, then that feeds the hope for carving out a gateway to a common, global understanding of the world and our options for governing it. It could lead the way towards an inhabitable future for all of us.

Chapter III.5

Power of the invisible

> Im ganzen habe ich jedenfalls erreicht, was ich erreichen wollte. Man sage nicht, es wäre der Mühe nicht wert gewesen. Im übrigen will ich keines Menschen Urteil, ich will nur Kenntnisse verbreiten, ich berichte nur, auch Ihnen, hohe Herren von der Akademie, habe ich nur berichtet.
>
> *Franz Kafka*, in *Bericht fur eine Akademie* [1]

In this concluding chapter we briefly recapitulate our journey through the quantum wonderland. It is a kind of mirror image of the introduction. The difference is that with the knowledge we have acquired along the way there is more room to reflect on the places we visited. This also means that there is some room for more subjective statements.

Figure III.5.1: A modern pillar of wisdom? (Source: Pete Ryan, NYT, Jan. 7, 2022)

A pillar of wisdom? The cartoon on the right by Pete Ryan appeared in the *New York Times*. For me it is an ironic pillar of wisdom depicting not only the wisdom itself, but also our winding roads towards it. That process starts in quite an orderly way at the bottom with a number of parallel strands going straight up. At some point you start wondering why the strands go up so perfectly straight and parallel. And as soon as you start to question the given narrative things start to diverge. The lines start wiggling and before you know you are caught up in a huge entanglement, a huge confusion, a spaghetti like mess of doubt and contradiction. How to move forward? How to get out of this mess? And yes, every time, as by some miracle you manage to surmount the problems and look what

[1] On the whole, at any rate, I have achieved what I set out to achieve. But do not tell me that it was not worth the trouble. In any case I am not appealing for any man's verdict, I am only imparting knowledge, I am only making a report. To you also, honored Members of the Academy, I have only made a report. (translation: Willa and Edwin Muir)

happens: things come together again, and they coalesce into a new perception of reality symbolized by the beautifully ornamented capital. Like a crown on your labor. You managed to beat the minotaur hidden in that labyrinth of strands.

I suppose the artist has forgotten about the many dead-end streets that are also part of the tangle. Maybe the artist was inspired by the path integral approach to wisdom where only paths from A all the way to B have to be included. In fact *all* of them have to be included, not just the shortest or the most beautiful, but also the less obvious, maybe obscure and low probability routes. Anyway, after working your way through all the possible paths you are bound to end up at a next level of knowledge and understanding. Yet another shoulder of a giant to stand on, yet another step on Cantor's devil's staircase to ultimate knowledge and may be wisdom....

Summary and outlook

To see the power of the invisible in a way that supersedes blind faith, it has to be made discernible first. And that is what empirical science is about, inventing the observational tools that allow us to see those things that have always been there, but were hidden from the naked human eye. Why worrying about the invisible, you may ask, as long as the visible suffices to keep us busy and to fully occupy our fragile minds? Curiosity to know what may or may not be beyond what we can see is one of the ultimate drivers of our existence, of discovery, and in the long run of understanding, reason and survival.

Who am I? If you would ask me who I really am, I may start by telling a nice story, probably a dressed up CV of some sort centered about my major accomplishments. In certain cases I may even disclose some personal details. And if you keep pushing me, it may turn into a narrative about my childhood, my family and its traditions. And by talking about family treats I have, without mentioning, entered the realms of heredity and of genetics. The narrative loses some its ultra personal features and turns into a more generic, though still fully anthropocentric, perspective. I will for example not mention that features like my sense of humor, or need to physically be in touch, or my habits of impressing others, or getting enraged about futilities, probably go all the way back to my primate or for that matter rabbit-like ancestors.

You understand what I am driving at: the deeper I search myself and the world in which I live, the less personal the story becomes, the more abstract it will be, and the less it will refer to the plainly visible or the specifically human. If your interrogation were to go on indefinitely, I might just jot down some quantessential formulas in the end. And that is how the science of the invisible enters our conversations as a relevant resource of reliable knowledge, leaving the limitations of anthropocentricity behind. Maybe that is the power of the invisible.

The mission of physics. Physics is an empirical science which concerns the art of making discoveries through making ever more sophisticated observations. It wants to know what nature looks like and how it works on all scales. We have to admit that it certainly paid off when Galileo supposedly threw stones and wooden balls from the Pisa tower and carefully listened to them hitting the pavement! We make progress by building models and improving on them. The models are supposed to not just fit data but more in particular to explain the different patterns of data by relating them through causal relationships expressed through mathematical equations.

On all scales there is the question what the relevant degrees of freedom are, and to understand their behavior, like structure formation through binding or a particular dynamics, we need to understand the interactions between these relevant constituents. Dynamical processes are generated by interactions or forces between constituents and that makes their overall effect often hard to predict, exactly because coupling systems introduces feedback loops. This is a general feature that holds both on the classical and quantum level. It is particularly true for many particle systems, but as we have seen, it also holds for space-time. So, let us once more look at the quantessence at large.

This book's approach. This three volume book is a somewhat experimental and ambiguous 'go in between' in the sense that it tries to interpolate between a 'laymen account' and a – I hate to say this – 'textbook' of a sort. Is it possible to go in-between without losing two audiences at once? My publisher will undoubtedly let me know immediately, I am sure!

Another question that crosses the mind is whether all those *Wikis* make books like these not obsolete? I think the answer is a firm 'no' and would claim the opposite. These books attempt to be more than a encyclopedia and give a coherent account of large range of topics that together form a huge subject in science. The aim is to provide a critical guidance for which items out of the small infinity of *Wikipedia* entries are actually relevant if you want to go quantum. I can only hope that these books did indeed give you an informed steer on when and where to go for additional *Wiki-wisdom*, and what the keywords were to look for.

It's the math, stupid! In confronting quantum realities this could be the analogue of the political maxim 'It's the economy, stupid!,' that was coined by the American political analyst James Carville in 1992. He wanted to emphasize that even the most basic knowledge of economy would stop people from making absurd claims about everyday economic realities. We have used a lot of mathematical language mainly in order to keep the arguments transparent and unambiguous and to prevent us from committing crimes against logic. But we softened our approach by paraphrasing the math with lots of prose as to keep the story accessible. However, making that choice we sacrificed a principal asset of mathematics, namely, that it is extremely concise and allows you to make precise yet brief arguments. The true aesthetics of mathematics is deeply rooted in this idea of eliminating all the unnecessary. In that respect math is the opposite of show business: no window-dressing allowed. We exploited the unambiguous and transparent character of the mathematical formalism, but at the same time blurred its purity by – in parallel – talking extensively about what it means and using lots of illustrations. We immersed our math formulas in the 'unnecessary' to keep them accessible and part of the conversation. You could say that we fell back on show business after all.

The three track narrative. In an attempt to help overcome the common fear of formulas, and keep the contents manageable I adhered to a storytelling philosophy where the narrative followed three tracks in parallel. The first was a pictorial one, as I included over 450 illustrations, the second was the rather extensive use of equations, and the third track consisted of extensive prose. The latter is there in its own right, but also to bridge the gaps between pictures and formulas. The interplay between these tracks hopefully allowed you to grasp this wonderful body of fundamental knowledge in the heart of science. I am convinced that it made you at least 'conversant' about the *quantessence* of things.

The *quantessence* in retrospect.

Let us briefly look back at the three volumes that make up this quantum trilogy with Figures III.5.2 in mind. The reason why this trio has such a wide scope is the plain fact that quantum theory is a general set of principles that nature appears to obey on all scales, at least as far as we have been able to test. It applies to different types of systems, where the translation of the fundamental quantum principles get a different mathematical implementation and outlook.

Three volumes.

Volume I. In the first volume we have devoted quite a bit of time and room to provide a wide background by recalling the basic concepts of classical physics. This in order to provide a setting in which the quantessential parts of the subsequent volumes stand out more clearly.

In Chapter I.1 we briefly reviewed of the central achievements of classical physics. And in Chapter I.2 we extended that with the basics of relativity, geometry, and classical information theory.

Chapter I.3 looks at the universal constants of nature and what their meaning is. We showed how through dimensional analysis these constants set natural scales linked to certain classical and quantum phenomena.

In Chapter I.4 we descended the quantum ladder in a systematic way from the atomic scale down. This culminated in a description of the Standard Model for the elementary particles and the fundamental forces between them. We then continued with excursions into the speculative domains of supersymmetry and string theory as possible approaches to a consistent quantum theory that includes gravity: a quantum theory that would unify matter, radiation and space-time.

Volume II. In the second volume we introduced the mathematical framework and mostly applied it to basic systems like qubits, electron spins, particles and simple field theories.

In the Chapter II.1 we discussed concepts like the Hilbert space of states, a vector space where the linear superposition principle holds which quite directly leads to the possibility of *entangled states* which are uniquely quantum. These states lead to intriguing paradoxes like 'Schrödinger's cat' and the EPR paradox, but at the same time opened the possibility of quantum teleportation and quantum key distribution.

In Chapter II.2, we introduced the observables as operators acting on Hilbert space. This identification led to quantessential notions like the incompatibility of observables, which in turn give rise to the fundamental uncertainties as expressed by Heisenberg's uncertainty relations. We also went into various aspects of particle-wave duality, leading to particle interference phenomena as discussed in Chapter II.3.

We demonstrated that the vastly different quantum setting allows for a new type of information processing and computing with a far-reaching technological potential. This is a major challenge and has become a high priority effort for the worldwide community of quantum condensed matter physicists. And in parallel to the struggle to produce scalable and reliable hardware there is now also a booming branch of quantum software developments.

In Chapter II.5 we explored a topological argument for the exclusion principle and the spin/statistics properties of quantum particles.

Symmetry considerations play a central role in all fields of modern physics and chemistry. We therefore concluded the second volume with a chapter entirely devoted to the meaning and quantum implementations of symmetry and its breaking.

Volume III. In the third volume we showed how the physics of the early cosmic evolution in an expanding and cooling universe is completely governed by the quantum laws. The resulting structural hierarchy of matter reflects how the various fundamental forces played dominant roles in suc-

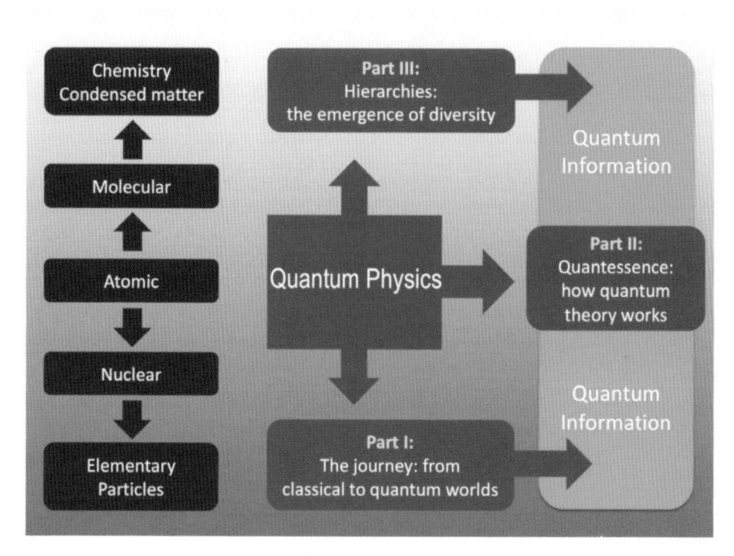

(a) The book at large.

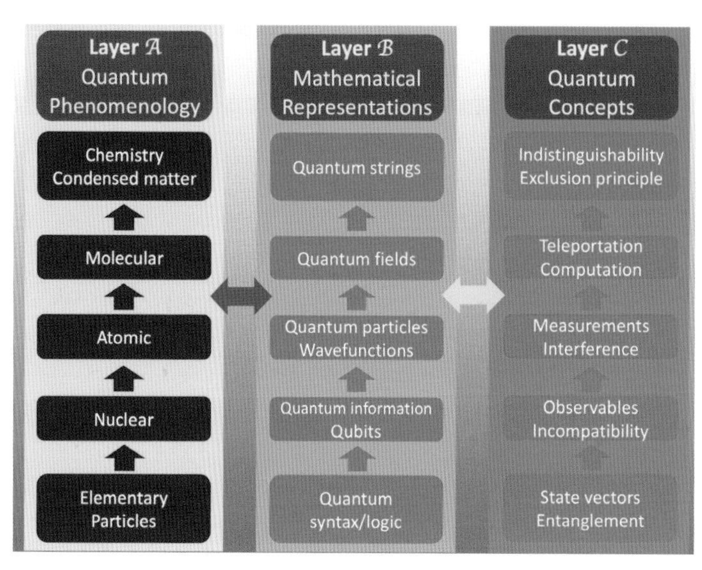

(b) Quantum layers.

Figure III.5.2: *Book summary.* The quantessence in retrospect.

cessive stages of that evolution.

After discussing the basics of molecular (chemical) physics, we turned to the many-body physics of condensed states of matter. First we described the types of order that the substrate of atoms or ions may exhibit, like crystal lattices of all sorts and their symmetries. We also considered the defects or imperfections that may form in such highly ordered states of matter. These defects often carry quantum numbers that are conserved for topological reasons.

In Chapter III.3 we turned to the electron collective and how that gives rise to many surprising quantum phenomena like various types of conductivity and magnetism, from semi- to superconductors, quantum Hall states etc. It is amazing to see how many novel states of matter are possible in the quantum regime.

We closed our quantum excursions with Chapter III.4 on the properties of scaling, first in the realms of geometry and then in context of dynamical systems. In the quantum regime leading the notion of *renormalization*, which boils down to a systematic scale dependent redefinition of the parameters that define the model. In quantum field theory this stands for sophisticated procedures of juggling with infinities leading to a state of peaceful coexistence with them, by producing unambiguous finite answers. In addition to the understanding of phenomena like the *confinement* of quarks, the *renomalization group* approach provided a powerful approach to critical phenomena in general.

Three layers.

Layer $\mathcal{A}$: Down and up the structural hierarchy. There is a subtle difference between the first column of the Figure III.5.2(a) referring to the Volumes and Figure III.5.2(b) referring to the layers. In the first figure the arrows are pointing downwards from the atomic scale to the scale of quarks and leptons, while in the second they are all pointing upwards. We recall that in Chapter I.4 we followed the quest for ever more fundamental building blocks of matter indeed following the arrows down. However, in Chapter III.1 we did the opposite, and followed the time path, not of the human quest, but of the true cosmological history by showing how the hierarchy of matter starting from the Big Bang all the way up to the molecules of life came into being. This perspective was of course forced upon us after understanding the evolution of space-time according to the Big Bang scenario described by the theory of General Relativity.

Layer $\mathcal{B}$: The hierarchy of mathematical realizations. The mathematical realizations of the basic quantum principles are shown in the second column of the figure. Simply stated, the system one considers defines what the basic degrees of freedom or dynamical variables are. Given the Hamiltonian one may then define the operators for the 'coordinates' and conjugate 'momenta' and postulate their canonical commutation relations. The structure of the corresponding Hilbert space of quantum states then follows. If the system cannot be solved exactly which is mostly the case, one usually starts from the non-interacting system, and uses that as the starting point for a perturbative approach of the system with interactions.

What the middle column shows is that at the bottom of the hierarchy, the most elementary quantum system is in fact the *qubit* or the spin-1/2 degree of freedom, with its two-dimensional Hilbert space. This system was extensively analysed in Chapters II.1 and II.2.

One step up we have the framework of *quantum mechanics* for a single particle, typically in an external potential leading to an infinite-dimensional Hilbert space of normalizable wave functions. These notions were introduced in Chapter I.4 in the section on 'Atomic structure' and we repeatedly returned to this topic in the second volume, and in particular in Chapter II.5.

At the next level of generality we include special relativity which forced us to move from quantum mechanics to the framework of *quantum field theory*. Here the fields and their conjugate field-momenta are the basic degrees of freedom, leading to the multi-particle Hilbert space. This framework centers around *field operators* that allow for the creation and annihilation of particles and therefore allows for the implementation of the famous equivalence relation $E = mc^2$, for example as we see it in processes like pair creation and annihilation in QED. Field theory is the language of the Standard Model, but also for most of condensed matter physics. Quantum field theory is introduced in Chapter I.4 in the context of the Standard Model. We returned to some of the formal aspects in Chapter II.5, and apply it to the electron collective in Chapter III.3. Finally, the scaling and renormalization aspects of field theory were discussed in Chapter III.4.

A yet more general framework would allow for the consistent inclusion of general relativity: in other words the inclusion of the gravitational force implying the quantization of space-time itself. This mission is not completed yet. The most advanced models of this type are the *superstring theories* which we described towards the end of Chapter I.4. In this framework each string mode corresponds to a different quantum field. The string idea therefore unifies all fields and thus all particle types into a single theory. This theory has certainly deepened our understanding of the quantum properties of gravity, like black holes and resolved some of the outstanding paradoxes, but the theory has not yet led to unique explanations of observed phenomena like dark energy. And the predictions it does make, like the 10-dimensional structure of space-time, or the existence of a myriad of super particles, have not (yet) been confirmed by experiment.

Layer $\mathcal{C}$: Quantum concepts and their meaning. The third layer shows how the mathematically consistent framework raised a number of conceptual issues physics had to face. These issues concern the question of how to interpret the core of physical reality. The subtitle of the book is 'The *quantessence* of reality' because that quantessence has been shaking the foundations of many of our cherished beliefs about what seemed to be self-evident features of reality, features reflecting our classical intuitions. These intuitions concern what the properties of physical systems were supposed to be, and what the role causality and predictability in their mathematical framing amounted to. What we have learned in a century of quantum developments is that these changes are radical and will be long lasting.

Starting at the bottom of the third column of Figure III.5.2(b), we see the that the structure of the space of states of any quantum system is a vector (Hilbert) space, meaning that the superposition principle holds, and that physical states are represented by normalized vectors. If we combine subsystems the total Hilbert space becomes to the (tensor) product space, implying that the dimension of the total space is the product of the dimensions of the subspaces. This structure implies the existence of *entangled states*, which are states that correspond to normed vectors in the total space that are *not factorizable*, that *do not* correspond to a direct product of two vectors in the subsystems.

Entanglement allows for the possibility of strong, very quantessential, instantaneous correlations between outcomes of measurements separated by arbitrary large distances. This led to a profound debate often referred to as the *Bohr-Einstein* debate about the locality and causality properties of physical reality. Experiments like the GHZ experiment that we discussed in Chapter II.4 convincingly showed the quantum interpretation to be correct.

Moving one step up in the column we mention that the mathematical structure of quantum mechanics implies that observables should be interpreted as (bounded) operators acting on vectors in Hilbert space. These should be thought of as (finite or infinite) matrices or differential operators which by acting will in general change the state. The fact that observables are no longer real-number-valued variables like in classical physics immediately leads to the problem of what a measurement exactly means. In the Copenhagen interpretation it means that the measurement outcome is a probabilistic one and furthermore that the act of measurement will generically change the state of the system. There is no longer a strict separation between object and subject when observations are made. We can no longer predict precisely what happens but can only calculate the odds. This in turn means that we leave the notion of classical determinism behind. Quantum means indeterminism.

Another important consequence of the fact that observables are operators is that they do not necessarily commute. The outcome of their successive action on a given vector may depend on the order in which you apply them. If the operators do not commute, the corresponding observables are called *incompatible*. This incompatibility lies at the root of the intrinsic quantum uncertainties in measurement outcomes so beautifully encoded in *Heisenberg's uncertainty relations.*

The structure of quantum reality also implies that we cannot copy a quantum state while keeping the original, this is known as the *no-cloning theorem.* However, what *is* possible is to transfer a quantum state from one system to another, and because of the entanglement property this can in principle be done instantaneously over arbitrary large distances. This possibility of *quantum teleportation* turned the entanglement property into a blessing in disguise. It enables another level of cyber security in data transfer.

Further conceptual consequences are evident if one thinks about the quantessentials from the point of view of information. The quantum states allow for storage of information, and this naturally leads to the introduction of the *qubit* as the quantum analogue of the digital bit. Quantum mechanics allows for unheard possibilities to process this quantum information. We see all around us that a major quantum information revolution is on its way, a revolution that both on the hard and software side will radically transform our computational abilities.

A final radical ingredient of quantum reality manifests itself if one studies the collective behavior of many particle systems. First of all because particles of a certain type correspond to basic modes of a single quantum field, they are *indistinguishable*, they have a family name but no first name, so to speak. In addition there is the possibility of *exclusion*, saying that there cannot be more than one particle in a given quantum state. This verdict is anchored in the quantum interpretation of the Dirac field. We addressed these fundamental properties of quantum particles in Chapter II.5, and linked them to the topological properties of the two-particle Hilbert space. Indistinguishability and exclusion each modify the statistical properties of many body systems and create entirely novel possibilities for the physical states of these systems. These possibilities have made quantum condensed matter physics into an inexhaustible source of technological innovations.

Altogether the beauty of the conceptual notions which surfaced in the third layer are a direct and therefore necessary consequence of the basic logical structure of quantum theory. There appears to be no way around them and more and more we start to appreciate how they enriched and broadened our perception of the roots of reality. They embody a true revolution in our understanding of the physical universe that found its translation into powerful new technologies that radically transformed our daily lives, and will keep doing so.

The many topics we didn't talk about. Many of the quantessential subjects we only touched upon superficially deserve chapters or books on their own. We spent a section on the miraculous properties of Carbon but what about a chapter on the virtues and technological blessings of silicon? What about the nano-sciences? What about an extensive review of an ever-growing list of alternative interpretations of quantum theory, like the 'many-worlds interpretation' proposed by the American physicist Hugh Everett in his doctoral thesis at Princeton University in 1957? Indeed, there are many topics which are relevant that I chose not to focus on and only mentioned in passing.

The main reason for these shortcomings is that I wanted to stay faithful to the subtitle of the book and focus on the *Quantessence*, the well-established fundamental aspects of the quantum reality. The perspective that shook the scientific world a century ago and lead to an unlimited extension of technological opportunities and realities that has by far not been exhausted or even been fully explored. As I emphasized all along, the era of quantum information technologies for example has only just started.

Common denominators.

The power of information as fundamental concept. Figure III.5.2(a) is just like the figure we presented in the Introduction to the book except that on the right we added a full column referring to the notion of information. It underscores that on all levels we may include an information science and computational perspective in the framework. All systems are in a sense information carriers and information processing devices, meaning that we set up paths with preset interactions between these carriers. Execution of a program or algorithm can be thought of as a particular class of dynamical processes. In this book we have repeatedly noted that the information science perspective involving algorithmic thinking is in an interesting way complementary to the more conventional theoretical physics approach involving calculus and differential equations, and it has led to surprising insights.

We encountered the notion of information towards the end of Chapter I.1 while introducing the notion of entropy as the

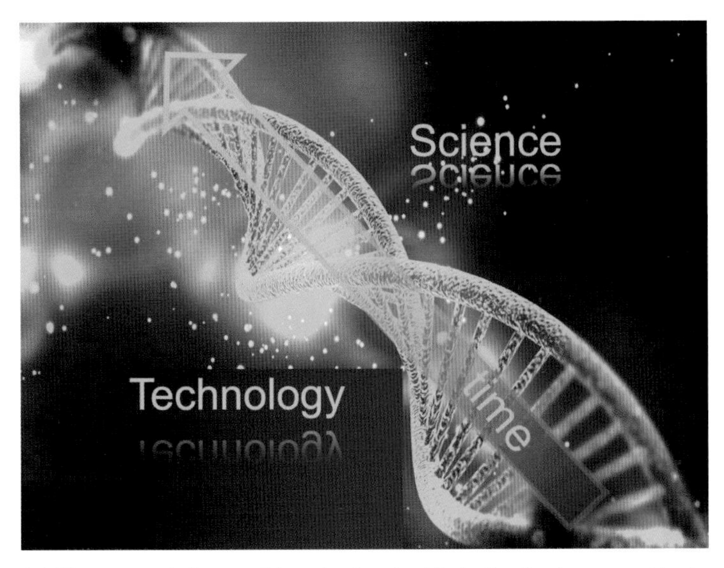

(a) Human evolution as driven by the double helix of science and technology.

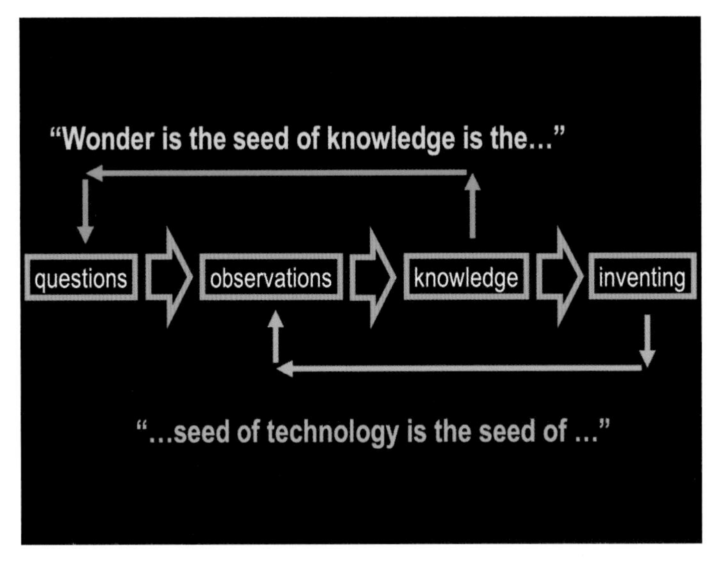

(b) The positive feedback loop of science and technology producing knowledge, technology and the human expertise.

Figure III.5.3: *The double helix of science and technology.*

logarithm of the number of micro-states corresponding to a given macro-state. It is a measure of information capacity of the system, or stated differently, for the information loss in going from the micro- to the macro-description of that system. It involves the aggregation of micro degrees of freedom into far fewer macro degrees of freedom. In that sense entropy is a measure for hidden information. In Chapter I.2 we gave a small introduction to the basics of information theory as initiated by Turing and Shannon, and in the section on black holes we discussed the Bekenstein-Hawking entropy and the famous black hole information paradox.

In the quantum realm, we introduced in Chapter II.1 the idea of a 'bit mechanics' as the most basic of all dynamical systems leading to the notion of a qubit, with its two-dimensional Hilbert space. In the following chapters we illustrated many fundamental quantum concepts referring to this basic quantum system. In Chapter II.4 we talked about teleportation of quantum information, about quantum gates and circuits, and went into a rather detailed discussion of Shor's quantum factorization algorithm.

So indeed, the notion of information popped up everywhere justifying the blue column on the right-hand side of Figure III.5.2(a).

The power of symmetry as guiding principle. We saw that symmetry is a powerful notion with applications on all levels of the quantum ladder. This is reflected in the rich nomenclature involving symmetry concepts, like global versus local (gauged), space-time versus internal, exact versus approximate, and broken versus unbroken synmmetry. It is not surprising that the notion of symmetry popped up in many chapters. We decided to devote Chapter II.6 to the many ways symmetry concepts have entered physics. In a sense it also deserves just like information a full column in Figure III.5.2(b).

Symmetries in classical as well as quantum physics are

linked to conserved quantities.Therefore they lead to a transparent labeling of the physical properties of states. It allows us to give names to things like 'energy,' 'angular momentum,' 'charge,' or 'isospin.'

Symmetry considerations play a crucial role in analysing and understanding the solution spaces of the fundamental equations of quantum physics, like the spectra of single atoms and molecules as well as the states of many-body condensed matter systems. And symmetry served as a successful guiding principle in the uncovering of the underlying structure of subatomic physics encoded in the Standard Model as an expression of the underlying gauge symmetry.

Symmetry-breaking turned out to be a key concept to explain the many different guises in which symmetry manifests itself on all levels in nature. From Zeeman splitting on the atomic level to spontaneous magnetization or superconductivity on the macroscopic level, to the existence of the Higgs particle on the subnuclear level. Indeed the idea of symmetry-breaking led to a unified understanding of the phase structure predicted by a wide variety of theoretical models.

The power of modelling as a discourse. Most models are quantitative in nature and by construction logically consistent. An ever-expanding body of symbolic relations that may be used to represent anything you can imagine. A human-made symbolic language ideally suited for a truly scientific discourse. Many of the great scientific turning points are cast in simple mathematical equations, or mathematically defined rules.

State of the art modelling. Modelling is not only a way to talk *about* reality; it is also a way to talk *with* reality. It is a productive way of framing the scientific discourse. A state of the art model is rarely completely correct. It has its strong and illuminating sides but also its weaknesses. So especially once the systems become complex with many hidden feedback loops and many coupling parameters one doesn't expect perfect predictions, and less so on the long-term future. What you gain in adaptability you lose in predictability. Think of modelling the climate or the spreading of viruses like Covid-19 or Ebola, or the endless efforts to properly model the good old economy.

The modelling activity furnishes a platform to study the effect of possible interventions. This is an interactive platform that can bring opposing interest groups together in a reasonable debate or negotiation, assuming both share enough purpose. Playing with the parameters of models gives a clear impression of what might go wrong, what the vulnerabilities of the system are, and what type of tipping points can occur. Models thereby can forge the highly needed compromises in order to be able to deal with the problems one is faced with.

Analytic versus algorithmic thinking. We have stressed that a crucial aspect of scientific progress is the parallel development of mathematics as a language for modelling nature. Nowadays we should also include the crucial importance of computation and algorithmic thinking as powerful means to achieve progress in science. This concerns a wide range of methodologies, beginning with simple numerical methods to solve systems of mathematical equations to advanced simulation methods for complex systems like agent-based modelling. But also methodologies like machine learning to collect and analyse large data sets, algorithms to detect correlations, that make predictions possible without an actual understanding of the causal mechanisms underlying them.

Rule-based models. In this era of computational empowerment, we are increasingly driven away from completely analytical, closed systems of equations like those of Newton or Maxwell, to more evolutionary approaches like simple rule-based models. Rules that are iterated very, very many times and may lead to structural entities in which we may recognize fundamental aspects of reality. This ap-

(a) The structural hierarchy mapped onto a circle.

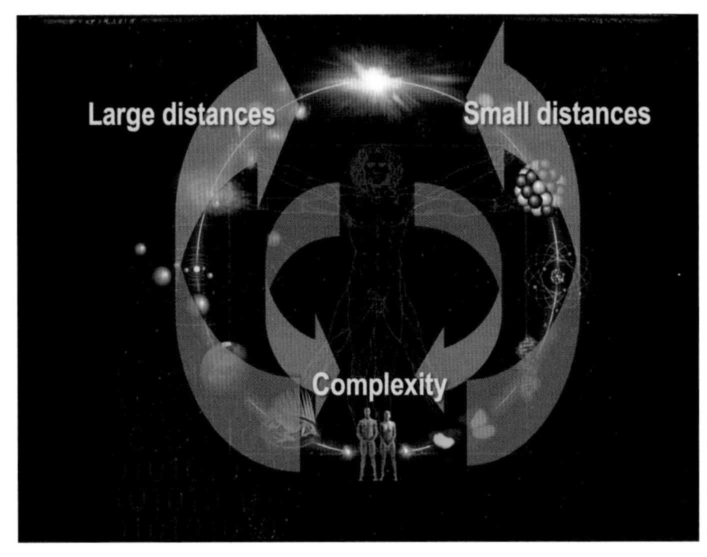

(b) Three fundamental frontiers.

Figure III.5.4: *The structural hierarchy of the material world and the basic frontiers of science.* In (a) we mapped the structural hierarchy onto a circle. Moving clockwise is moving towards larger scales, starting from 10^{-20} and extending all the way to 10^{+25} meters. The human scale is kind of in the middle. In (b) we indicated the three fundamental frontiers. On the left the large-scale frontier of astronomy pursued through space observatories like the Hubble and the James Webb. On the right the small-scale frontier of high-energy physics pursued at CERN and Fermilab for example. The arrows pointing towards the bottom symbolize the multiple frontiers of the life sciences including neuroscience. These naturally expand into the vast domain of information and computer science that are redefining the range and ambitions of the social sciences including economics.

proach involves a shift from analytic to more algorithmic thinking.

A key feature is that simple algorithms can generate extremely complex patterns with all kinds of emergent order. That emergent order is very hard to predict in advance using tools from standard analysis and geometry; its complexity can only be understood from actually running the algorithm for a sufficiently long time. We speak of *irreducible complexity* inherent to certain simple rule-based dynamical systems: for example cellular automata, or evolutionary pattern growth algorithms on networks, like John Conway's *Game of life.* The simplest way to find out what the structures are that emerge from a certain rule is to run the corresponding program long enough. We refer to the extensive literature on this subject by its pioneer and protagonist Stephen Wolfram who is also the founder and CEO of the successful software environment called Mathematica and Wolfram language. In his latest project aimed at 'finding a new fundamental theory of physics' he argues that all of quantum may be the product of iterating a simple rule-based algorithm! Another great mission, but for now also incomplete.

Scenarios for past and future

Science at large. In this final section I would like to put the whole quantum story in the wider context of science in general, a perspective that derives also from my earlier book titled *In Praise of Science: Curiosity, Understanding and Progress*. And in doing so I have adapted some of the imagery created for that book.

To me one of the most remarkable facts we are aware of is that nature evolved from a random and structureless initial state with a uniformly distributed low information density, to a state of very high information content, very much localized in the most advanced of biological organisms such as human beings. It did so by following a set of strict rules we call 'laws of nature.' The most stupefying twist is that these rules have been hidden until we as human beings became aware of them after millennia of carefully researching and modelling what we observed. Indeed, nature seems to be in search of itself, becoming aware of itself through this concerted yet indefinite human effort.

The double helix of science and technology.

Let us focus a bit more on the mechanism underlying this process of progress as depicted in Figure III.5.3, On the left we see a schematic of what I have called 'the double helix of science and technology.' It is like a mutually inspiring, almost ritual dance, generating knowledge and technology, but also the expertise of scientists and engineers who are able to create and apply that knowledge. Paraphrasing Francis Bacon it visualizes the idea that 'wonder is the seed of knowledge' and 'knowledge is the seed of technology,' which in turn is the seed of new 'wonder' and scientific discovery.

This perpetual machine works because technology also involves the invention of new instruments that shift the boundaries of what is observable. It pushes the observable in an objective sense. The domain of empirical investigation keeps expanding, generating an ever-growing body of knowledge! From instruments like microscopes and telescopes, all the way up to MRI machines, accelerators, and not to forget computers. The power to compute, to simulate numerically, as well as screening immense quantities of data for all kinds of correlations and patterns which are hidden from the human eye, is invaluable for human progress.

This human-made evolutionary process overtakes biological evolution in the sense that it continuously offers new options to humanity to move forward. I use the term options on purpose because it implies the notion of choice. The term progress suggests that society will always benefit, but that is not necessarily the case. What is certain, however, is that society will keep being bombarded with ethical and moral dilemmas, because those are inherent to that double helix of innovation.

History has taught us that technology is a double-sided sword which may be used in constructive as well as destructive ways. And that means that it requires a society that has the ability to make the right choices and in particular manages to avoid a proliferation of the evil aspects of technological achievement. I think there is ample room for optimism but to close one's eyes for the risks and the dark sides that are certainly there, is dangerously naive.

Looking at the double helix of Figure III.5.3(b) one realizes that it is a magical machine that is not easy to stop. It is a positive feedback loop. It is hard to forbid curiosity or creativity by law but there have been regimes that did exactly that, a game only with losers. This machine is much more autonomous than most people are aware of. It takes a great deal of expertise and scientific awareness to navigate society in a way that the constructive opportunities get amplified and the destructive ones are eliminated as far as possible. It is quite evident that good science does not work by popular vote. The scientific method is open to critique and rigorous analysis, but it is not democratic in the 'one man one vote' sense. That does not preclude that by the time new technological options present themselves to society one may hope that well-informed crowds will demonstrate their wisdom in governing their implementation.

This observation once more underscores the importance of fighting scientific illiteracy through broad educational programs introducing science and technology and raising the awareness of the social impact they may have. It is our duty to educate a critical audience, that is conversant about topics that will shape our common future. In my opinion those topics include the possible ways in which we may steer and regulate future applications of science and technology so that they improve the human condition not for the few but for the many.

What adds to the complexity of this process is the fact that the plusses and minuses of novel technologies are in most cases not evident at the moment of their inception. Unfortunately they are often even intertwined. And that is precisely why the incorporation of up-to-date scientific expertise in the political arena is necessary in any well-functioning, future oriented democracy.

Trees of knowledge

What we learned in this process of scientific discovery is presented schematically in a series of four subsequent images. You may call it a display of the harvest of the double helix.

The structural hierarchy. In the first picture III.5.4(a) we mapped the structural hierarchy of the material world onto a circle, where moving clockwise we go to ever larger distances. At the bottom, roughly in the middle, we see ourselves, and it is from that position that we started to explore the order of things in- and outside of us, diving ever deeper in the microcosmos and looking ever further out in the macrocosmos. So one way to look at this figure is that it depicts the human effort to understand the world we are living in, basically following the double helix of science and technology.

Three fundamental frontiers. The arrows we superposed on the circle in the second picture III.5.4(b) indicate how the basic frontiers of knowledge have moved forward. On the left from starting with Galileo all the way up to the Hubble or Webb space telescopes, and on the right from Antonie van Leeuwenhoek all the way down to the LHC at CERN. Very large and very small scales meet and merge in the Big Bang where modern research fields like astroparticle physics came to flourish. The Big Bang is the event where today's largest and smallest scales of the universe meet and that is why I have put the scales on a circle and not on a line.

The inside arrows pointing down to us humans clearly represent the evolutionary perspective on structural complexity like the phenomena of life. The arrow on the left represents the study of biology from the macroscopic Darwinian perspective on the speciation of plants and animals, and on the story told by the fossils they left behind in the earth's crust. The downward arrow on the right represents the unstoppable advance of molecular thinking in the life sciences, symbolized by the DNA-molecule. And indeed the genes on the DNA molecules tell that same Darwinian story but then on the molecular level. These two complementary views on evolution therefore meet and merge in the modern life and the earth sciences. And in a sense this 'closes' the circle at the bottom in us humans.

Three domains: Relativity, Quantum and Evolution. As indicated in the third picture III.5.5(a), the arrows in the background represent the large domains of fundamental scientific inquiry which are anchored in the leading conceptual frameworks like the *domain of relativity* (concerning space-time and gravity), *the domain of quantum* (covering all forms of constituent matter and the forces between them), and finally the *domain of evolution*, the con-

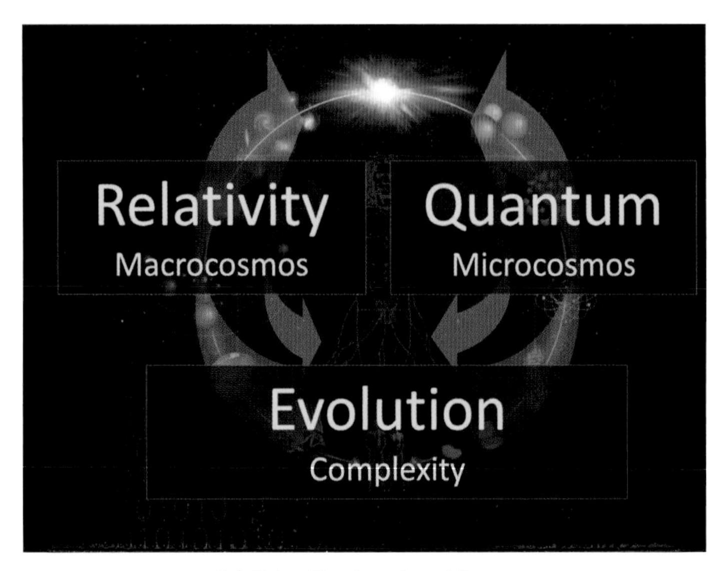

(a) Scientific domains at large.

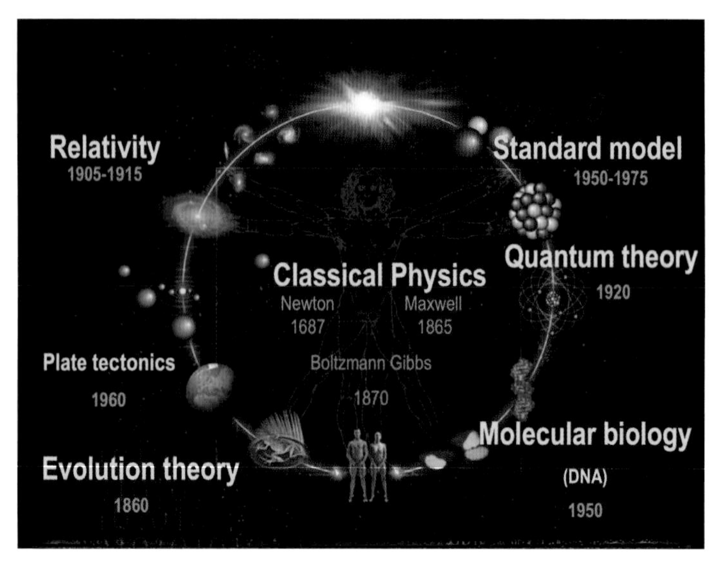

(b) Turning points in our understanding.

Figure III.5.5: *The structural hierarchy unravelled by the sciences.* On the left in the circle it is basically the gravitational force that causes structure, while on the right it is due to the other forces. Top down we see basically how time evolution both from the left (from large scales down) and the right (from small scales up) lead to ever more complex structures. The turning points in our understanding of nature can also be mapped on the circle.

certed effort to gain a unified understanding of the tremendous diversity and complexity that evolved in nature over time.

Quantum versus Relativity. Quantum theory is less accessible than relativity, because as we saw it is the impressive legacy of a great number of outstanding scientists that filled over a century of successful groundbreaking research. For that reason quantum has not been personalized to the degree that relativity has been identified with the person of Albert Einstein, and maybe that also explains why intellectual giants like Bohr, Schrödinger, Heisenberg and Dirac never reached the status of a public idol like Einstein. The painful paradox is that whereas their profound work is leaving ever deeper marks in modern life, most people bitterly complain that they do not understand a single word of it. And that was one more reason to write these books.

It is interesting to note that a Nobel prize for the theory of relativity as such has never been awarded, while there have been more than fifty linked to quantum theory as witnessed by the tables in appendix B on 'Chronologies, ideas and people.' Indeed, the prize awarded to Einstein, was in recognition of his explanation of the photo-electric effect, which is a fundamental contribution to quantum theory and has nothing to do with relativity. So the irony is that he received the Nobel prize for his contribution to a theory he basically didn't believe in!

With so many Nobel prizes awarded, it is no surprise that a book that aims slightly higher than just summing up the basic results is bound to be voluminous indeed. Be my guest!

Turning points. In the fourth Figure III.5.5(b) we show how this endeavor to advance knowledge gave rise to a

(a) The Big Bang and the subsequent cosmic evolution.

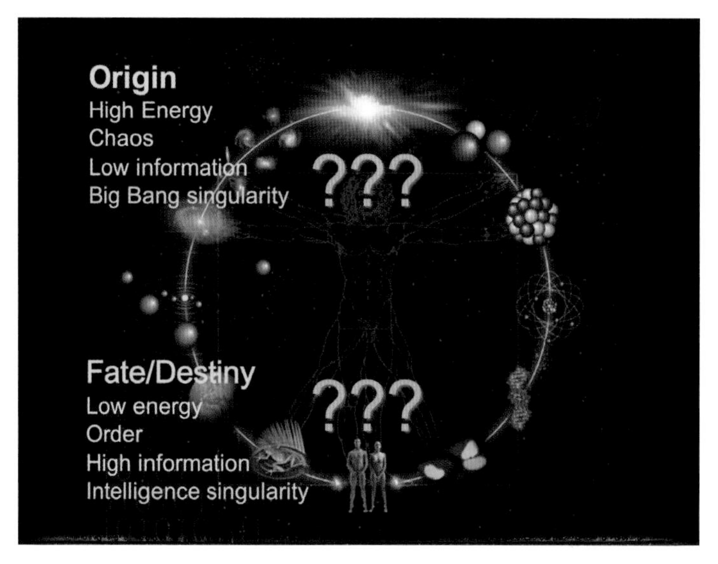

(b) Ultimate questions that concern our deep origins and our long-term future (if we have one).

Figure III.5.6: *Science appears caught between two singularities.* The cosmic evolution at large according to the Big Bang scenario is depicted in Figure (a). The ultimate questions in Figure (b) concern on the one hand the origin somehow hidden in the Big Bang, and on the other is about where this evolution will bring us and to what extent we can shape that future ourselves. So it concerns nothing less than the quest for the interpretation or meaning of our universe as a whole, and its present and possible future contents.

rather limited number of truly fundamental turning points that stand for the great leaps forward in our scientific understanding of the natural world, the world we ourselves are part of. It is striking to see that there are only so few. It is also striking that so much novel science and technology derives from such a small number of truly fundamental insights.

Cosmic evolution. Let us continue with the two pictures of Figure III.5.6. In the first one we depict the actual process of cosmic evolution according to the hot Big Bang scenario. Where the increasing complexity in dead matter smoothly turns into the Darwinian story of life. This took altogether almost 14 billion years, where the Darwinian episode 'only' covers the last 4.5 billion years. Clearly the full story is by no means complete. The figure nicely shows how material complexity sequentially evolved as a necessary consequence of an expanding universe slowly cooling down. It is this story of cosmic evolution that brought most of the empirical natural sciences together so harmoniously, that makes the narrative or perspective of science on the whole of nature so clarifying and illuminating. It is in that story that reductionism meets holism. A beautiful product of brainpower, enlightenment and perseverance.

Ultimate questions: from origin to fate. Science is a systematic process of advancing understanding by creating ever better observational abilities, which in turn allow for ever better modelling of reality. The circle that appears in all the figures by no means tries to convey the idea that science is a closed body of knowledge, a narrative completed. Science is always 'work in progress,' and may on the one hand be characterized by the questions it *did* answer, but on the other hand by the questions it raised but did *not* answer. This is indicated by the question marks at the top and bottom of the would-be circle. They represent ultimate questions that in fact rip open the circle allowing for additional realities we have not yet any idea about. It illustrates how the whole of science is basically caught in between two essential but enigmatic singularities.

On top we have what I called the 'cosmic short' between the physics of the smallest and largest conceivable scales which somehow meet in the Big Bang. We like to think of the Big Bang as an event, but may be it is better to think of it as a gate to an unknown territory where relativity and quantum presumably govern in a truly unified fashion. In that point there is room for fundamentally new insights. That gate would give access to the physical origins of the Big Bang itself. Our lack of understanding is probably best characterized by the term 'Big Bang singularity,' which of course refers to the unphysical extrapolation of the early universe to the quite unphysical initial state with an infinite temperature and energy density.

The arrows of time move downward towards the domain of human evolution, of the human brain, and of human society. Clearly also at that point our understanding is very much incomplete. The present state of science poses hard questions, like asking how the process of evolution will further unfold. It is a fact that the theory of evolution, in spite of having an incredible explanatory power with respect to our past, is surprisingly weak as a predictive model. It predicts a process of the increasing complexity of organisms but is not specific about where the breakthroughs of – let us call it – biological self-transcendence will take place. And this question of predictability has not become easier as we humans have become the dominant species on Earth. As indicated in the figure we have moved from an initial state, which is characterized by extremely high energy, chaos, a uniform distribution of a low information content or capacity, towards the present state which has the signature of very low temperature and energy, allowing for highly localized forms of complex order and high information capacity like the brains of human beings for example.

Evolution at large. In Figure III.5.7 I have presented an alternative visualization of the cosmic evolution at large, and marked the most consequential branchings of the evolutionary tree. I like to think of these branchings as moments of radical innovation, as irreversible transitions or tipping points. Indeed we went through the evolution of dead matter all the way up to the production of the chemical elements which were a necessary prerequisite for the creation of sustainable life on Earth and may be elsewhere on what are called *exoplanets*. In a universe with some 10^{21} stars that probability of extraterrestial life can't be negligible I would think.

In order to cope with the unknowns of the future a solid knowledge of our past appears to be a crucial prerequisite. So we should celebrate collaboration in scientific research efforts addressing such questions, like the launch and operation of the James Webb space telescope that allows us to look deeper in the universe than we ever did before, exactly to better understand its remote past. It is a splendid international collaboration of NASA and the European and Canadian Space Agencies. Its mission is to collect hard data concerning the beginning of structure formation and the births of stars as well as the possibility of extra terrestrial life (see Figures III.5.8 and III.5.9).

Once life began we had another 4.5 billion years of biological evolution culminating in such attributes as consciousness and intelligence which allowed humanity to basically take over their planet. Human evolution transformed us from just inhabitants to the custodians of planet earth. It appears that we have taken our fate in our own hands. We have become responsible for our own future. At present that means that we have to face such inconvenient truths like the climate crisis and we need to urgently act in order to keep the planet inhabitable. Al Gore, the former vice president of the US and a powerful voice in favor of direct

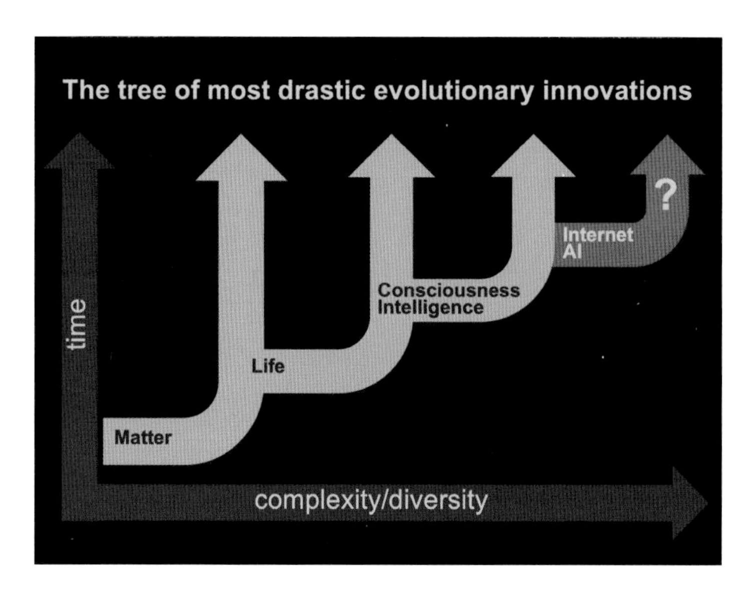

Figure III.5.7: *Cosmic evolution at large.* Does human evolution, driven by the double helix of science and technology, allow for a post-biological branch dominated by artificial intelligence, machine learning and quantum computing?

action to avoid climate catastrophies, once noted that by broadcasting an inconvenient truth one is bound to wake up the most powerful enemies, which makes taking proper action even harder.

We also have to seriously analyse the consequences of the great information revolutions that obey Moore's law, and the introduction of internet and its radically novel way of 'connecting people.' The introduction of these new technologies that allow for instantaneous and global human interaction clearly implies a fundamental change in the human condition which has caused a tipping point in social awareness and coherence. It started a process of a global restratification of society, and the unfolding of unheard of concentrations of power and wealth. This process is full of social risks and has to be critically monitored and controlled by governments and international institutions that should be endowed with both sufficient funding and executive power. This is a far cry from today's reality.

To cope with the many negative aspects of these developments requires the development of the notion of global citizenship. People should be educated to be aware of what is happening, and institutions should insist on openness, accessibility and transparency. This may necessitate adding new chapters to the declarations of fundamental human rights, which extend and define these rights to their existence on the World Wide Web and other cyberworlds. It teaches us, as the dominant inhabitants of planet Earth, that the tremendous amount of freedom we have achieved implies a huge undeniable responsibility.

A post-biological branch? Information philosophers and futurists like Max Tegmark, Nick Bostrom and Yuval Harari warn us that with the rapid advances in artificial intelligence, like machine learning, and quantum computing, machines may well take over completely as we become more and more dependent on them. Not just for gathering relevant information, but also for making rational, optimal decisions. There are major obstacles to be taken, namely to extend the abilities of artificial intelligent algorithms to have 'general intelligence.' This is a much harder problem than acquiring expertise in a limited context and domain in which algorithms already outperform humans. General intelligence is the outcome of our biological evolution and unsurprisingly, that is what humans excel in.

Anyway, the question posed by the orange branch in the figure is whether we are on the verge of a transition towards a radically different post-human, post-biological evolutionary phase. This does not mean that we could no longer exist, bacteria after all managed to survive in many ways too well for billions of years after more complex organisms took over. What the post-human branch presumably implies is that we are no longer the glamour boys of creation, but rather that we may turn into somewhat outdated pieces of biological apparatus of reduced relevance, compared to our super intelligent silicon or quantum brothers and sisters to be. Maybe the optimal way forward is to engage in further exploring symbiotic options.

The intrinsic value of science. We should be aware that politicizing science is a threat to its primary objective: the search for objective truths. The risk of trying to politicize that aspect is not just that it leads to crimes against logic, but also to corrupting scientific integrity. It often involves a form of 'passive lying,' which refers not to directly telling plain lies (active lying) but rather to not telling the truth, that is, the whole truth. It is like leaving important terms out of the equation and thus propagating models that fail reality. It is like the often applied strategy of spreading misinformation to gain political or commercial support and influence. 'The goal justifies the means,' is the slogan that easily comes along and allows the most well-funded lobbyists to dominate the political landscape. Indeed, the success of advertising is justifying the goal of better sales often by not telling the truth.

But doesn't science do the same, you might object? Yes and no! It is certainly true as I have noted repeatedly in the book that science is 'work in progress,' and therefore also scientific 'truths' are relative and should be subject to refutation if decisive arguments or data are being brought forward at some point. Indeed the notion of an absolute truth is basically incompatible with the notion science as an incomplete body of knowledge. And it is this aspect that makes the scientific infrastructure, its institutions and funding strategies vulnerable to abuse. This is a paradoxical aspect of the role that science plays in society: in spite of the fact that there is no such thing as an absolute truth, we do not hesitate to board planes, go to hospitals, and get addicted to our cell phones. It appears that scientific truths, if not absolute, are at least extremely robust!

The symbiotic relationship between science and technology is harder to disentangle. As stated before they need each other in essential ways, and yet technology is per definition a double-sided sword. The best we can do is to insist that the discourse on science and technology at all stages be a hundred percent transparent and respects the principles of a solid democracy. This refers to a higher

Figure III.5.8: An artist impression of the James Webb space telescope (JWST) unfolding in space at a distance of 600.000 km from the Earth. Its mission is to look at the very early stages of the universe as a whole and the very early stages of structure formation. It is furthermore the first space telescope to study the possibility of extraterrestrial life by analysing the chemical composition of the atmosphere of exoplanets. The slogan would be: Are there somewhere in the universe alternative humankinds? (Source: Adriana Manrique Gutierrez/NASA)

vocation, and adds elements of ideology and wishful thinking to the notions of science, technology and innovation, which in turn make them more vulnerable!

In my opinion what we need is quite the opposite of what is trending: we need to have more science, scientific literacy and expertise into the political arena to bring the necessary amount of integrity into the political discourse. Unfortunately science as the evidence-based cornerstone of human culture remains a vulnerable institution that should be protected and defended against the arrogance of power, media popularity, the spreading of misinformation, and lobbying practices that turn into corruption. In the words of the well-known spy novel author John le Carré:

> One day somebody will explain to me why it is that,

> at a time when science has never been wiser, or the truth more stark, or human knowledge more available, populists and liars are in such pressing demand.
>
> *John le Carré*

Indeed, as soon as we allow the politicization of the funding structure, and make it a prey to lobbyists and commercial interests, or force it to serve the vested interests and privileges of some ruling class, irrespective of the political system we adhere to, we are sure to lose science. It will decay from a devoted search for truth – also if that truth turns out to be inconvenient – to some kind of hidden or even blatant form of lopsided advocacy. Legal experts or lawyers, in contrast to scientists, are allowed to limit their sources for research and part of their skill requires craftfully selecting the evidence that supports their client's case.

Here is a large-scale perspective offered by the eminent quantum scientist Charles Bennett:

> The Enlightenment inspired Universal Declaration of Human Rights promulgated in 1948 after a decade of technical sophistication accompanied by inequity and cruelty on an unprecedented scale, exemplifies the seemingly still attainable goal of an equitable, peaceful society that manages its environment and itself well enough to last millions of years.
>
> *Charles H. Bennett*

Human history looks like a perpetual battle between power and knowledge, with power always calling victory in the short term (under the argument of improving efficiency and 'the' economy) and knowledge always being the winner in the long term, even though the price for society for finding out can be disproportionally high. We have created dangerously pervasive constructs like the military-industrial complex, or the medical-industrial complex and now also the information-industrial complex, which have turned into autonomous self-inflating entities thoroughly intertwined with human society. These thrive on a delicate interplay between innovation and commercialism using the creation of fake needs and fake fear. They embody an abuse of power that is derived from knowledge. The sobering fact is that lies and misleading accounts spread fast and one can only hope that truth will ultimately prevail. I myself firmly believe that to be the case, but over all it remains an open question. Too much science/technology based power in too few hands is a recipe for societal disasters. Let me close with quoting Bennett once more:

> Unfortunately due largely to the increased range and speed of communication, misinformation has emerged as a meta-threat to equity and civilisation. By luring people into self-isolating bubbles, to be soothed, entertained and incited by incompatible versions of reality, it empowers autocrats and demagogues, it hobbles democracies and makes co-operation on globally urgent problems like climate change almost impossible.
>
> *Charles H. Bennett*

Addressing scientific illiteracy.

> *Heisenberg? Huh, isn't that the guy from* Breaking Bad*?*

After the red light started flashing, the radio host nodded to me and asked: 'Well, professor, can you tell us in a few lines what quantum physics is?' And I said: ' Hm, yes of course, hmm I mean No! Hmmm, I mean yes, but ...' Talking quantum to family and friends at a birthday party often feels like being a tour guide in London for extra-terrestrials who don't happen to know what a bridge, a museum or a traffic light is. As I mentioned before, the fact that quantum things are to a large extent invisible does not mean that they are not there. They certainly are. And as we have learned, the fact that most quantum things are not discernible by the naked eye doesn't mean that they are

Figure III.5.9: *Starbirths in the Carina Nebula as seen by the James Webb space telescope.* This image made in July 2022 is divided horizontally by an undulating line between a cloudscape forming a nebula along the bottom portion and a comparatively clear upper portion. Speckled across both portions is a starfield, showing innumerable stars of many sizes. The smallest of these are small, distant, and faint points of light. The largest of these appear larger, closer, brighter, and more fully resolved. The upper portion of the image is blueish, and has wispy translucent cloud-like streaks rising from the nebula below. The cloud-like structure of the nebula contains ridges, peaks, and valleys - an appearance very similar to a mountain range. (Source: NASA, ESA, CSA, and STScI.)

not relevant or important. In spite of being unknown and widely ignored, the *quantessentials* are here to stay. This leaves us with the sobering fact that they are still surprisingly unfamiliar. This in my opinion is a strong call for worldwide efforts to educate, to fully develop the tremendous intellectual potential that is present everywhere at any instant.

I have spent about half a century in that invisible quantum world, doing a lot of active research, but also getting slightly frustrated not being able to share much of it at everyday occasions like birthday parties. That made me sad but also aware that I should stop whining and just sit down and write a book about what I learned on my journeys through that amazing quantum world. A modest attempt to help alleviate the burden of scientific illiteracy. And that is how the three lines allowed to me by that sympathetic interviewer gave rise to these three volumes about the *Power of the Invisible: The Quantessence of Reality*.

Further reading.
Classics of popular physics:

- *Cosmos*
  Carl Sagan
  Random House (1980)
- *A Brief History of Time*
  Stephen Hawking
  Bantam Dell Publishing Group (1988)
- *Cosmic Code*
  Heins Pagels
  Dover Publications (2012)

On Science and the Future of Human Culture:

- *Superintelligence: Paths, Dangers, Strategies*
  Nick Bostrom
  Oxford University Press (2016)
- *Sapiens*
  Yuval Harari
  Penguin books (2015)

Complementary reading:

- *A Project to Find the Fundamental Theory of Physics*
  Stephen Wolfram
  Wolfram Media (2020)
- *In Praise of Science: Curiosity, Understanding, and Progress*
  Sander Bais
  MIT Press (2010)
- *Mysteries Of The Quantum Universe*
  Thibault Damour and Mathieu Burniat
  Penguin (2020)

Appendix A

Math Excursions

♣ On functions, derivatives and integrals

> Do not worry about your difficulties in mathematics.
> I can assure you that mine are greater still.
>
> *Albert Einstein*

Functions. Functions are a general class of objects in mathematics that have endless applications in all fields of science. A function is an object – let us denote it by the symbol f – that may depend on a set of variables (arguments) – say $\{x_a\}$. As such it assigns a value to f for any allowed point in the space of variables $\mathcal{X} \sim \{x_a\}$: in other words it provides us with a map $f : \mathcal{X} \rightarrow \mathcal{F}$. The domain $\mathcal{F}$ of the function denotes the space where f itself lives, and can be many things, we think in particular of the real numbers $\mathbb{R}$, the complex numbers $\mathbb{C}$, or some (other) vector space $\mathcal{V}$.[1]

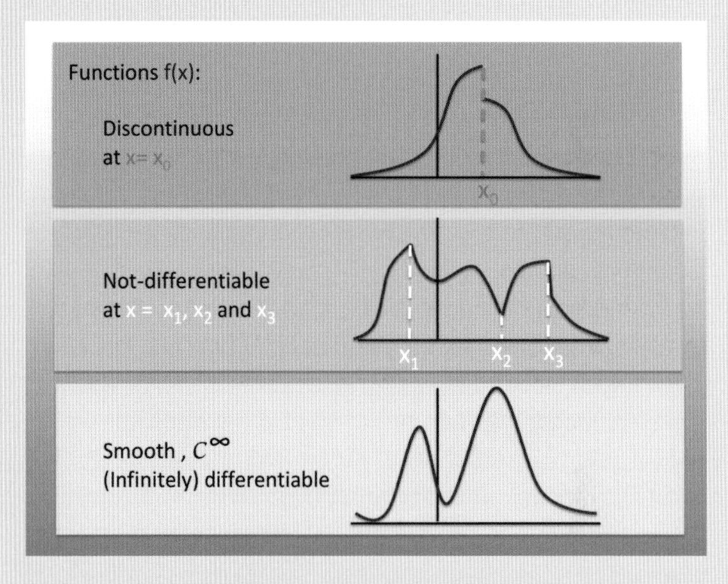

Figure A.1: *Function classes.* We have plotted three functions which belong to different classes. A *discontinuous* function on top (the function value jumps at $x = x_0$). In the middle a continuous function but *not-differentiable* at $x = x_1, x_2$ and $x = x_3$, where the slope is discontinuous when approaching the points from the left and the right. At the bottom a *smooth* function which is per definition *infinitely differentiable*, meaning that all higher derivatives exist and are continuous.

Think of the temperature T in the room you are in. It is a function that depends on where and when, i.e. on the set of variables $\mathcal{X} \sim \{x, t\}$, you could say $T : \{x, t\} \rightarrow \mathbb{R}$ and we indicate this dependence by writing $T = T(x, t)$. The potential energy $V(x)$ of a particle is a real function defined over the real position space, and like the temperature, V may differ from place to place. If we plot the value of a real function f as the 'height' above the point x then $f(x)$ defines a kind of *landscape* over $\mathcal{X}$. Very basic features of functions are given in Figure A.1 which refer to whether they are continuous and or differentiable. We will

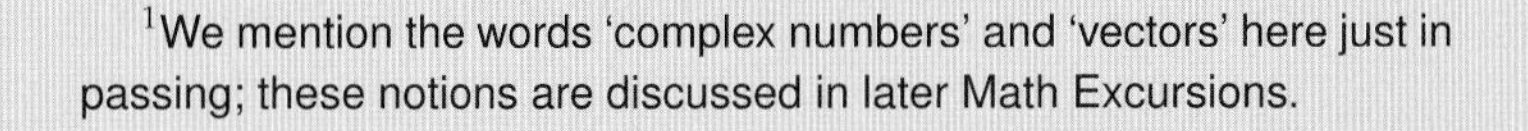

[1] We mention the words 'complex numbers' and 'vectors' here just in passing; these notions are discussed in later Math Excursions.

mostly assume that we are dealing with *smooth* functions: those are functions for which all derivatives exist and are continuous.

We have mentioned other quantities which are basically functions: the position and velocity are functions of the time variable. In d-dimensions these are vectors ("vector" functions) with d components. Vectors have not only a magnitude but also a direction which makes them different from being just a number. A number can be written down and be communicated by mail; this is not true for a vector because the direction can get messed up. The electric and magnetic fields are both vector-valued functions or vector fields in short. The same is true for the velocity field of a river, it encodes the direction in which the fluid flows at any given point in the fluid. So even if you were not aware of the notion of (vector) functions, you presumably now realize that you are quite familiar with them. To give you an impression, we have plotted some typical elementary (real) functions of a single variable in Figure A.2.

With real functions you can do what you can do with numbers if you do it point wise, i.e. in every point of $\mathcal{X}$. For example, we define the product h of functions f and g by the function $h(x) = f(x)g(x)$. The limitations on what you do with functions is of course determined by which operations are defined in $\mathcal{F}$.

Of interest are two natural operations one may define on smooth functions that play a fundamental role in many applications. These operations are basically each other's 'inverse'; one is called *differentiation* or taking a derivative, the other is *integration*, or taking the integral. We discuss them for the case of real functions.

Differentiation. Think of a real function $f(x)$ of one real variable, then we may draw it as a curve on a graph paper, putting x along the x-axis and $f(x)$ along the y-axis, as we did in Figure A.3(a). The derivative with respect to the variable x in a point x_0 of the function denoted as $\frac{df}{dx}$, or simply with a prime, i.e. $f'(x_0)$ is just the *slope* of that curve above the point x_0.

For example, if the function is linear in x , $f(x) = 3x$, then that function has a constant slope equal to 3 and thus is the derivative a constant, $f'(x) = 3$. Having given this heuristic definition of the derivative, I should hasten to say that this is a phenomenally important concept in science, as it embodies the mathematical statement that exactly quantifies the otherwise rather vague notion of 'change'.

Looking at the derivative operator more abstractly it can be considered as a map $\frac{d}{dx} : \mathcal{F} \to \mathrm{Slope}\,\mathcal{F}$. Points where the derivative of a function vanishes correspond to points where the slope is zero and the function has a maximum or a minimum, as we have indicated in Figure A.3(a). Note that if one knows a function in the neighborhood of a point x_0 one may calculate its derivative in that point. This is clear from the formal definition of the derivative: $f'(x) = (f(x + \Delta x) - f(x))/\Delta x$ taken in the limit of ever smaller Δx. This definition implies another useful relation (also in the small Δx limit) namely that we may write: $f(x + \Delta x) = f(x) + f'(x)\Delta x$. This provides a clear statement of the use and meaning of a derivative: if we make a tiny move from x to $x + \Delta x$ in space, then the corresponding change in any function $f(x)$, is from $f(x)$ to $f(x) + f'(x)\Delta x$ to lowest order in Δx.

Let us finally mention that calculating the derivatives of many standard functions and expressions containing them is not so hard and usually part of a science high school math curriculum. We have listed a few derivatives of standard functions in Table A.1 below. Another way to think about differentiation is therefore to say that it is an operator d/dx which applied to a function $f(x)$ generates a translation (or change) in function space $\mathcal{F}$ induced by a small translation in the underlying configuration space $\mathcal{X}$. We will make use of this interpretation later on.

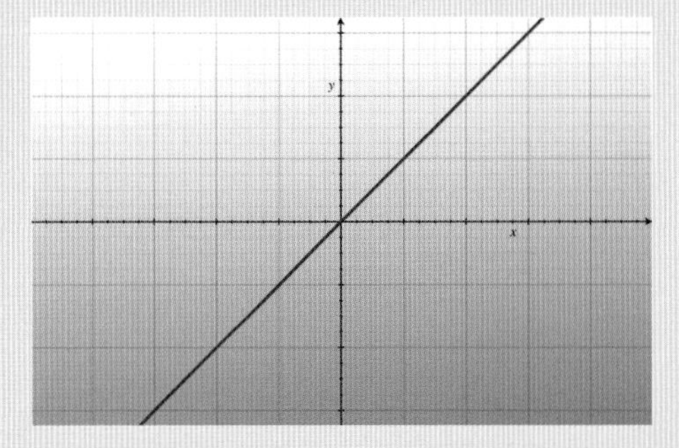

(a) The linear function $f(x) = x$. It has a constant slope. It is the simplest *odd* function as it satisfies $f(-x) = -f(x)$

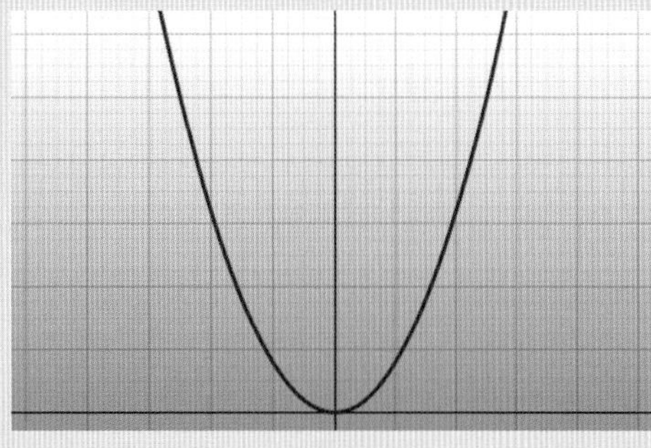

(b) The quadratic function $f(x) = x^2$. It has a constant curvature or second derivative. It is the simplest even function (except the constant function) satisfying $f(-x) = f(x)$.

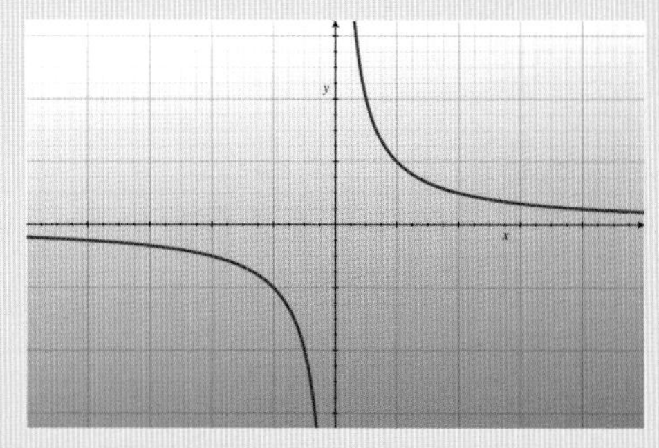

(c) The inverse function $f(x) = 1/x$. The function slowly tends to zero for $x \to \pm\infty$, while it becomes infinite (or singular) for $x \to \pm 0$. It is only defined for $x \neq 0$.

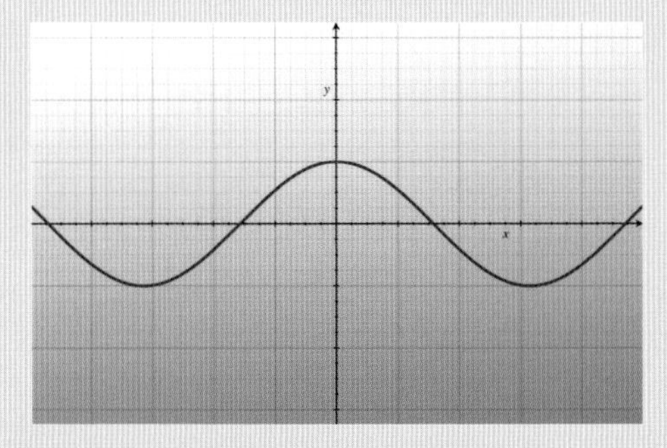

(d) The periodic function $f(x) = \cos(x)$. It satisfies the property $f(x) = f(x+2\pi)$. Shifting the cosine by $1/4$ period to the right one obtains the sine function.

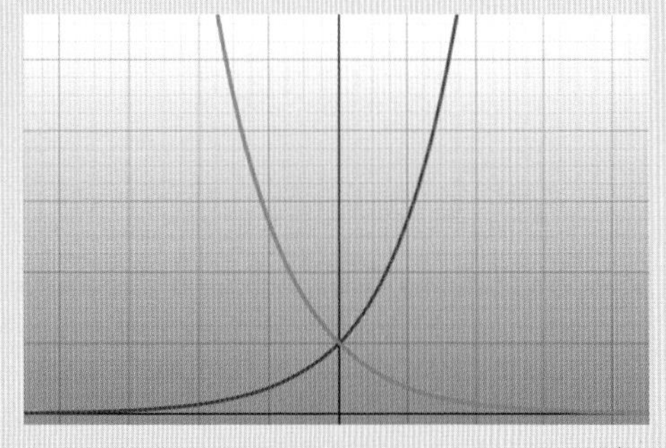

(e) The exponential functions $f(x) = e^{\pm x}$. these grow rapidly to ∞ for $x \to \pm\infty$ and decay rapidly to zero for $x \to \mp\infty$.

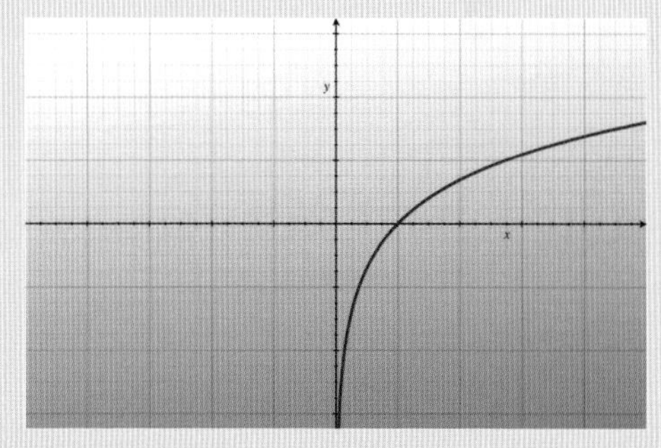

(f) The logarithmic function $f(x) = \ln(x)$ is a slowly but ever-growing function. It has a singularity for $x \to +0$.

Figure A.2: The graphs for some typical elementary real functions f(x), showing their salient features.

An example: dispersion. We have been discussing the energy E of a particle as a function of the momentum p for the non-relativistic and relativistic cases with a parametric dependence on the mass m_0. There is another quantity of importance and that is the *dispersion* defined as the derivative of E with respect to p. The term dispersion originates in optics where in a given medium one has that the frequency will depend on the wavelength, which manifests itself for example in the fact that the angle of refraction of light will depend on the angle of the incident beam. For matter waves we have that $E = \hbar\omega$ and $p = \hbar k$, so we can express the dispersion also in terms of E and p. In Figure A.4, I have plotted the relativistic expression for the particle energy, $E = \sqrt{m_0^2c^4 + p^2c^2}$, and below it the dispersion $dE/dp = pc/\sqrt{m_0^2c^2 + p^2}$. There are roughly three regimes: (i) on the left we have the non--relativistic regime where $p \ll m_0c$ where the energy approximates tp $E \simeq m_0c^2 + p^2/2m_0$ with linear dispersion $dE/dp \simeq p/m_0$, and the expression up to the mass-energy reduces to the familiar Newtonian form, (ii) in the

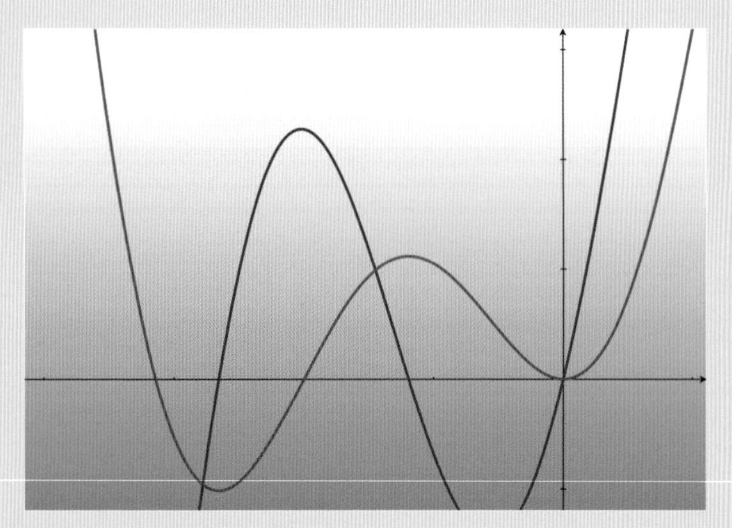

(a) The *derivative* df/dx (purple) of a function $f(x)$ (red). At the extrema of $y(x)$ the derivative (= slope) is zero.

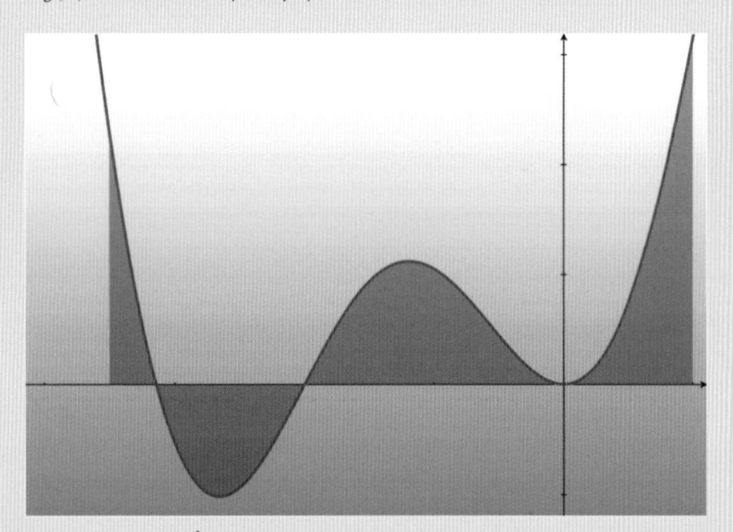

(b) The *integral* $\int_a^b f(x)\,dx$ of $f(x)$ is the area below $y(x)$ above the x-axis minus the area belowthe x-axis, between the points $x = a$ and $x = b$.

Figure A.3: A function, its derivative, and its integral.

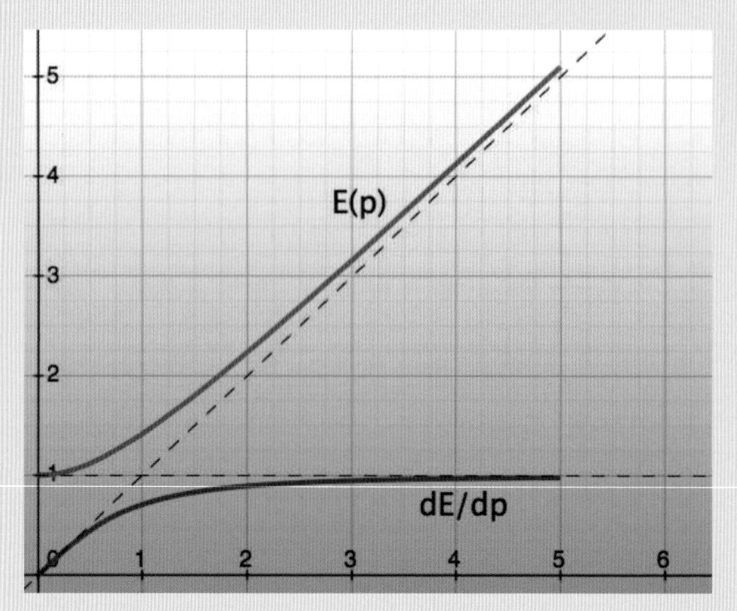

Figure A.4: *Relativistic energy.* The particle energy E as a function of p in red, and the dispersion defined as the derivative dE/dp in purple. We have chosen m_0 and c equal one.

middle we need the fully relativistic expression, and (iii) on the right we have the ultra-relativistic regime where $p \gg m_0 c$, and we have the approximation $E \simeq pc$ with dispersion $dE/dp \simeq c = \text{constant}$, which effectively corresponds to the expression for a massless particle.

Integration. Having the red curve in the example of Figure A.3(b) the (definite) integral F_{ab} of a function $f(x)$ between two points $x = a$ and $x = b$ is just the area under the curve between the two points. One may also define an 'indefinite' integral $F(x)$ or primitive of $f(x)$, which is mathematically represented by the integral symbol:

$$F(x) = \int f(x)dx\,. \qquad \text{(A.1)}$$

F(x) has the property that $F_{ab} = F(b) - F(a)$. If a function is constant $f(x) = c$ then the integral is thus simply $F_{ab} = c(b - a)$ and $F(x)$ would be $F(x) = cx + d$ where there is an arbitrary constant d that one can add. Now we are also in a position to appreciate the remark that these operations are in a sense each other's inverse: if we differentiate $F(x)$ we get the original function $f(x)$ back.

The definition of the integral involves a limiting procedure of an approximation that is not so hard to imagine. To calculate the definite integral F_{ab}, we divide up the interval

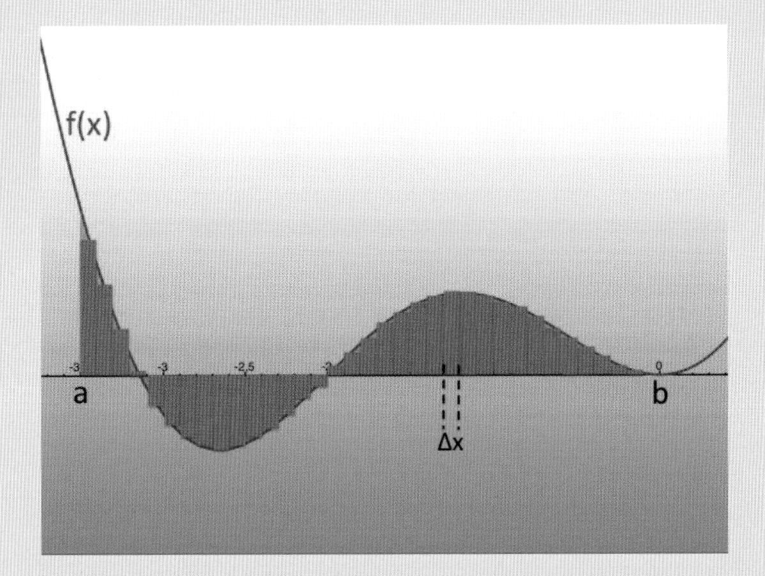

Figure A.5: *The integral as area.* The definition of the definite integral of $F(x)$ between points $x = a$ and b is the sum of the positive and negative contributions from the areas of the small rectangles, in the limit that $\Delta x \to 0$.

$b - a$ on the x-axis up in a large number N equal little segments Δx, then we define the centre of each segment by its coordinate $x_i : i = 1, \ldots, N$. The integral is then defined by:

$$F_{ab} = \int_a^b f(x)dx = \lim_{N\to\infty} \sum_i^N f(x_i)\Delta x, \qquad \text{(A.2)}$$

as is illustrated in Figure A.5.

Calculating the integrals of elementary functions is not too hard, but often integrating is hard and not possible in 'closed form'. Therefore numerical approximations are of crucial importance in most applications, and those are usually based on approximations in the spirit of equation A.2. The problem of integration is at the heart of physics and engineering, exactly because in most cases the laws that govern nature are formulated as so-called differential equations, that means that the equations contain derivatives of quantities one would like to solve for. Many equations are 'equations of motion'. The equations of Newton determine the time evolution of a particle's position end momentum. The Maxwell do that for the electromagnetic fields, and the Schrödinger for the wavefunction of a quantum system, while Einstein's equations describe the time evolution of the universe. Solving those equations corresponds in some sense to finding ways to 'integrate' the equations for specific boundary or initial conditions.

derivative : $\frac{df(x)}{dx}$	**function :** $f(x)$	**integral :** $F(x) = \int f(x)dx$
a	ax	$\frac{1}{2}ax^2$
nx^{n-1}	$x^n (n \neq -1)$	$\frac{1}{n+1}x^{n+1}$
$\frac{-1}{x^2}$	$\frac{1}{x}$	$\ln\lvert x\rvert$
$\cos(x)$	$\sin(x)$	$-\cos(x)$
$-\sin(x)$	$\cos(x)$	$\sin(x)$
ke^{kx}	e^{kx}	$\frac{1}{k}e^{kx}$
$\frac{1}{x}$	$\ln x$	$x\ln x - x$
$\Longrightarrow$ differentiation	$\Longrightarrow$ $\Longleftarrow$	Integration $\Longleftarrow$

Table A.1: A list of some elementary functions (see also Figure A.2) in the middle column, with their derivatives on the left and their integrals or primitives on the right. Taking a derivative moves you to the left, integrating moves you to the right. Integration means that one always can add an arbitrary constant to the integral; this constant is not included in the table.

In Table A.1 we have listed some well-known functions, their derivatives, and their primitives (i.e. integrals).

Example: the harmonic oscillator. The force on a particle is defined as minus the derivative of the potential energy: $F = -dV/dx$, indeed with $V = ax^2/2$, this yields the harmonic force $F = -ax$. But given the force we can also calculate the potential energy by integrating it. We have to move the particle up the hill form $x = 0$ to, say, $x = x_0$. To do so we have to do an amount of work on the particle which equals the (opposite) force times the distance, integrated from zero to x_0:

$$V = -\int_0^{x_0} F(x)\, dx = \int_0^{x_0} ax\, dx = \{\frac{1}{2}ax^2 \;\; {}_0^{x_0} = \frac{1}{2}ax_0^2 .$$

Differential equations. Differential calculus is basically the calculus of changes, and differential equations are typically the equations that govern the change in time or space of any dynamical system one might think of, equally applicable to modelling in classical physics as it is for quantum theory, but it is equally well employed in modelling economics, ecological systems or the climate. As we have seen, many 'laws of nature' take the form of a system of differential equations. This means that on the left-hand side of the equation we have the changes of the system's variables in time and space, while on the right-hand side they are expressed as functions of the variables themselves, i.e. the point in the space of states the system could be in. Examples were already provided by Newton's equations (I.1.3) and the Maxwell equations (I.1.28). The solutions of these equations describe therefore the dynamical trajectories in the configuration space that the system traverses in time. The trajectory depends of course on the starting point or initial condition. Obtaining solutions to differential equations has to involve some kind of integration because we want to get rid of the derivatives, and that is exactly what makes solving differential equations so hard. If the equations are linear, meaning that the unknowns one want to solve for only appear linearly in the equation, solutions can often be obtained in closed analytic form, but if the equations are nonlinear that is only rarely the case.

Let us conclude this excursion by looking at two differential equations of particular interest, a growth/decay equation and a wave equation.

Example: the equation for exponential growth or decay. We have a container with N_0 radioactive nuclei. Then the remaining number $N(t)$ at time t will decrease in time at a rate dN/dt. This rate will be proportional the number N(t), which is just saying something like, 'if the population is twice as big, twice as many people will die.' So the equation we like to solve reads:

$$\frac{dN}{dt} = -\lambda N . \qquad \text{(A.3)}$$

this can be cast in the form:

$$\frac{dN}{N} = -\lambda dt . \qquad \text{(A.4)}$$

Now the left-hand side and the right-hand side can be 'integrated', which by using Table A.1 yields the solution:

$$\ln|N| + d = -\lambda t \;\; \Rightarrow \;\; N(t) = N_0 e^{-\lambda t} , \qquad \text{(A.5)}$$

where the constant e^{-d} has to equal N_0, the number of nuclei at time $t = 0$. Note that the solution corresponds to the green curve depicted in Figure A.2(e). The solution tells us that the decay is exponential, and we will refer to this result if we talk about radio-active decay in chapter I.4. And if we change the sign in front of λ in the equation, we of course get the red curve in the figure corresponding to exponential growth, describing some stages of epidemics or a post on Facebook 'going viral.'

Example: the wave equation. This equation is of interest because waves appear all over the place in physics. Not just water or sound waves, also light is a wave phenomena, and also in quantum theory we encounter wave equations in many guises. Most prominent is the Schrödinger equation, but also the Maxwell and Dirac equations are basically wave equations, which after quantization will have interpretations in terms particles. And it is here that the well-known quantessential catch phrase *particle-wave duality* originates.

In one space and one time dimension the relativistic wave equation takes the form of a differential equation with two derivatives working subsequently on a function $f(x,t)$ of space and time:[2]

$$\frac{\partial^2 f}{\partial t^2} - c^2 \frac{\partial^2 f}{\partial x^2} = 0 \,. \tag{A.6}$$

The solutions for f are waves that move with a velocity equal $\pm c$ for example:

$$f(x,t) = a\cos(\omega t - kx)\,. \tag{A.7}$$

This solution has besides the *amplitude* a, two parameters, the *angular frequency* $\omega = 2\pi\nu$, and *wavenumber* $k = 2\pi/\lambda$, and looks like the wave pattern of Figure A.2(d) moving either to the left or the right. Indeed, taking two derivatives means in Table A.1, that we move from the column on the right to the column on the left. If you put this into the equation and take the derivatives, you get an algebraic equation $\omega^2 - c^2k^2 = 0$ for the parameters ω and k, telling us exactly, that – as advertised – there are propagating waves satisfying the equation with $\omega = \pm ck$ which amounts exactly to the wave relation $\nu = c/\lambda$. Later on we will see that quantization of this relation leads to the linear dispersion relation $E(p) = \hbar\omega = c\,\hbar k = cp$, which is characteristic for a massless particle. This reflects the similarity of the above equation with the electromagnetic wave equation (I.1.47). ♣

◇ On algebras

In high school we have to learn *elementary algebra*, where one represents variables – mostly corresponding to real numbers – as abstract letter symbols, and one learns how to manipulate the expressions according to certain rules or operations that apply to real numbers, such as addition and multiplication. The principle application is to solve equations by exploiting these manipulations. For example having the quadratic equation $ax^2 + bx + c = 0$, the question is to solve for the variable x in terms of the constants a,b and c. One proves that there are two real solutions given by $x_\pm = (-b \pm \sqrt{b^2 - 4ac})/2a$, provided the expression under the square root is positive. So the advantage of the abstract notation is that the answer applies for any choice of the constants a, b and c: it gives the general solution.

Abstract algebra. Generally the subject of *abstract algebra* deals with collections of objects such as numbers, vectors, matrices, polynomials and functions for which binary operations like addition and multiplication and possibly more are defined (the inverse operations like subtraction and division for example). The binary operations may or may not be *distributive*: $a \times (b + c) = a \times b + a \times c$, *commutative*: $a + b = b + a$ and *associative*: $a + (b + c) = (a + b) + c$. You see that for the algebra of ordinary numbers both the addition and multiplication operations are distributive, commutative and associative (subtraction should be thought of as addition of a negative number $a - b = a + (-b)$, and division by a number as multiplying by the inverse of the number). If you read the next *Math Excursion* you will find that for the algebra of $(n \times n)$ matrices the sum and product are distributive and associative, but whereas matrix addition is commutative, matrix multiplication is not.

A particularly simple algebra we will use in the next chapter is the *Boolean algebra* of binary numbers $\{0, 1\}$. The algebra is defined by the operations displayed in the table below. They are distributive, commutative and associative.

Algebraic structures that are widely applied in physics

[2] As f depends on two variables we have to distinguish the derivatives with respect to space and time, we write the curly derivative symbols called *partial derivatives*. The squares in the derivatives mean that you apply the derivative operator twice, so $\partial^2 f/\partial t^2 = (\partial/\partial t)^2 f$.

addition	multiplication
$0+0=0$	$0\times 0=0$
$0+1=1$	$0\times 1=0$
$1+0=1$	$1\times 0=0$
$1+1=0$	$1\times 1=1$

Table A.2: The Boolean algebra.

are vector spaces, rings, groups and spaces of functions. It turns out that often subjects that begin as pastimes for the mathematically minded end up having great practical use in the realms of science and engineering. What we will see in this book over and again is that in the description of quantum states the notions of vectors, complex numbers, and matrices arise naturally. All these ingredients have a specific underlying algebraic structure. We discuss the algebra of complex numbers in the Math Excursion on page 174, while matrix algebras are described in the next Math Excursion.

Of particular interest in quantum theory is the *algebra of observables* consisting of (hermitian) self-adjoint operators or matrices. These algebras correspond to so-called *Lie algebras*, which are directly linked to the theory of Lie groups, which in turn describe many of the symmetries that play a central role in (quantum) physics. Lie algebras are discussed in more detail on page 178, and Lie groups in the Excursion on page 179.

It is evident that math and physics have co-evolved over centuries leading to a situation where modern theoretical physics makes extensive use of modern and abstract mathematics. It is for that reason that I have decided to throw in some (in fact more than average) math in this semi-popular account of a subject like quantum theory. ♢

♡ On vectors and matrices

The reason for exploring vectors and matrices, is that they play a central role in the mathematical formulation of all of physics and in particular in quantum physics. In classical physics we think of positions, momenta, angular momenta and forces as ordinary three-dimensional vectors. These are *real* vectors because their entries or components are real numbers. In electromagnetism and relativity we have encountered so-called relativistic four-component vectors which are also real. Quantum states are represented by *complex* vectors and physical observables are represented by a class of complex matrices. This excursion highlights some of the more important properties of real vectors and matrices We return to complex vectors and matrices, which play a central role in part II of the book, in a separate *Math Excursion* on page 176.

Real vectors. A vector can be viewed simply as an arrow of a certain length in some n-dimensional Euclidean space $\mathbb{R}^n$. Note that we also have the *null-vector* corresponding to the origin. We denote column vectors by *ket* vectors $|w\rangle$: they are elements of a vector space $\mathcal{V}$, while the row vectors are denoted by so-called *bra* vectors $\langle v|$, and these are elements of a dual vector space $\mathcal{V}^*$. We can add and subtract vectors by just adding or subtracting their corresponding components, and scale the vectors by multiplying them by ordinary numbers. These are familiar properties to most of you.

Vector components and choice of basis. If the dimension of the vector space is n, we can choose sets of basis vectors $\{|i\rangle\}$ and $\{\langle i|\}$ and expand vectors as $|v\rangle = \sum_j v^j|j\rangle$ or $\langle v| = \sum_i v_i\langle i|$. You may think of these basis vectors as unit vectors along the different orthogonal axes of the vector space. The reason for this subtle distinction between row and column vectors is that we will encounter different types of vector spaces in this book. We have already seen the example of ordinary Euclidean vectors and the relativistic Lorentz vectors. The differences between these spaces becomes clear if we look at the definitions for the invariant squared 'length' or the inner product of vectors.

The inner, dot, or scalar product. Having a vector space $\mathcal{V}$ and its dual $\mathcal{V}^*$ we may define an *inner, dot* or *scalar product* between elements $v \in \mathcal{V}^*$ and $w \in \mathcal{V}$ as the number obtained after adding the products of the corresponding entries:

$$\langle v|w\rangle \equiv v \cdot w \equiv \sum_i v_i w^i .$$

As an example we calculate the dot product of two two-dimensional Euclidean vectors:

$$\begin{pmatrix} 2 & 1 \end{pmatrix} \begin{pmatrix} -1 \\ 1 \end{pmatrix} = -2 + 1 = -1 .$$

Taking the dot product of a Euclidian vector with itself, $\langle v|v\rangle = |v|^2$ always yields a sum of squares, corresponding to a real number larger or equal zero, which is defined as the *length* of the vector, $|v|$, squared. We also mention that for real vectors the dot product is real and symmetric, $v \cdot w = \langle v|w\rangle = \langle w|v\rangle = w \cdot v$.

As another relevant example we consider the Lorentzian four-momentum vector $p^\mu = (E/c, \mathbf{p})$. The inner product should produce the expression $p_\mu p^\mu = E^2/c^2 - p^2$. This means that the row vector (with lower indices) should be $p_\mu = (E/c, -\mathbf{p})$. It is extremely useful then to define a metric, which is just a matrix $\eta_{ij} = diag(1, -1, -1, -1)$, which maps a column vector to its corresponding row vector like $v_i = \sum_j \eta_{ij} v^j$. And therefore the inner product can be written using this metric as $v \cdot w \equiv \sum_{ij} g_{ij} v^i w^j$. For the Euclidean case this metric is just the unit matrix $g_{ij} = \delta_{ij} = diag(1, 1, \ldots, 1)$. Observe that the value of the inner product of a Lorentzian four-vector with itself is not restricted, it can be either positive, negative or zero. Furthermore, if this product is zero, this does not imply that the vector itself has to be zero. It just means that the corresponding particle has vanishing rest-mass.

We have given a graphical representation of the scalar or dot product of two vectors in Figure A.8(a), which underscores the fact that the dot-product produces a number, not a vector, and for that reason it is also called the scalar product.

The exterior or cross product of two vectors. In three dimensions one may indeed also define a 'vector', 'exterior' or 'cross' product between vectors which produces a vector w out of two vectors u and v, and one writes $w = v \times u$. There is no simple extension of such a vector product to general dimensions.

Matrices. Matrices are there in many kinds, appear all over the place and have zillions of applications through the sciences. It refers to a two-dimensional array of elements like for example the apartment building of Figure A.6. The entries of a matrix are often numbers that refer to information about the – in the example at hand – apartment: how many bedrooms, or how many people, or their income, their age etc. In this book we will only employ square $(n \times n)$ matrices that will satisfy various additional properties that derive naturally from certain physical requirements in the specific applications we discuss. There are many ways to look at a matrix: the most neutral way is to say that it is a square array of (real or complex) numbers (see Figure A.7(a)). For example a distance table between n cities would be like a real $(n \times n)$ matrix. Another way to look at a matrix would be to distinguish the set of diagonal elements, the elements in the upper triangle and the elements of the lower triangle (figure A.7(b)). And sometimes it is convenient to think of a matrix as a stack of n n-dimensional row or column vectors as indicated in Figures A.7(c) and A.7(d).

Matrix algebra. Now the matrices themselves also form a vector space, because we may add and subtract them, there is a 'null-matrix' (with all entries equal zero), and we may multiply a matrix by an arbitrary constant (by just multiplying each entry of the matrix by that constant). There is

Figure A.6: *The Matrix.* A matrix is a two-dimensional array of elements. You may think of this apartment building as a 6×4 matrix, with 6 rows and 4 columns, where the apartments are labeled like the corresponding matrix entries. The entries may refer to information about the inhabitants of the apartments, like the family size, their income, etc. But the analogy is of limited use as we are not adding or multiplying apartment buildings, or assign any meaninbg tot theior aigenvectors and such.. (Source: Alamy.)

more, we may also define a multiplication for matrices as we will see shortly. And in view of the previous *Math Excursion* this means that the set of $n \times n$ matrices form an algebra. To define division for matrices is a little more intricate: we basically define it by multiplying by the inverse of the matrix, where the inverse of A^{-1} of A is defined as the matrix that satisfies $A^{-1}A = AA^{-1} = \mathbf{1}$, where $\mathbf{1}$ is the unit matrix with only ones on the diagonal. This raises the follow-up question of under which conditions the inverse is a well-defined matrix itself. And this question may remind you of the serious elementary school dictum: never divide by the number zero! For matrices the rule is that the inverse exists, if the *determinant* of the matrix is non-zero. This is a number that that can be calculated given the matrix, but we will not go into detail here. Certain matrices have inverses and others have not and there is a relatively simple criterium which tells you if the inverse of a certain square matrix exists. Including the multiplication we speak of a matrix algebra, as we can perform algebraic manipulations with them similar to what we do with numbers. There is a well-established basic branch of mathematics called 'linear algebra', and there are many textbooks covering the world of matrices in great detail.

Matrix as linear transformation of vectors. Now vectors can also be multiplied by matrices to produce another vector, the way that is done is pictorially indicated for a column vector in A.8(b). This action of matrices on vectors is clearly most easily understood if you think of the matrix as a stack of row vectors. The action can also be considered as a *transformation* of a vector into another vector. A simple example may help:

$$\begin{pmatrix} 1 & 1 \\ 1 & -1 \end{pmatrix} \begin{pmatrix} 2 \\ 1 \end{pmatrix} = \begin{pmatrix} 2+1 \\ 2-1 \end{pmatrix} = \begin{pmatrix} 3 \\ 1 \end{pmatrix}.$$

The matrix acts as a *linear operator* on the vector space, as it reshuffles the components into linear combinations of them. We may say that $(n \times n)$ matrices map the vector space $\mathcal{V}$ onto itself and we write $A : \mathcal{V} \to \mathcal{V}$. There is for example a particular subset of (3×3) matrices whose action on 'ordinary' vectors corresponds to rotating of those vectors in three-dimensional space R^3.

Another example which shows the descriptive power of matrices as operators on state vectors is in (quantum) computation, where generically we think of computation as a sequence of gates, interactions/manipulations or measurements that change the states of a set of (qu)bits.

Such processes or computations can be represented by a product of matrices. Indeed the complete computation is just a matrix mapping the in-state on the out-state vector.

Eigenvectors and eigenvalues. Given a matrix A one defines the *eigenvectors* of A as a set of special vectors

(a) A 4×4 *square matrix* can be thought of as a table of $4^2 = 16$ numbers or symbols representing them.

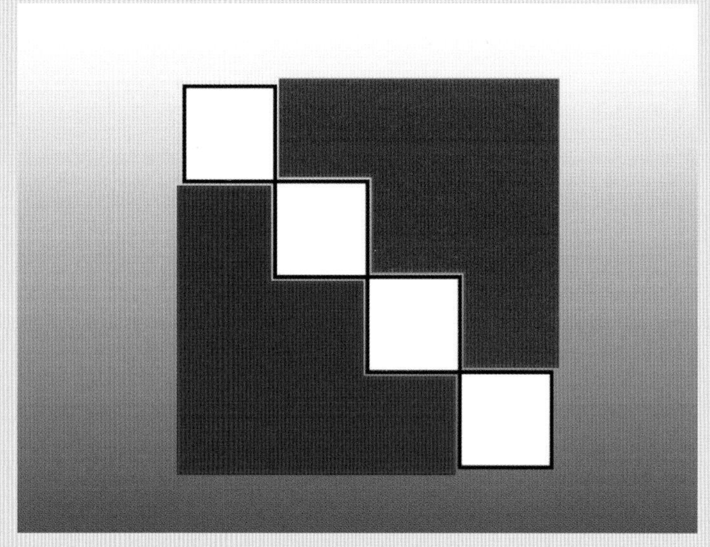

(b) Square matrix build up of three parts, upper triangular (red), diagonal (white) and lower triangular (blue).

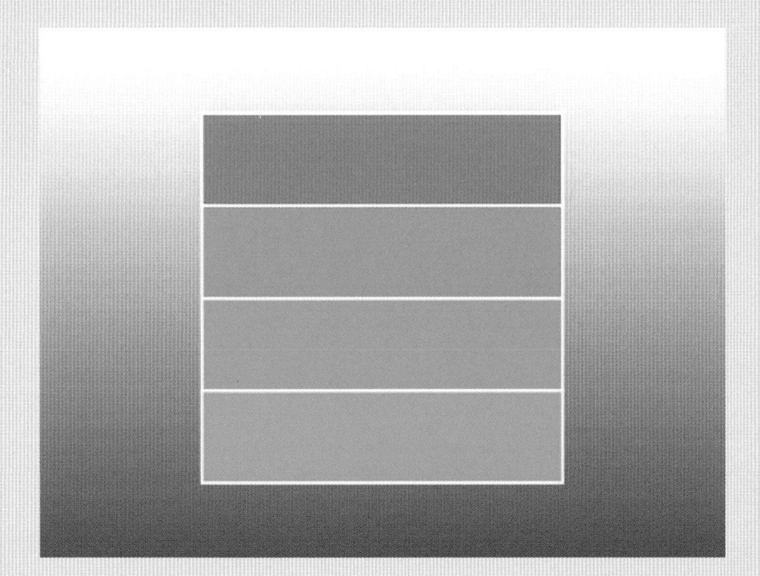

(c) A matrix can also be viewed as a stack of row vectors.

(d) A matrix can also be viewed as a stack of column vectors.

Figure A.7: *Four ways to think about a matrix.* Graphical representation of the many guises of a matrix (artist impression).

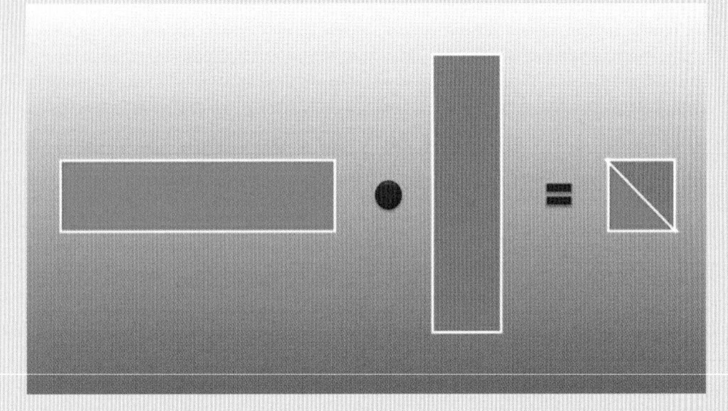

(a) The *inner, scalar or dot product* of a row and a column vector yields the single number obtained by adding the product of subsequent row entries with the corresponding column entries: $\langle g|b\rangle = g^* \cdot b = \Sigma_i g_i^* b_i$.

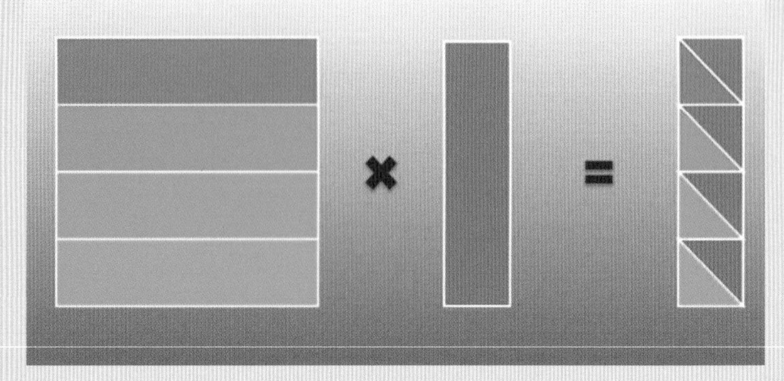

(b) The product of a matrix G with a column vector b yields again a column vector c obtained by taking the dot product of subsequent row vectors of G with the column vector b : $|c\rangle = G|b\rangle = G \cdot b$ meaning $c_i = \Sigma_j G_{ij} b_j$.

(c) The matrix product. Each entry in the product matrix C equals the dot product of the i-th row vector of the first matrix A with the j-th column vector of the second matrix B , so $C_{ij} = \Sigma_k A_{ik} B_{kj}$.

Figure A.8: *Multiplications.* Graphical representation and building up of products of vectors and matrices.

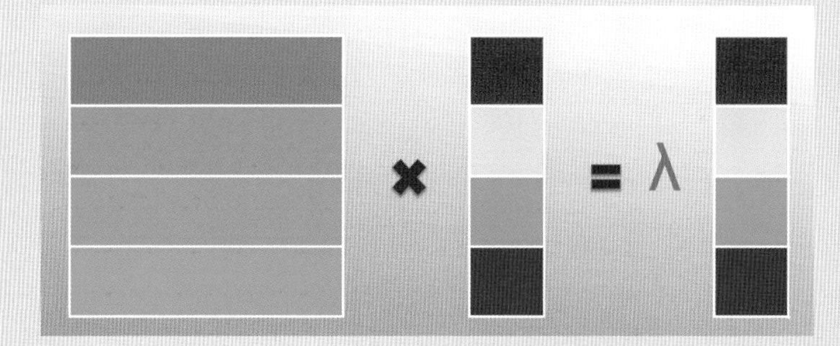

Figure A.9: *Eigenvectors and eigenvalues.* Given a matrix one defines the eigenvectors as a set of special vectors which satisfy an eigenvalue equation (A.8).

$\{|a_k\rangle\}$ that satisfy the following equation:

$$A\,|a_k\rangle = a_k\,|a_k\rangle\ , \tag{A.8}$$

where the numbers a_k are the corresponding *eigenvalues*. So acting on an eigenvector the matrix A gives that same vector back up to a constant, which is by definition the eigenvalue. This is illustrated in Figure A.9. The set of eigenvalues $\{a_k\}$ is called the *spectum* of the matrix. In quantum theory the observables are represented by Hermitean matrices and in that case the eigenvalues are real and the spectrum is called the *sample space* of the operator A.

The matrix product. Once we have defined the action of matrices on vectors the step to the multiplication of matrices is straightforward and we have indicated it in Figure A.8(c). The (ij)-entry of the product matrix $C = AB$ is obtained by the dot product of the $i-th$ row vectors of A with the $j-th$ column vector of B. Let us again give a simple example:

$$\begin{pmatrix} 1 & 2 \\ -2 & 1 \end{pmatrix}\begin{pmatrix} 1 & 1 \\ 1 & -1 \end{pmatrix} = \begin{pmatrix} 3 & -1 \\ -1 & -3 \end{pmatrix}. \tag{A.9}$$

Types of matrices. A distance table between n different cities is a square $(n \times n)$ matrix, a rather special one for sure, because its diagonal elements are all zero and it is symmetric with respect to that diagonal: the upper diagonal and lower diagonal matrices are each other's mirror image. Such a matrix is completely determined by specifying its $n(n-1)/2$ upper triangular entries.

Depending on the situation we may want to put additional constraints which define a subset of matrices. If the additional properties are preserved under the basic matrix operations, the subset forms a subalgebra of the original algebra. The additional properties involve typical matrix manipulations which we have represented symbolically in figure A.10. A fundamental notion is the *transpose* of a matrix denoted by the matrix A^{tr}, which is obtained from A as indicated in Figures A.10(a) and A.10(b), written in terms of its entries one has $(A^{tr})_{ij} \equiv A_{ji}$. The transpose can be obtained by mirroring the matrix in the diagonal, but can also be obtained by interchanging rows and columns. Repeating the operation brings you back to the original matrix. What happens if we take the transpose of a product of matrices? Referring again to Figure A.8(a), one sees that taking the transpose of matrix $C = AB$ on the right-hand side we get a matrix which is the product of the transposes, but in the opposite order: $C^{tr} = B^{tr}A^{tr}$.

Now it is also straightforward to define a symmetric or antisymmetric matrix as the ones that satisfies $A = \pm A^{tr}$ (see Figure A.10(c)). Note that a symmetric $(n \times n)$ matrix contains $n(n+1)/2$ real numbers, while the antisymmetric one has only $n(n-1)/2$, because the diagonal elements have to be zero for the latter.

Invariance of the inner product. We have shown that the product of a vector with itself defines the length of a vector, and we all know that the length of a vector does not change if we rotate the vector around. So we say that the length of a vector is *invariant* under rotations. Also the angle between two vectors is invariant under rotations. In other words the inner product of two vectors is invariant under rotations.

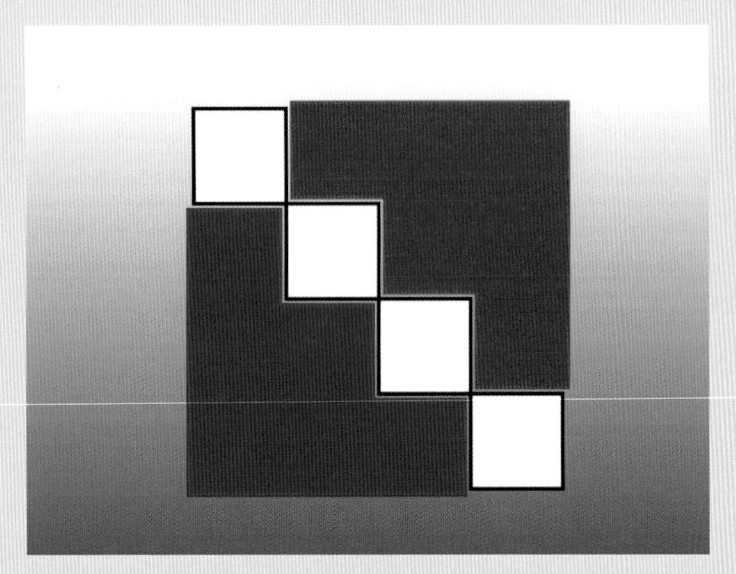

(a) A *square* matrix build up of three parts, upper triangular (red), diagonal (white) and lower triangular (blue).

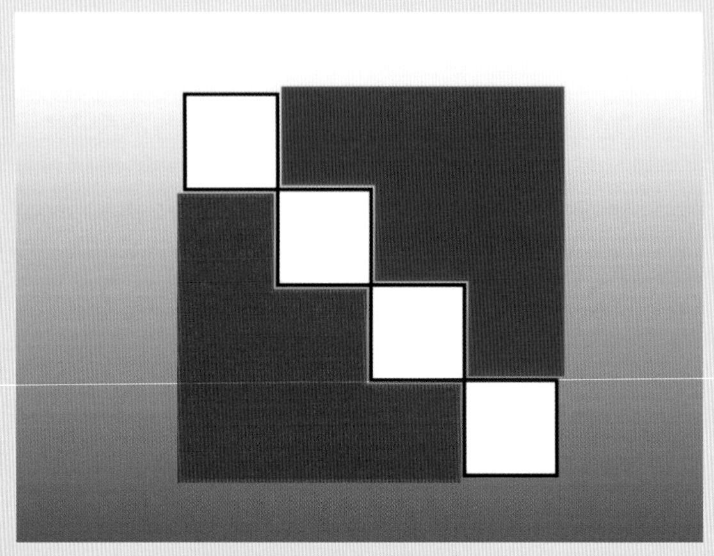

(b) *Transpose* of the matrix depicted in (a), obtained by reflecting in the diagonal, or by interchanging the rows and columns of the matrix.

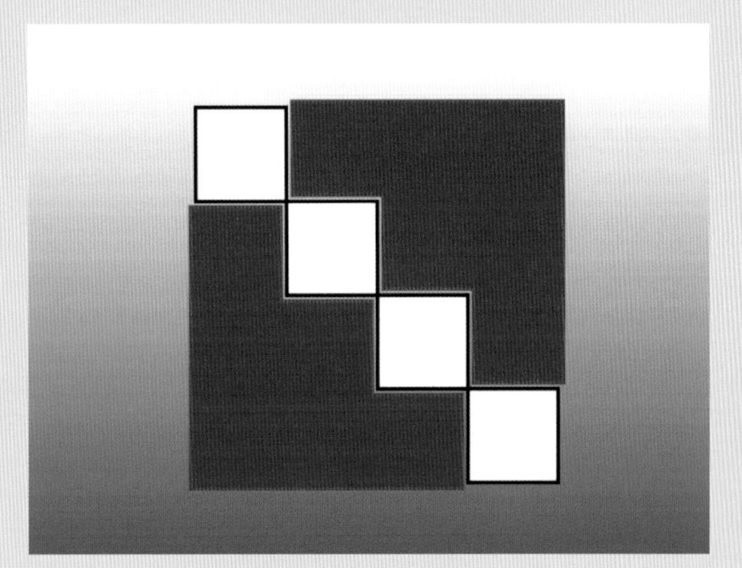

(c) A *symmetric* matrix is equal to its transpose. A distance table between four cities would be a symmetric matrix with zeros along the diagonal.

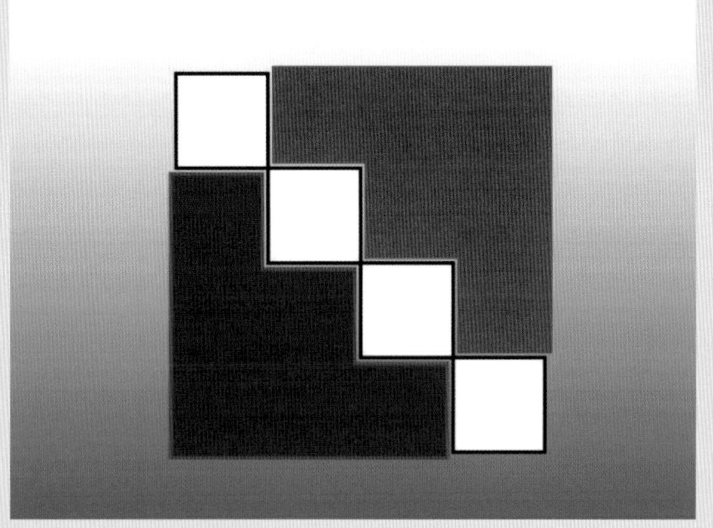

(d) An *antisymmetric* matrix is a matrix whose transpose equals minus that matrix. In other words: $A_{ji} = -A_{ij}$.

Figure A.10: *Matrix properties.* Graphical representation of some basic properties of matrices.

As the rotations involve a transformation of the vector into another vector, it follows that rotations can be represented by matrices acting on the vector space $\mathcal{V}$. And for real vectors this matrix has to be a real matrix. Imagine we act with a rotation matrix R on $|v\rangle$. We may write $|v'\rangle = R\,|v\rangle$, and it then follows that $\langle v'| = \langle v|\,R^{tr}$. Invariance of the inner product of two arbitrary vectors now requires that

$$\langle v'|w'\rangle = \langle v|\,R^{tr}R\,|w\rangle = \langle v|w\rangle \quad\Rightarrow\quad R^{tr} = R^{-1}\,. \qquad (A.10)$$

What this equation is telling us is that the matrices R that represent rotations have to satisfy the property that their transpose equals their inverse. Matrices that have that property are called *orthogonal* matrices. There is an additional important property that these matrices have to satisfy. If you realize that if we do two subsequent rotations on a vector, then that is the same as doing a single rotation that brings the vector directly from its original to its final orientation. Translated in the language of rotation matrices this means that the product of two orthogonal matrices is again an orthogonal matrix. And one says that the collection of all such matrices define a *group*, for the case at hand this is the so-called rotation group in n-dimensions denoted by $SO(n)$. The $SO(n)$ group has $n(n-1)/2$ independent elements.

What about the four-vectors whose inner product involves not the unit matrix, but rather the diagonal 4×4 matrix $\eta_{\mu\nu} = diag(1,-1,-1,-1)$? Now we have to impose a different invariance condition on the transformation matrices Λ, it reads $\Lambda^{tr}\,\eta\,\Lambda = \eta$. The Lorentz transformations are defined by the condition that they leave the inner product matrix or metric, η, invariant. The associated, so-called Lorentz group is then denoted as $SO(1,3)$, as the metric has one plus sign and three minus signs. ♡

♠ On vector calculus

In this excursion we touch on three important theorems with respect to integrating equations involving the vector derivative ∇ of fields. These theorems refer respectively to the line integral, an integral over an area and a volume integral.

Operators involving the vector derivative ∇.
We have been talking about fields such as a force field $\mathbf{F}(x)$, a current density $\rho(x)$ or the electric and magnetic fields $\mathbf{E}(x)$ and $\mathbf{B}(x)$. Such a vector field defines a vector at any point in space(time). We have also encountered the vector of derivatives called *nabla*:

$$\nabla = (\partial_{x_1}, \partial_{x_2}, \partial_{x_3})\,,$$

which plays a fundamental role in the calculus of (vector) fields which features as we have seen in the Maxwell equations of electromagnetism, but as a matter of fact it plays an equally important role in the subject of fluid dynamics. If the equations involve the nabla operator, then solving the equation means that we somehow have to 'integrate' the equation. The mathematics involved is denoted as *vector calculus* in contradistinction to *vector algebra*, which only involves algebraic manipulations of vectors.

The **gradient** of a scalar function yields a vector field. In this chapter we have encountered various definitions where a vector field was defined as the vector derivative or *gradient* of a scalar potential function $V(x)$, like for example the relations:

$$\begin{aligned}\mathbf{F}(\mathbf{x}) &= -\nabla V(x)\,,\\ \mathbf{E}(\mathbf{x}) &= -\nabla V(x)\,.\end{aligned}$$

When discussing the Maxwell equations we also encountered vector derivatives of vector functions. Here we distinguish the following two possibilities:

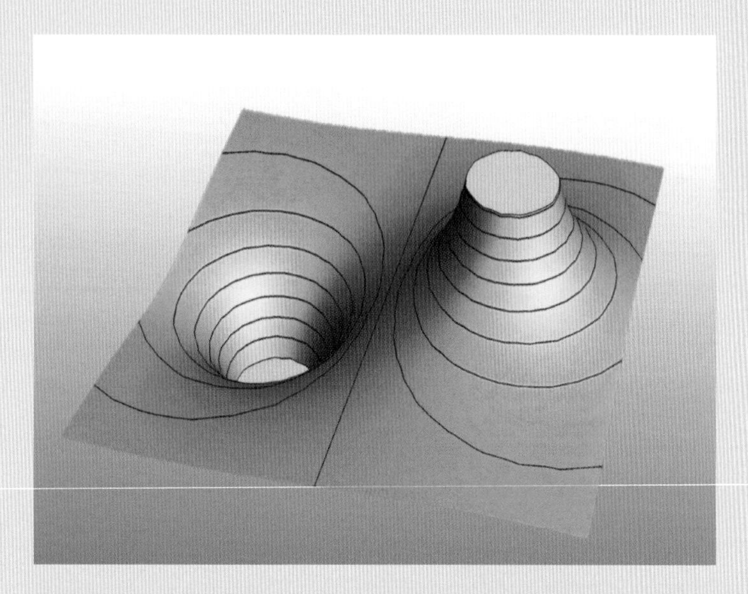

Figure A.11: *The electrostatic potential for a dipole.* This is the potential $V(x, y)$, with some equipotential lines, resulting from two opposite charges placed placed at opposite points on the x axis.

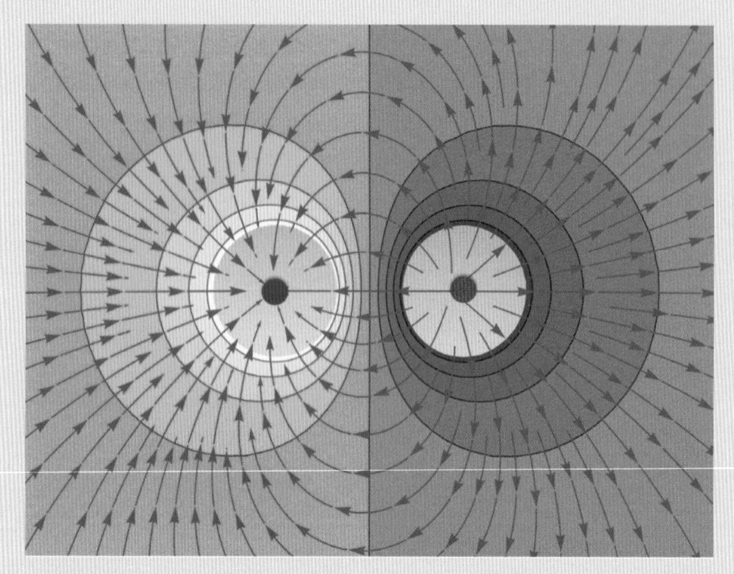

Figure A.12: *The electric dipole field.* This is the dipole field $\mathbf{E}(x, y)$ corresponding to minus the gradient of the potential depicted in the previous figure. We have drawn the *field lines*, these are the stream lines of the field. At any point the field is directed along the tangent of the line going through that point, and the magnitude is proportional to the density of lines around that point. The closed *equipotential lines* are projected in the plane and we see that the field lines are orthogonal to them. This means that the field lines are the projections of the lines of *steepest descent* on the surface of the previous figure.

(i) The **divergence** of a vector field, which yields a scalar function, for example:

$$\rho(x) = \nabla \cdot \mathbf{E}(\mathbf{x})\,.$$

(ii) The **curl** of a vector field, which yields another vector field, for example:

$$\begin{aligned} \mathbf{j} &= \nabla \times \mathbf{B}\,, \\ \mathbf{B} &= \nabla \times \mathbf{A}\,. \end{aligned}$$

These operations contain first-order derivatives and are thus linear in nabla. We also need higher-order derivatives, apart from definitions like the 'Laplacian' $\Delta \equiv (\nabla \cdot \nabla)$, there exist additional mathematical identities. In Chapter I.2 we used already two of them:

$$\nabla \cdot (\nabla \times \mathbf{A}) = 0\,, \qquad \text{(A.11a)}$$

$$\nabla \times (\nabla V) = 0\,. \qquad \text{(A.11b)}$$

One more useful identity is basically rewriting the repeated vector product of the nabla operator:

$$\nabla \times (\nabla \times \mathbf{A}) = \nabla(\nabla \cdot \mathbf{A}) - (\nabla \cdot \nabla)\mathbf{A}\,, \qquad \text{(A.12)}$$

where the Laplacian in the last term is understood as acting on the components of vector $\mathbf{A}$ individually.

We emphasize that the above are identities, meaning that they hold for any vector field $\mathbf{A}(\mathbf{x}, t)$ and any scalar field $V(\mathbf{x}, t)$.

To solve systems like the Maxwell equations we are interested in 'integrating' expressions involving the basic vector derivatives, this is facilitated by some powerful theorems that we will look at next.

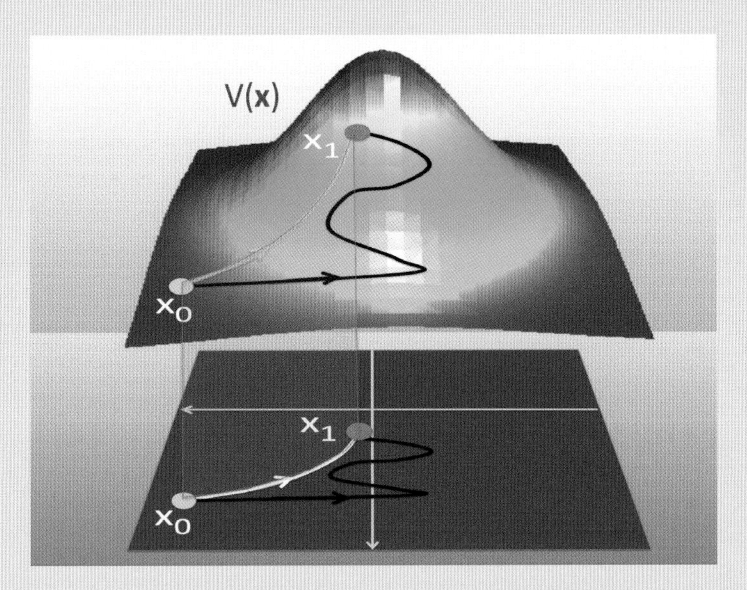

Figure A.13: *A line integral.* In the upper picture we give a two-dimensional potential surface $V(\mathbf{x})$. The force field is defined as $\mathbf{F}(\mathbf{x}) = -\boldsymbol{\nabla} V(\mathbf{x})$. If we choose a path from point $\mathbf{x}_0$ to $\mathbf{x}_1$, we can integrate $\mathbf{F}$ along that path, meaning that we integrate the component tangential to the path. This line integral yields the value $W = V(\mathbf{x}_0) - V(\mathbf{x}_1)$ which equals the work performed by the force, which in this is negative. We had to perform a force to go uphill and therefore the potential energy was increased. Note that the outcome is *independent* of the path chosen.

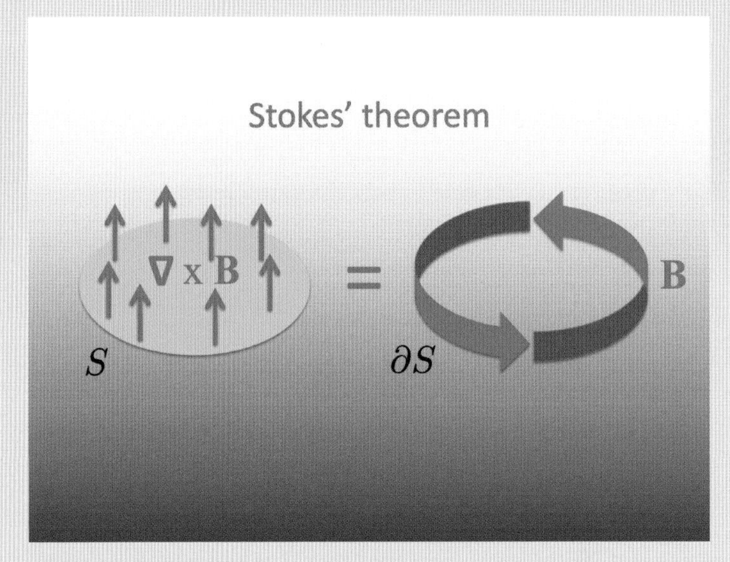

Figure A.14: *A surface integral.* The figure is a pictorial representation of Stokes' law, which says that integrating the component of the curl of a vector field ($\boldsymbol{\nabla} \times \mathbf{B}$) orthogonal to an arbitrary surface, over an area A, equals the line integral of that vector field along the closed boundary contour ∂A of that area.

Integration theorems for vector derivatives. 🌶🌶

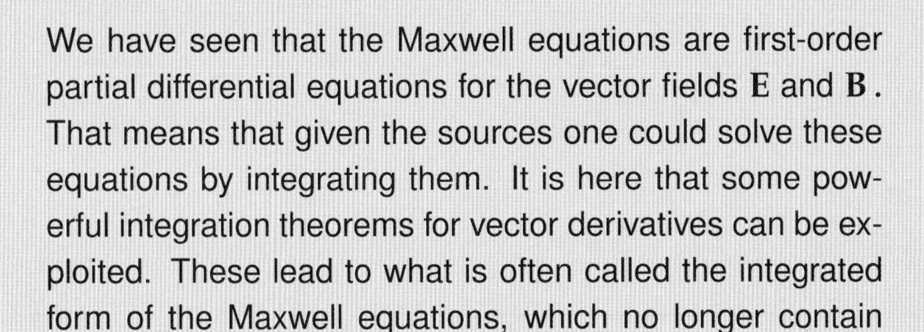
We have seen that the Maxwell equations are first-order partial differential equations for the vector fields $\mathbf{E}$ and $\mathbf{B}$. That means that given the sources one could solve these equations by integrating them. It is here that some powerful integration theorems for vector derivatives can be exploited. These lead to what is often called the integrated form of the Maxwell equations, which no longer contain any spatial derivatives of the fields.

We will consider the following cases :

(i) The *line integral* of a gradient field along a curve γ, for example:

$$\int_{\mathbf{x}_0}^{\mathbf{x}_1} \mathbf{F}(\mathbf{x}) \cdot \mathbf{dl} = -\int_{\mathbf{x}_0}^{\mathbf{x}_1} \boldsymbol{\nabla} V(\mathbf{x}) \mathrm{d}\mathbf{x} = V(\mathbf{x}_0) - V(\mathbf{x}_1),$$

where the line element $\mathbf{dl}$ is the unit vector tangent to the curve. We discussed this example already in Chapter I.1. In ordinary language this refers to the statement that if you apply a force on an object, then the integral of that force along a given path corresponds to the work applied to the object and that equals the increase of the potential energy of the object, as we have indicated in Figure A.13. This increase equals the difference of the potential energies at the endpoints of the path. The fact that the difference only depends on the endpoints means that the increase of energy is *not* dependent on the particular path chosen. If you want to climb to the top of a mountain you can choose between a path that is long and not so steep or a very short very steep path in either case you would have to deliver the same amount of energy.

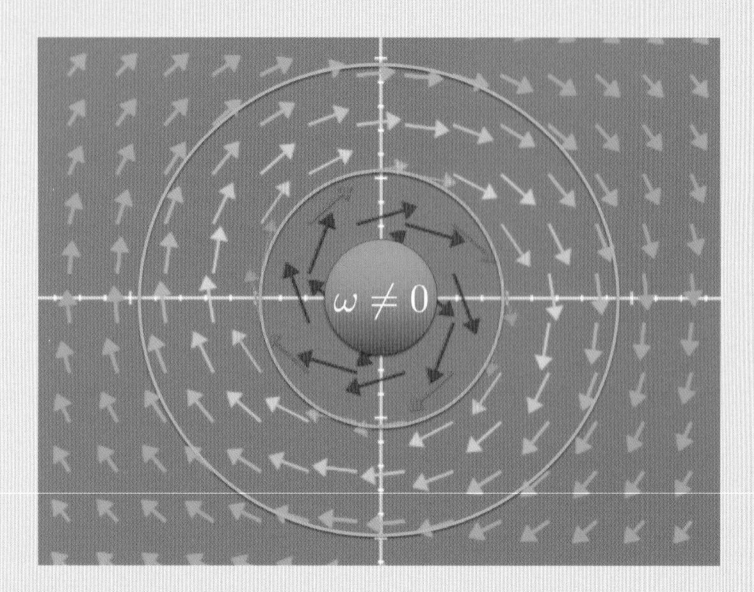

Figure A.15: *A vortex field.* The velocity field $\mathbf{v}(\mathbf{x})$ of an ideal or free vortex around a source where the vorticity $\boldsymbol{\omega}$ is non-zero in a small region around the origin and pointing along the axis perpendicular into the plane of the figure.

Figure A.16: *A tornado.* A tornado is an aerodynamical flow pattern with vorticity and a non-zero circulation.

(ii) The *surface integral of a curl* over a given area A, known as Stokes' theorem:

$$\int_A \boldsymbol{\nabla} \times \mathbf{B} \cdot \hat{\mathbf{n}}\, \mathrm{d}^2 S = \oint_{\partial A} \mathbf{B} \cdot \mathbf{dx}\,,$$

where on the left-hand side $\hat{\mathbf{n}}$ is the unit vector perpendicular to the surface element $\mathrm{d}^2 S$, and on the right-hand side we integrate the vector field $\mathbf{B}$ along the boundary ∂A of the surface area. This mathematical theorem is illustrated in Figure A.14.

The most familiar application is in fluid mechanics where the vector field defining the flow is the velocity field $\mathbf{v}(\mathbf{x}, t)$. The *vorticity* $\boldsymbol{\omega}$ of the fluid is then defined as the curl of the velocity field:

$$\boldsymbol{\omega} = \boldsymbol{\nabla} \times \mathbf{v}\,.$$

The simplest example is a situation where the vorticity to be non-zero only on the z–axis, as a constant vector in the positive z–direction. Then the solution for the velocity field is the familiar cylindrical free vortex flow around the z axis, corresponding to an ideal vortex. A related quantity is now the *circulation* of the flow as a surface integral of the vorticity, which then equals the line integral of the velocity around a closed loop bounding surface area. In the example where $\boldsymbol{\omega} = k\hat{\mathbf{z}}$ only on the z–axis, one obtains that for a loop winding once around the z–axis, the circulation γ equals $\gamma = n\,k$. Taking a horizontal circle around the z-axis we get a cylindrically symmetric, *free vortex field* with an angular velocity that drops off inversely proportional with the radius: $v(r) = k/2\pi r$, as depicted in Figure A.15. A beautiful, not so ideal vortex is the tornado depicted in Figure A.16.

In electrodynamics one applies Stoke's theorem to Ampère's law yielding

$$\oint_{\partial A} \mathbf{B} \cdot \mathbf{dx} = \int \mathbf{j} \cdot \hat{\mathbf{n}}\, \mathrm{d}^2 S\,.$$

This is basically the 'integrated form' of Ampère's law, the equation $\boldsymbol{\nabla} \times \mathbf{B} = \mathbf{j}$, that was already depicted on the left in Figure I.1.18.

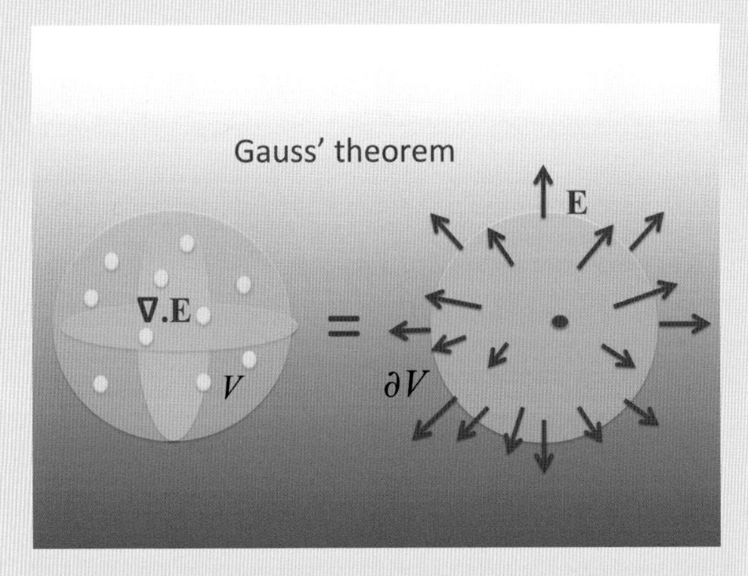

Figure A.17: *A volume integral.* The figure illustrates Gauss' law states that the volume integral of the divergence ($\boldsymbol{\nabla} \cdot \mathbf{E}$) of a vector field $\mathbf{E}$ equals the surface integral of the perpendicular component of that vector field over the closed surface (∂V) bounding the volume V.

Stoke's theorem also applies to the magnetic flux through a bounded surface, which becomes equal to the loop integral of the vector potential $\mathbf{A}$, which is defined by the equation $\mathbf{B} = \boldsymbol{\nabla} \times \mathbf{A}$:

$$\Phi = \int \mathbf{B} \cdot \hat{\mathbf{n}}\, d^2S = \oint_{\partial S} \mathbf{A} \cdot \mathbf{dx}.$$

(iii) The *volume integral of a divergence* over volume V known as Gauss' theorem :

$$\int \boldsymbol{\nabla} \cdot \mathbf{E}(\mathbf{x}) d^3V = \int_{\partial V} \mathbf{E} \cdot \hat{\mathbf{n}}\, d^2S,$$

where the integral on the right-hand side is over the closed surface S bounding the volume V. This theorem is depicted in Figure A.17.

We can apply it to the first Maxwell equation I.1.26 as follows:

$$\int_V \rho(x) d^3V = \int_{\partial V} \mathbf{E} \cdot \hat{\mathbf{n}}\, d^2S = Q,$$

telling us that integrating the perpendicular component of the electric field over a closed surface bounding a volume yields the total electric charge inside that volume. ♠

♣ On probability and statistics

> . . . But ignorance of the different causes involved in the production of events, as well as their complexity, taken together with the imperfection of analysis, prevent our reaching the same certainty [as in astronomy] about the vast majority of phenomena. Thus there are things that are uncertain for us, things more or less probable, and we seek to compensate for the impossibility of knowing them by determining their different degrees of likelihood. So it is that we owe to the weakness of the human mind one of the most delicate and ingenious of mathematical theories, the science of chance or probability.
>
> (Laplace, 1889)

Probabilities. A variable x can take on values, in a discrete or maybe a continuous set, a *domain* or a *sample space* we will denote by $\mathcal{X} = \{x_i\}$. A *random* or *stochastic variable* is one where we associate with that variable a *probability distribution* over the domain, so we introduce a probability function $p_i = p(x_i)$ that gives the chance or probability that x will have the value x_i. As the variable x always carries some value, we have to require that the probabilities add up to one:

$$\Sigma_i \, p_i = 1 \, . \qquad \text{(A.13)}$$

Given a random variable and its probability distribution, we can calculate the average outcome of a number of statistically independent measurements of x or for that matter any function $f(x)$ of x . It is simply given by the *expectation value* or *average* defined as:

$$< f >= \Sigma_i \, p_i f(x_i) \, . \qquad \text{(A.14)}$$

So for a fair dice we have that $\mathcal{X} = \{1, 2, \ldots, 6\}$ and $p_i = 1/6$ for all i, and therefore one calculates for example that $< x >= \frac{1}{6}\Sigma_i \, i = 7/2$ and $< x^2 >= \frac{1}{6}\Sigma_i \, i^2 = 91/6$.
We can ask the same questions for the sum outcomes if we throw two dice, we have now to first determine the domain of $x = x(1) + x(2)$ to obtain $\{2, 3, \ldots, 12\}$. The probabilities for each outcome equals the number of distinct combinations for the two dice to get the given answer. For example from the $6 \times 6 = 36$ possible combinations, the outcome $x = 7$ can be obtained in 6 distinct ways, namely,

$$(x(1), x(2)) = (1, 6), (2, 5), (3, 4), (4, 3), (5, 2), (6, 1) \, .$$

So, the probability $p(x = 7) = 6/36 = 1/6$. One can similarly construct distributions $P(x, n)$ for n dice, and these are depicted in Figure A.18 for an increasing number of dice.

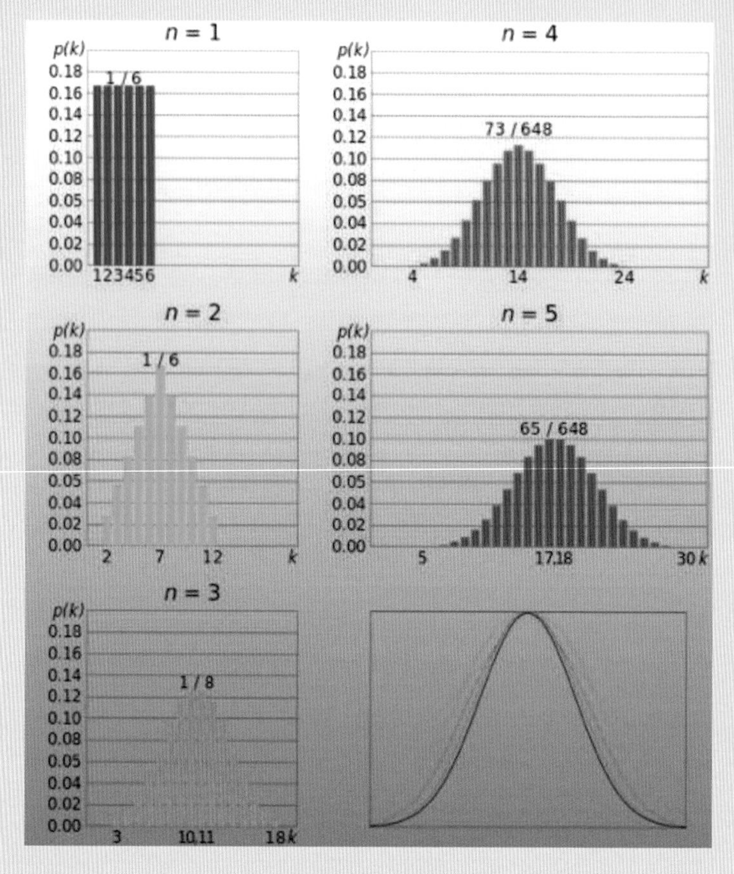

Figure A.18: *The distributions* $P(x, n, 6)$, with $x = x(1) + \ldots + x(n)$ for throwing n fair dice. For large n this symmetric distribution approaches the normal or Gaussian distribution.

Another important quantitative measure of a distribution is the *standard deviation* σ and its square, called the *variance* or *mean square deviation*, which is defined as:

$$\sigma^2 =< (x- < x >)^2 >=< x^2 > - < x >^2 . \quad \text{(A.15)}$$

The variance is a measure of the width of the distribution. For the dice examples one finds that for one dice $\sigma = \sqrt{35/12} = 1.71$ and for the pair $\sigma = \sqrt{35/6} = 2.42$.

Statistics. Having a stochastic variable one can make measurements at a series of times t_m, and one may study the frequency distribution of outcomes and compare it for example with a theoretically predicted probability distribution. Here we enter the field of statistics, of statistical analysis. The challenge of statistical analysis is to understand from the measurements, what the set of sample values you have taken tells you about the true distribution. The central and vital question is what conclusions can you draw from some experiment and with what degree of certainty or confidence.

Say the length of males in *cm* for a certain country has a certain distribution $H(h)$, which may peak around $170\ cm$. Now we can take a sample of the population and from the sample construct the sample distribution, which now is like an approximation of the real distribution, and it will not surprise you that by making the sample ever larger the approximation will get better. It may also be that you are probing a space of choices that people make and try to predict the probability of the next choices that will be made. The business of polling is in this category. Politicians and public media frequently demonstrate their ignorance where it comes to understanding statistics, and sometimes proudly so. In science, however, we have to insist on a solid understanding of statistics to interpret what we see, or think to see, and in order to draw balanced and reliable conclusions, taking the uncertainties which are always there, properly into account.

Central limit theorem. Often one is interested in a quantity y, which is dependent on many different independent random variables. The height of people for example may be written as the sum of other random variables $x^{(m)}$ with $m = 1, \ldots, M$, where each may have its own distribution $p(x^{(m)})$. Under general conditions on the distributions $p(x^{(m)})$ the distribution $P(y)$ we are interested in will approach the *Gaussian* or *normal distribution*. So quantities that equal the sum of many random variables, which need *not* be normally distributed themselves, tend to be normally distributed! This is as true for the velocity distribution of particles in a gas kept at a given temperature, as it is for the height distributions in a population, or for the frequency of errors, but also for the minimal uncertainty wave packet describing a quantum particle. The importance of this normal distribution cannot be overstated as it pops up in any serious field of study. This is nicely expressed in the following quote of Sir Francis Galton, the Victorian progressive, polymath, statistician, sociologist, psychologist, anthropologist, eugenicist, tropical explorer, geographer, inventor, meteorologist, proto-geneticist, and psychometrician:

> I know of scarcely anything so apt to impress the imagination as the wonderful form of cosmic order expressed by the 'law of frequency of error' [the normal or Gaussian distribution]. Whenever a large sample of chaotic elements is taken in hand and marshalled in the order of their magnitude, this unexpected and most beautiful form of regularity proves to have been latent all along. The law . . . reigns with serenity and complete self-effacement amidst the wildest confusion. The larger the mob and the greater the apparent anarchy, the more perfect is its sway. It is the supreme law of unreason.
>
> (Galton, 1889)

The normal distribution depends on two parameters, its *mean* or *expectation* μ and its *variance* σ^2, and it is given

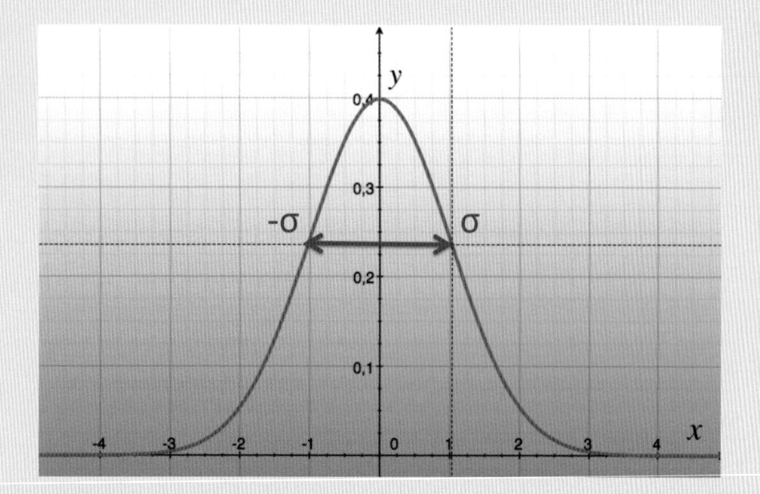

Figure A.19: *The Gaussian or normal distribution,* with variance $\sigma^2 = 1$ and mean $\mu = 0$.

by the following expression,

$$f(x) = \frac{1}{\sqrt{2\pi\sigma^2}} e^{-(x-\mu)^2/2\sigma^2}. \tag{A.16}$$

We have depicted the normal distribution in Figure A.19 with its familiar bell shape.

Statistical physics. To describe the macroscopic properties of systems like gases, fluids, plasmas one does not need to know the precise properties of all individual particles making up the system. Fortunately, because that would amount to solving some 10^{23} coupled partial differential equations. If we put the particles say in a container, then each of the particles has a well-defined phase space that is the same for all of them, but each particle may sit in a different corner of the phase space. Boltzmann made the assumption that such a macro-system may then be characterized by some distribution of the particles over phase space.

For a simple gas or fluid, he introduced the distribution function $f(\mathbf{x}, \mathbf{v}, t)$, giving the probability density for a particle in the gas to have position $\mathbf{x}$ and velocity $\mathbf{v}$ at time t. This function will have some generic features. He in fact showed that this distribution function had to satisfy some fundamental equation which now carries his name. From f one can derive the number density distribution, $n(\mathbf{x}, t) = \int f(\mathbf{x}, \mathbf{v}, t)\, d^3\mathbf{v}$.

If the system is in equilibrium, one has that the distribution f is time independent. In a gas in equilibrium (without external forces) we expect the particles to spread out evenly over the volume, so f will also be $\mathbf{x}$ independent, and because of the interactions one expects that the energy will be quite equally distributed over the particles. If we keep the gas at a fixed temperature, so that the average energy per particle equals $3kT/2$, this leads to the well-known Maxwell-Boltzmann equilibrium velocity distribution:

$$f(\mathbf{v}; T) = \left(\frac{m}{2\pi kT}\right)^{3/2} e^{-m|\mathbf{v}|^2/2kT}, \tag{A.17}$$

which is a 3-dimensional Gaussian distribution.

Entropy. With a given distribution p, one can always associate a certain Gibbs-Shannon or *information entropy* $S(p)$ with,

$$S(p) = -\Sigma_i p_i \log_2 p_i . \tag{A.18}$$

The entropy is thus a number that you can calculate given a distribution. If the outcome is certain, then one has for one particular i that $p_i = 1$ while the others are zero, and one finds that $S = 0$. On the other hand if the outcome is maximally uncertain we will have that N states $p_i = 1/N$ for all i, implying that the entropy will attain its maximal value $S = \log_2 N$. Another interesting property is that entropy is an additive quantity, if one combines two independent distributions. Imagine throwing simultaneously a fair coin and a fair dice with distributions $p^{(1)}$ and $p^{(2)}$, then there are $2 \times 6 = 12$ states with a combined distribution $p = p^{(1)} \times p^{(2)}$. The entropies then satisfy the additive relation: $S = S^{(1)} + S^{(2)}$. In other words, if one finds in an experiment that the additive property does not hold this indicates some interdependence between the variables, which in physical terms means that the two components of the system interact. It is therefore certainly possible to have a closed system consisting of two interacting subsystems, where the entropy of one subsystem actually decreases, as long as the entropy of the other subsystem increases by an equal or larger amount, as to make sure that the whole systems satisfies the second law. For example, if one has a mixture of different particle types, which at some point will start binding, the bound state represents a lower energy state, and thus in this transition heat will be released, which corresponds to pure entropy production. Here we see that on the one hand the interactions cause more structure, a higher level of order and thus less entropy in the particle component of the system, but at the same time the entropy of the system as a whole will increase because of the amount of heat that is produced.

Maximal entropy principle. If you have a certain sample space, you may want to consider different distributions $p^{(m)}$ over that space and compare their entropies. Then an interesting fact is that the distribution that maximizes the entropy over the set of distributions $\{p^{(m)}\}$ is the best guess you can make, assuming that you know nothing else about the process or the distribution you are studying except that the probabilities add up to one. But in many cases you do know more, for example you know the average outcome of some observable $\lambda(x)$, so $< \lambda(x) >= \lambda_0$. Then you want to maximize the entropy under the additional constraint that $< \lambda(x) >= \sum_i p_i \lambda(x_i) = \lambda_0$, and that will lead to another maximal entropy distribution. So the maximal entropy distribution is the least biased probability distribution under the given set of constraints. Many of the distributions that play an important role in nature are maximal entropy distributions. Let us look at some of the familiar cases:

(i) We define the information entropy $H(\{p_i\};\{\lambda_k\})$ as the entropy but with the constraints added with a parameter λ_k. The trivial case is where we impose that the sum of the probabilities equals one:

$$H(p_i;\lambda_k) = -\sum_i p_i \ln p_i - \lambda_0(\sum_i p_i - 1)\,. \qquad \text{(A.19)}$$

We maximize H with respect to the $\{p_i\}$ and $\{\lambda_k\}$ by requiring the partial derivatives to be zero:

$$\left(\frac{\partial H}{\partial p_i}\right) = -\ln p_i - 11 - \lambda_0 = 0\,, \qquad \text{(A.20)}$$

$$-\left(\frac{\partial H}{\partial \lambda_0}\right) = \sum p_i - 1 = 0\,. \qquad \text{(A.21)}$$

The first equation yields that p_i is constant $p_i = p$; substitution in the second equation yields $Np - 1 = 0$, so that $p = 1/N$, corresponding to the well-known case of fixed energy or the micro-canonical ensemble.

(ii) Let us now take a continuous energy type distribution where we know the average energy to be ε^*. Then we have to add to the expression (A.19) the constraint term $-\lambda_1(\int_0^\infty p_i \varepsilon - \varepsilon^*)$, yielding for the first equation:

$$-\ln p - 1 - \lambda_0 - \lambda\varepsilon\,, \qquad \text{(A.22)}$$

with solution

$$p(\varepsilon) = Ce^{-\lambda\varepsilon}\,.$$

From the first constraint we get:

$$\int p(\varepsilon)\,d\varepsilon = C(-\frac{1}{\lambda})\,e^{-\lambda\varepsilon}\Big]_0^\infty = \frac{C}{\lambda} = 1\,, \qquad \text{(A.23)}$$

so we learn that $C = \lambda$. Substitution in the second constraint yields another relation that we can solve for both parameters :

$$C\int \varepsilon\, e^{-\lambda\varepsilon}\,d\varepsilon = \varepsilon^*\,. \qquad \text{(A.24)}$$

Let us rewrite

$$-C\frac{d}{d\lambda}\int e^{-\lambda\varepsilon}\,d\varepsilon = -C\frac{d}{d\lambda}(\frac{1}{\lambda}) = \frac{C}{\lambda^2} = \varepsilon^*\,, \qquad \text{(A.25)}$$

which yields $C = \lambda = 1/\varepsilon^*$ and we obtain the simple exponential distribution:

$$p(\varepsilon) = \frac{1}{\varepsilon^*} e^{-\varepsilon/\varepsilon^*} . \tag{A.26}$$

(iii) A similar calculation can be set up for the case where we have prior knowledge about the variance of the distribution, in which case one obtains a Gaussian distribution, like the celebrated Maxwell-Boltzmann distribution.

The maximal entropy principle is a powerful tool for constructing the optimal distribution satisfying a certain number of constraints. And we see that this is completely consistent with our discussion of statistical mechanics in chapter I.1. A virtue of the maximal entropy principle is that it nicely separates the purely statistical and the more physical aspects in the approach to macroscopic systems. This approach to statistical mechanics, inspired by the work of Gibbs and Shannon, was introduced in 1957 by the American physicist Edwin Thompson Jaynes.

Quantum entropy. In quantum theory, probability plays an important role even if we consider a system consisting of a single particle, as its wave function or state vector is a probability amplitude that encodes the probability for obtaining certain outcomes of measurements of an observable. Therefore probability is built in right from the start for any quantum system. and you expect that there is some meaning to the notion of entropy as well. Indeed, there is, the quantum entropy was defined by Von Neumann much in parallel with its classical precursor:

$$S = -\mathrm{Tr}\, \rho \log \rho . \tag{A.27}$$

In this expression, ρ is the so-called density matrix of the system as discussed in Chapter II.1, which represents the state of the system. The symbol Tr stands for the trace of a matrix, which equals the sum of its diagonal components. The Von Neumann entropy is a measure for the degree of *entanglement* of a multicomponent quantum system. ♣

♠ On complex numbers

Mathematics is one of the few places where complexification often stands for simplification.

Number systems. It is interesting to note how number systems have been extended through history. A natural starting point are the *natural numbers* or positive integers, and we know how to add and subtract them, where to stay within the set of natural numbers the subtraction is restricted to numbers smaller (or equal if we include zero in the set). We can extend the definition of subtraction to all natural numbers but that forces us to augment the set with the exquisite number 'zero' and the negative integers. One defines multiplication as an operation on the integers and then we see that the inverse operation called division is restricted and forces us to introduce the *rational numbers* or fractions. The next step is taking powers, and defining their inverse as taking the corresponding roots. Applied to positive numbers this leads to the *real numbers*, with the remark that of course all rational numbers are real but not the other way around, such as for example the real number $\sqrt{2}$. If we extend the definition of roots to negative numbers we are lead to the introduction of the *complex numbers*, where indeed the fundamental new element is the *imaginary unit* $i = \sqrt{-1}$.

Definition of a complex number. A complex number α has a real and imaginary part $\alpha = a_1 + ia_2$, where a_1 and a_2 are both real, and i is the *imaginary unit* with the defining property $i^2 = -1$. Note that a complex number can therefore also be thought of as a vector in a two-dimensional real space also called the *complex plane*, by taking the real part as the x-component and the imaginary part as the y-component, and thus writing $z = x + iy$. The length of the vector is called the *magnitude or absolute value* of α and denoted by $|\alpha|$, and the angle it makes with the real (x) axis is called its *argument or phase.*
The *complex conjugate* of α is defined as $\alpha^* = a_1 - ia_2$,

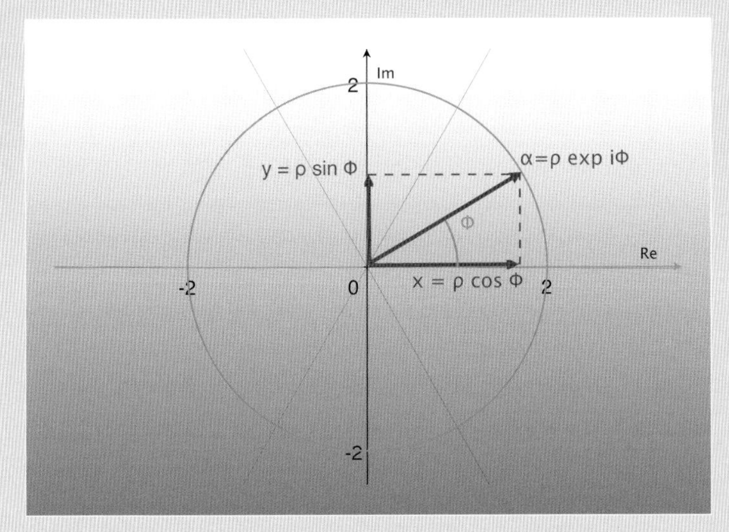

(a) Polar representation of a complex number $\alpha = \rho \exp(i\varphi)$.

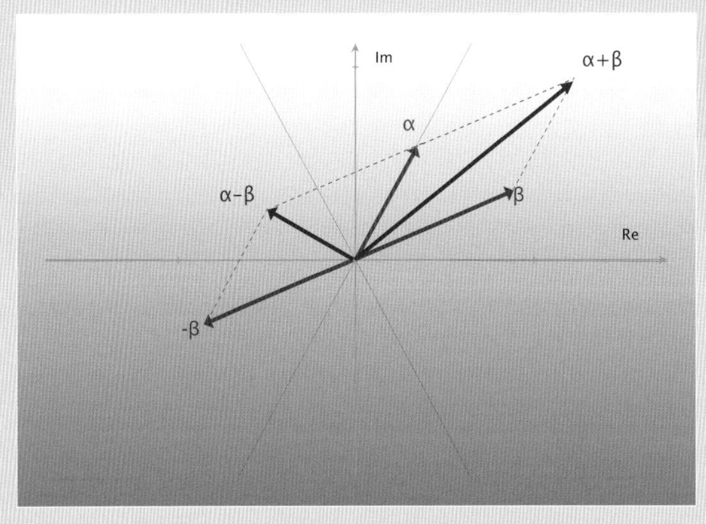

(b) Adding and subtracting two complex numbers α and β by the 'parallelogram' rule.

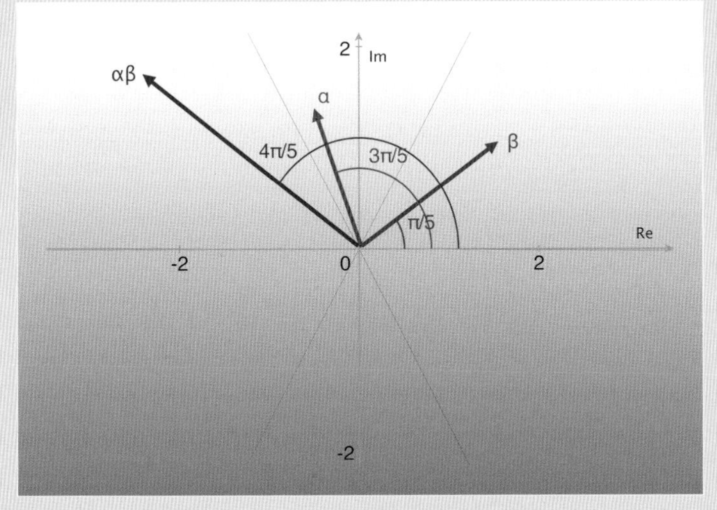

(c) Multiplying two complex numbers α and β amounts to multiplying their magnitudes ($\rho_{\alpha\beta} = \rho_\alpha \rho_\beta$) and adding their phase angles ($\varphi_{\alpha\beta} = \varphi_\alpha + \varphi_\beta$).

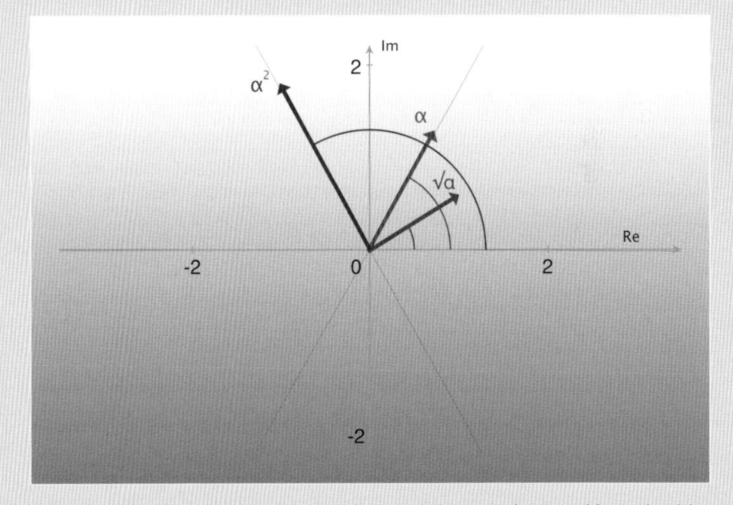

(d) The square and square root of a complex number α. Here the blue angle is half and the purple angle is twice the red angle.

Figure A.20: *Complex numbers.* Graphical representation of some basic operations with complex numbers.

it is obtained by replacing i by $-i$. The value of $|\alpha|$ is defined by the relation $|\alpha|^2 = \alpha^*\alpha = a_1^2 + a_2^2$., where one obtains the result by multiplying out the expressions and remembering that $-i^2 = +1$, so, $(a_1 + ia_2)(a_1 - ia_2) = a_1^2 - i^2 a_2^2 = a_1^2 + a_2^2$. This indeed equals the length of the corresponding vector.

Polar decomposition. There is an alternative but equivalent way to think of complex numbers explicitly using their two-dimensional vector property. If one thinks of a planar vector in polar coordinates, one may specify it by giving its magnitude ρ and the angle φ it makes with the x–axis. The complex number is then written as $\alpha = \rho e^{i\varphi}$: the terminology is that φ is called the *argument* or phase angle, and $e^{i\varphi}$ the *phase factor.* We see that $|\alpha| = \rho$ and $|e^{i\varphi}| = 1$. The phase factor describes therefore a point on the unit circle in the complex plane which makes an angle φ with the real axis. This is depicted in Figure A.20(a) from which one also sees that the real part of the phase factor equals $\cos\varphi$, while the imaginary component equals $\sin\varphi$, which leads to a famous mathematical identity originally due to Euler:

$$e^{i\varphi} = \cos\varphi + i\sin\varphi \,. \tag{A.28}$$

This formula is a source of numerous amusing number theoretical identities like $e^{i\pi} + 1 = 0$ and $e^{i\pi/2} = i$. In this parametrization of complex numbers it is easy to perform complex multiplication and division and taking powers or roots.

Algebraic properties of complex numbers. To add or subtract two complex numbers, one just adds or subtracts their real and imaginary parts separately: $\alpha \pm \beta = (a_1 \pm b_1) + i(a_2 \pm b_2)$. This corresponds to adding (subtracting) two vectors in the plane by the 'parallelogram' rule as indicated in Figure A.20(b). Multiplying two complex numbers α_1 and α_2 amounts top multiplying the magnitudes, i.e. $\rho = \rho_1\rho_2$, while the phase angles add, $\varphi = \varphi_1 + \varphi_2$ as in Figure A.20(c). Similarly when dividing two complex numbers one divides the magnitudes and takes the difference of the phase angles. Taking a complex conjugate amounts to replacing φ by $-\varphi$, i.e. mirroring the vector in the x-axis. We see that the polar representation of complex numbers makes it particularly easy to visualize the multiplication and division operations, but also to take their powers and roots, as we did in Figure A.20(d).♠

♡ On complex vectors and matrices

We have discussed real vectors and matrices in the Math Excursion on page 158. But in quantum theory everything gets complexified, meaning to say that states are represented by complex vectors and observables by complex (hermitian) matrices. Therefore we will summarize here some additional material specific to complex vectors and matrices.

Complex vectors. Think of our vectors as *column* or *ket* vectors $|v\rangle$ which are complex, which means that the entries or components are complex numbers. Then we may define a space of dual vectors, the dual of a column vector is a *row* or *bra* vector $\langle v|$, *with complex conjugate entries.*

The inner- or dot-product. Having a vector space $\mathcal{V}$ and its dual $\mathcal{V}^*$ the *inner product* between elements of $v^* \in \mathcal{V}^*$ and $w \in \mathcal{V}$ is defined as the number obtained after adding the products of corresponding entries:

$$\langle v|w\rangle = v^* \cdot w = \Sigma_i v_i^* w_i \,.$$

We calculate for example the dot product of two two-dimensional complex vectors as:

$$\begin{pmatrix} 2i & 1 \end{pmatrix} \begin{pmatrix} i \\ 1 \end{pmatrix} = 2i^2 + 1 = -1.$$

The property of the inner product that,

$$\langle w|v\rangle = \langle v|w\rangle^* \,,$$

still implies that $\langle v|v\rangle = \langle v|v\rangle^* = |v|^2$ is always a positive real number which is defined to be the length of the vector $|v|$ squared.

The state space of a qubit. The state of a qubit is by definition the two-dimensional complex vector $|\psi\rangle$ of equation (II.1.2). The normalization condition applied to the state can be written as:

$$\langle\psi|\psi\rangle = |\psi|^2 = |\alpha|^2 + |\beta|^2 = 1\,. \qquad \text{(A.29)}$$

If we substitute $\alpha = a_1 + ia_2$ and $\beta = b_1 + ib_2$, then we find

$$a_1^2 + a_2^2 + b_1^2 + b_2^2 = 1\,. \qquad \text{(A.30)}$$

This equation describes a (real) three-dimensional sphere, S^3, embedded in the four-dimensional Euclidean space, R^4, with coordinates (a_1, a_2, b_1, b_2).

Complex matrices acting on complex vectors. Now vectors can also be multiplied by matrices to produce another vector, the way that is done was pictorially indicated for a column vector in A.8(b). This action of matrices on vectors is clearly most easily understood if you think of the matrix as a stack of row vectors. This action can also be considered as a *transformation* of a vector into another vector. A simple example may help:

$$\begin{pmatrix} 1 & i \\ -i & 1 \end{pmatrix}\begin{pmatrix} 2 \\ i \end{pmatrix} = \begin{pmatrix} 2+i^2 \\ -2i+i \end{pmatrix} = \begin{pmatrix} 1 \\ -i \end{pmatrix}.$$

The matrix acts as a *linear operator* on the vector space, as it reshuffles the components into linear combinations of them. Or one may say that $(n \times n)$ matrices map the vector space $\mathcal{V}$ onto itself and we write $A : \mathcal{V} \to \mathcal{V}$. There is for example a particular subset of (3×3) matrices whose action on 'ordinary' vectors corresponds to rotating of those vectors in three-dimensional complex space C^3.

Another example which shows the descriptive power of matrices as operators on state vectors is in (quantum) computation, where generically we think of computation as a sequence of gates, interactions/manipulations or measurements that change the states of a set of (qu)bits.

Such processes or computations can be represented by a product of matrices and rescalings. Indeed the complete computation is just a big operator, mapping the in-state on the out-state vector.

The matrix product. Once we have defined the action of matrices on vectors the step to the multiplication of matrices is straightforward and it was visualized in Figure A.8(c). The (ij)-entry of the product matrix $C = AB$ is obtained by the dot product of the $i-th$ row vectors of A with the $j-th$ column vector of B. Let us again give a simple example:

$$\begin{pmatrix} 1 & i \\ -i & 1 \end{pmatrix}\begin{pmatrix} 1 & 1 \\ 1 & -1 \end{pmatrix} = \begin{pmatrix} 1+i & 1-i \\ 1-i & -1-i \end{pmatrix}. \qquad \text{(A.31)}$$

Types of matrices. As mentioned before, depending on the situation we usually have to put additional constraints defining subsets of matrices, which may or may not be preserved under the basic matrix operations. These definitions involve certain basic matrix manipulations which were represented symbolically in Figure A.10. A fundamental notion is the *transpose* of a matrix denoted by the matrix A^{tr}, which is obtained from A, as we illustrated in Figures A.10(a) and A.10(b). Written in terms of its entries one has $(A^{tr})_{ij} \equiv A_{ji}$. Taking the transpose can therefore also be defined as interchanging rows and columns. Repeating the operation brings you back to the original matrix. Taking the transpose of matrix $C = AB$ we get a matrix which is the product of the transposes, but in the opposite order: $C^{tr} = B^{tr}A^{tr}$. Symmetric or antisymmetric matrices satisfy $A = \pm A^{tr}$ respectively. Note that a symmetric complex matrix contains $n(n+1)$ real numbers, while the antisymmetric one has only $n(n-1)$, it adds up to $2n^2$, the number of real entries of a general complex $(n \times n)$ matrix.

Hermitean matrices. Of special importance in quantum theory are the *hermitian* matrices, because they represent observable physical quantities. To tell you what they look like we first define the hermitian adjoint $A^\dagger$ as $A^\dagger = (A^{tr})^*$ (see Figure A.10(d)). A hermitian (self-adjoint) matrix is just one that satisfies $A = A^\dagger$. It is not hard to see that a hermitian matrix can be decomposed in the sum of a symmetric real and an antisymmetric purely imaginary matrix, also implying that the diagonal elements are real. Such a hermitian matrix contains n^2 real numbers. Let us give a simple example of the above operations for a 2×2 matrix:

$$C = \begin{pmatrix} 1 & i \\ 1 & -1 \end{pmatrix}$$
$$\Rightarrow C^{tr} = \begin{pmatrix} 1 & 1 \\ i & -1 \end{pmatrix}; \; C^\dagger = \begin{pmatrix} 1 & 1 \\ -i & -1 \end{pmatrix};$$

we see that C is not hermitian because $C \neq C^\dagger$. Each of the Pauli matrices on the left-hand side of equation (A.32) however is hermitian. Note however that their product is *not*.

The Pauli matrices. Most famous are the set of three (2×2) hermitian matrices, which are called the *Pauli matrices* X, Y and Z. They are defined as:

$$X = \begin{pmatrix} 0 & 1 \\ 1 & 0 \end{pmatrix}, \; Y = \begin{pmatrix} 0 & -i \\ i & 0 \end{pmatrix}, \; Z = \begin{pmatrix} 1 & 0 \\ 0 & -1 \end{pmatrix}, \quad \text{(A.32)}$$

and have a quite unique combination of properties.
(i) They are hermitian: $X^\dagger = X$ etc.
(ii) They are unitary: $X^\dagger X = 1$.
(iii) From (i) and (ii) it follows that they square to the unit matrix: $X^2 = 1$ etc.
(iv) They form a basis of the $su(2)$ Lie algebra, which means that they form a closed algebra under commutation:
$[X, Y] = 2iZ$ etc. (see below).
(v) Their anti-commutator vanishes: $\{X, Y\} = XY + YX = 0$ etc.
(vi) The one qubit observables are linear combinations of the Pauli matrices, the spin-half operators correspond to: $S_x = \hbar X/2$ etc.
(vii) If we add the unit matrix (which commutes will all three of the Pauli matrices, and which is also hermitian), we get the algebra of $u(2) \simeq su(2) \oplus u(1)$.
(viii) Every 2×2 unitary matrix can be written as a linear combination of these four matrices (see below).

Lie algebras.

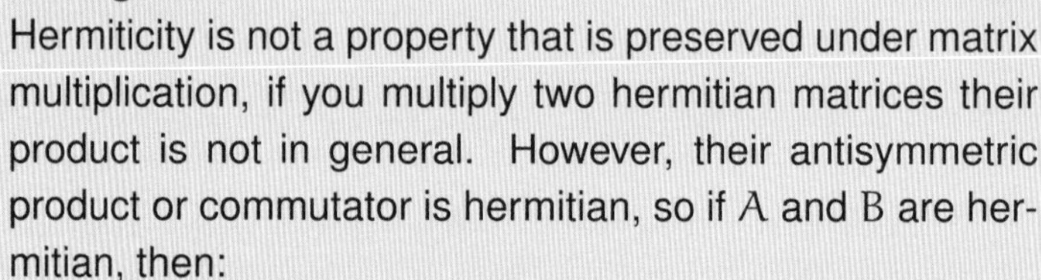

Hermiticity is not a property that is preserved under matrix multiplication, if you multiply two hermitian matrices their product is not in general. However, their antisymmetric product or commutator is hermitian, so if A and B are hermitian, then:

$$(i[A, B])^\dagger = -i(AB - BA)^\dagger = -i(B^\dagger A^\dagger - A^\dagger B^\dagger) = i[A, B]$$

In this sense the commutator of observables yields another observable, or to put it another way: the observables form a closed commutator algebra, where the 'product' operation of the algebra is then defined as the commutator: $A \cdot B \equiv i[A, B]$. We see a splendid example of this with the qubit where we had three basic observables $\{X, Y, Z\}$ that form a closed algebra under commutation:

$$[X, Y] = 2iZ \quad [Y, Z] = 2iX \quad [Z, X] = 2iY, \qquad \text{(A.33)}$$

this three-dimensional algebra is called $su(2)$. The beauty of the subject becomes clear if you think – for example – of the $su(2)$ algebra not as a set of relations that our spin matrices satisfy, but as an abstract set of commutators that define the algebra. In general one should think of a set of elements X_i that form the basis of the Lie algebra $\mathcal{A}$, satisfying commutation relations:

$$[X_i, X_j] = i \sum_k f_{ijk} X_k;$$

the specific set of constants $\{f_{ijk}\}$ are the so-called *structure constants* which define the Lie algebra.

Now you can turn the question around, and ask when given the structure constants, whether there exist any sets of matrices or other operators that actually do satisfy precisely the above relations. This is what one calls the *representation theory* of Lie algebras, an important part of the mathematical theory. In physics we encounter this all the time, for example the $su(2)$ algebra is basically the algebra of rotations in three-dimensional space.[3] It is the algebra satisfied by the angular momentum operators $\{L_x, L_y, L_z\}$ as differential operators, but the algebra has also irreducible representation as $(n \times n)$ matrices for any $n = 1, 2, 3, \ldots$. If we write $n = 2s+1$ then s is now defined as the spin, or the angular momentum, and we see that indeed all half-integral and integral values are possible. And the integer values we see recurring as the quantum number l in the spectra of atoms. The $s = 1/2$ case clearly corresponds to the 2×2 matrices S_i. The complex *Lie algebras* and their 'irreducible' representations have been classified completely and form an important subject in the mathematics and physics literature. ♡

[3]This algebra is defined by the commutation relations of equation (A.33) without the factor 2 on the right. In other words $S_x = X/2$ etc.

♢ On symmetry groups

Symmetries are a powerful guiding principle in identifying and understanding important properties of physical systems. The notion of symmetry can be applied to objects, to spaces or lattices, to equations, to the degeneracies in the spectra of atoms and molecules, but also of the electron bands of materials where the ions form an underlying lattice structure. Here we limit ourselves to the basic mathematical background concerning the symmetry groups, which we will refer to throughout the book. In Chapter II.6 we have an extensive section devoted to the physical aspects of symmetries and their breaking.

Groups: the language of symmetry. When we talk about order we usually refer to some regularities, some predictable pattern that has some or many symmetries. The word symmetry in physics has many different meanings and is like the word 'snow' for the Inuits. One speaks of finite or infinite, discrete or continuous symmetries. Symmetries of objects, of spaces, and of equations. And on another level one speaks of global or local, exact or approximate symmetries. We encountered already the notion of frame rotations, of space-time rotations, and of gauge transformations. And the elaborated structure of fiber bundles as described in chapter I.1, involved the concept of a local or gauge symmetry.

The notions just mentioned are relevant in different contexts but they share the underlying mathematical concept of a *group*. Let us introduce this concept in its elementary easy to grasp form as a *group of transformations*. One can indeed think of transforming an object as applying some operation on it, like rotating it, or moving (translating) it in some direction, or mirroring it (like transforming your left shoe in your right shoe), or scaling the object by changing its size but not its shape. Generally we think of the group as acting on some vector space, where the objects, like fields or states, are defined as vectors.

Defining properties of a group. Mathematically a group is just a set of elements and a 'product rule' that satisfy some rather obvious axioms, and interestingly those axioms are so restrictive that basically everything is known about the groups that play a role in physics. Group theory is a rich branch of mathematics and we will only scratch the surface here.

We denote the group by G : it is a set of elements (i.e. transformations or operations) g_i and we write $G = \{g_i\}$ and conversely $g_i \in G$. There are four defining properties:

(i) *composition rule*: if $g_1 \cdot g_2 = g_3$ with $g_1, g_2 \in G$ then $g_3 \in G$, this composition rule is often referred to as the *group multiplication*.

(ii) *associativity*: the group multiplication is associative, which means that the outcome of a product does not depend on the order we perform the multiplication, so,

$$(g_1 \cdot g_2) \cdot g_3 = g_1 \cdot (g_2 \cdot g_3) = g_1 \cdot g_2 \cdot g_3 \, .$$

(iii) *identity*: there always is the trivial transformation of doing nothing, it corresponds to the identity element e, which satisfies

$$e \cdot g = g \cdot e = g \text{ for all } g \, .$$

(iv) *inverse*: as you can always transform back, meaning that each element g has a unique inverse g^{-1} with

$$g \cdot g^{-1} = g^{-1} \cdot g = e \, .$$

Numbers or matrices certainly can form groups, but note that we only refer to a single 'composition rule' or 'product' of elements. They do not form a linear space, or an algebra. A set of objects that is closed under some kind of product is maybe the easiest way to think about them. In that sense a group is an elementary and natural notion, and you may be more familiar with it than you think.

Some examples. The set of all integers n form a group

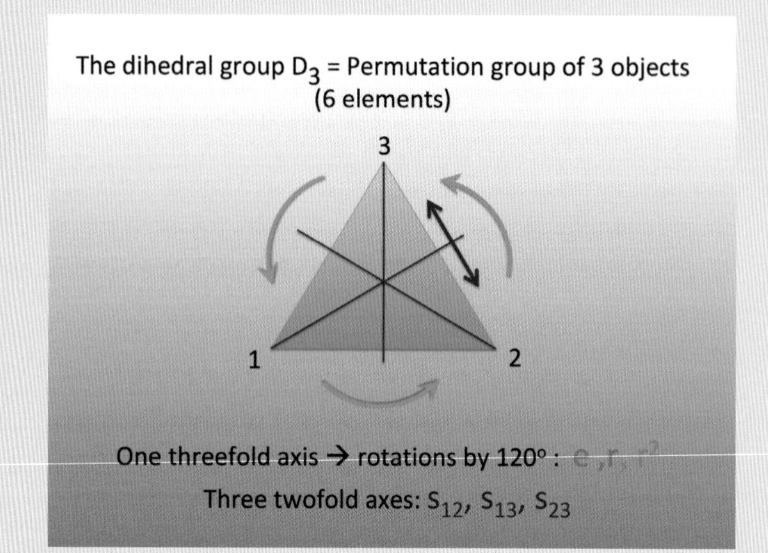

Figure A.21: *The dihedral group* D_3. The symmetry group of an equilateral triangle is the group D_3 consisting of 6 elements. There is one threefold axis, and three twofold axes.

$G = Z$ where the composition rule is addition, the identity element is $n = 0$ and the 'inverse' of n is $-n$. This is an *infinite discrete* group. Note that the integers do *not* form a group under multiplication, because of the problem caused by the inverse operation; zero has no inverse while just dividing two integers brings you outside the integers in to the set of fractional numbers.

The real numbers which correspond to an infinite line form a *continuous* group of translations $T = R$ again under addition (subtraction). Yet another example is by rotations in the plane. We may rotate a two-dimensional object by a certain angle ϕ where $0 \leq \phi < 360^o$. Now the group is not a line but a circle, rotating by 360° is like doing nothing. This two-dimensional rotation group denoted by $SO(2)$ is the same as the 'phase group', denoted by $U(1)$.

Let us now discuss the group of transformations that leaves some object (or space, or equation) *invariant*, in which case we speak of the *invariance* or *symmetry* group of that object. Consider an equilateral triangle like in Figure A.21;

it is easy to list the transformations that leave it invariant: (i) rotations over 120° about its center $\{r, r^2\}$, (ii) mirroring it through the bisector of one of the angles $\{s_1, s_2, s_3\}$. This group $G = \{e, r, r^2, s_1, s_2, s_3\}$ has 6 elements and is denoted as the dihedral group D_3. This group is the same as the permutation group S_3 of three objects. The group D_3 readily generalizes for regular polygons (square, pentagon, hexagon,...) to groups D_n.

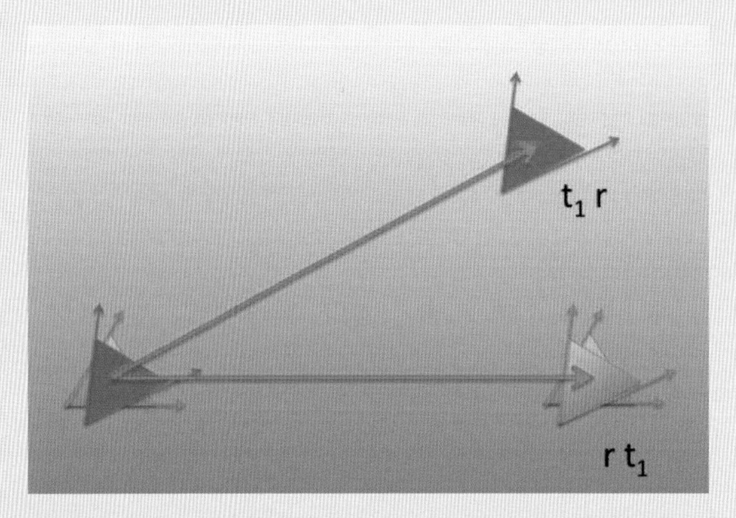

Figure A.22: *The symmetries of two-dimensional Euclidean space.* Picture showing that translations and rotations (of a triangular object) do not commute. It is a fact we are all familiar with: if you make first a step sideways and then turn, you end up in a different place then if you first turn and then make a step sideways. Formally stated: if we first translate along the bottom side of the triangle and then rotate over 30°, we act with $r \cdot t_1$, and we end up with the rotated triangle in the lower right-hand corner; if we first rotate and then translate, we act with $t_1 \cdot r$, and we end up with the rotated triangle in the upper right-hand corner. The operations are clearly not the same.

Another important class of groups are groups that leave the inner product of some vector space invariant. For ordinary three-dimensional vectors, the inner product is $a \cdot b = |a|\,|b| \cos\phi$ and the invariance group is the rotation group $SO(3)$. For relativistic four vectors we defined the inner product as $a \cdot b = a_\mu b^\mu = \eta_{\mu\nu} a^\mu b^\nu$, with $\eta_{\mu\nu} = diag(1, -1, -1, -1)$, and it is invariant under the Lorentz group $SO(1,3)$. In the n-dimensional complex Hilbert space we have state vectors and the hermitian inner product $\langle \Phi | \Psi \rangle$, and as we discussed in this chapter the invariance group is the unitary group $U(n)$. We will have more to say about the unitary groups at the end of this *Math Excursion*.

Space (time) symmetries. In physics and chemistry one type of order refers to the situation where the atoms form a lattice in space and so it is of interest to look at the symmetries of a lattice. If we look at a triangular lattice, or triangular tiling of the plane like in Figure III.2.24(a), we see that we not just have the rotations by multiples of 60°, but also translations along the sides of the triangles. Those translation can be generated[4] by the two basic translations t_1 and t_2 of the discrete translation group $G = T^2 = T \times T$. Note that each translation group is the same as the group of the integers: $T \simeq Z$.

Abelian versus non-abelian groups. If we now combine the rotations and the translations, we learn something interesting about the structure of the group, namely that the group composition rule is not necessarily *commutative*, which just means that in general we have that $g_1 \cdot g_2 \neq g_2 \cdot g_1$. The group is then called non-commutative or non-abelian. And this is clearly different from the multiplication and addition of ordinary numbers which are commutative. Ordinary division is of course not, as in general $a/b \neq b/a$, but if you define division as multiplication by the inverse it is, as $a\frac{1}{b} = \frac{1}{b}a$.

The rotations (in a plane) by themselves do commute, if I first rotate by an angle ϕ_1 and then ϕ_2 the net result is a rotation by $\phi_1 + \phi_2$, and that is the same as first rotating by ϕ_2 and then by ϕ_1. The same is true for the translations by themselves as $a + b = b + a$.

[4]Generated means that all translations can be obtained by repeated application of the two basic translations.

It is no longer true if we combine rotations and translations as we did in in Figure A.22. If we choose r with $\phi = 60^o$ and $t_1 = na$ translation over n times side of a triangle, then both operations leave the lattice of Figure III.2.24(a) invariant. They belong to the invariance group of the lattice but correspond to different elements. The terminology is that we call the total invariance group of a lattice a *space group* whereas the rotational part of it forms a *point group* as it leaves a point of the space fixed. Note that if we think of the plane as a continuous space, usually denoted by R^2, then the space group would be the group made up by arbitrary rotations and arbitrary translations; this is a continuous group denoted by E_2, the Euclidean group in two dimensions. Also this group has of course higher n-dimensional analogues called E_n.

Groups of matrices. There are many groups that can be represented by matrices, because square matrices close under the matrix product. Generically such groups are non-abelian. But one can also make restrictions to subsets of matrices that form closed subsets under matrix multiplication. Of special interest for us are the *orthogonal* and *unitary* matrices $O(n)$ and $U(n)$. They act as non-abelian transformation groups of rotations on the real and complex spaces $\mathbb{R}^n$ and $\mathbb{C}^n$. The matrices satisfy $O\ O^{tr} = 1$ and $U\ U^\dagger = 1$ respectively.

The group $SU(2)$ of 2×2 unitary matrices.
Let us add an important remark on the relation between hermitian and unitary matrices. Let me recall the Euler formula for the exponential of imaginary number '$i\varphi$' (A.28):

$$e^{i\varphi} = \cos\varphi + i\sin\varphi\,.$$

The sine and cosine appearing show that it is indeed a periodic function, and therefore we choose an angular variable φ. You might wonder whether similar formulas can be written down for matrices. The answer is a full fledged yes, and that brings us to the relation between Lie algebras and Lie groups. Let me give you the extremely useful generalization of the Euler formula to the Hermitean (2×2) matrices. Consider an $su(2)$ matrix,[5]

$$A = (\hat{n}_x X/2 + \hat{n}_y Y/2 + \hat{n}_z Z/2)\,,$$

where $\hat{n}$ is some arbitrary vector of unit length and θ some angular variable, then in general the following relation holds:

$$e^{i\theta A} = \mathbf{1}\cos\theta/2 + iA\sin\theta/2\,. \tag{A.34}$$

This elegant equation has many applications in all venues of theoretical physics, and we will use it repeatedly later on. It does for example represent a rotation of a two-component spinor over an angle θ around the $\hat{n}$ axis, with the peculiar but characteristic property that a rotation by $\theta = 2\pi$ of any spinor maps it to minus itself. As mentioned before, that is a property that distinguishes spinors from 'ordinary' vectors. One thing that is immediately clear from the above formula, is that the expression corresponds to a unitary matrix. This holds in general: if we write a matrix U as an exponential of a hermitian matrix A, then we can write:

$$U^\dagger = (e^{iA})^\dagger = e^{(iA)^\dagger} = e^{-iA^\dagger} = e^{-iA} = U^{-1}\,, \tag{A.35}$$

which shows that U is a unitary matrix. This property that exponentials of hermitian matrices are unitary operators is widely used in quantum theory, in particular in the theory of (unitary) representations of symmetry groups that act on the Hilbert space of a system.

So to summarize this part we saw a close relationship between the 'algebra of observables' for a quantum system, being a Lie algebra, i.e. a closed commutator algebra, which when put in the exponent yields a corresponding Lie group. In that sense we say that the observables (the Lie algebra) generate small or infinitesimal transformations, while the exponents (elements of the Lie group) correspond to finite transformations.

[5] We have mentioned before that half the Pauli matrices $\{X/2, Y/2, Z/2\}$ do form a basis for the angular momentum or spin algebra, as they satisfy $[S_x, S_y] = iS_z$ etc.

Invariants. There are two more properties of matrices we want to discuss: these are what are called invariants under basis transformations. First observe that we may rotate the basis of a vector space. Then the components of the vector change and are obtained by acting with the corresponding matrix U. In the main text we showed that basis transformations have to preserve the scalar product of two arbitrary vectors and therefore will satisfy the unitarity condition $U^\dagger U = 1$, and therefore $U^\dagger = U^{-1}$. So if we have a matrix operator A acting on vectors in a given frame and we ask what the matrix looks like in the rotated or 'primed' frame we can see that from the following algebraic manipulations. First we define:

$$|\psi'\rangle \equiv U\,|\psi\rangle \text{ and } |\phi\rangle \equiv A|\psi\rangle\,,$$

which allows us to write:

$$\begin{aligned} |\phi'\rangle &\equiv U\,|\phi\rangle = U\,A|\psi\rangle \\ &= UAU^{-1}U|\psi\rangle = UAU^{-1}|\psi'\rangle = A'|\psi'\rangle \end{aligned}$$

Implying that $A' = UAU^{-1}$. Given these expressions for how state vectors and observables transform under unitary basis transformations, you might ask whether there are any quantities related to these observables that are preserved under such transformations. The answer is affirmative: the invariant quantity corresponds to the set of eigenvalues, particularly the sum and the product of all eigenvalues, denoted as the *trace* and the *determinant*.

The *trace* of a matrix A denoted by tr A is defined as the sum of the diagonal elements, so tr $A = \Sigma_i A_{ii}$. The trace is indeed invariant under basis transformations as one easily sees:

$$\text{tr}\,A' = \text{tr}\,(UAU^{-1}) = \text{tr}\,(U^{-1}UA) = \text{tr}\,A\,.$$

The trace satisfies the cyclic property meaning that the trace of a product is invariant under cyclic permutations, i.e. that is putting the matrices in the trace on a circle holding hands and moving them around:

$$\begin{aligned} \text{tr}\,(ABC) &= \Sigma_{ijk}(A_{ij}B_{jk}C_{ki}) = \\ &= \Sigma_{ijk}(C_{ki}A_{ij}B_{jk}) = \text{tr}\,(CAB) \text{ etc.} \end{aligned}$$

The point is that all indices are pairwise summed over. We will see that the trace, because it is frame independent, plays an important role in certain aspects of quantum theory. ◊

1994
CUBA
CORREOS
MAX PLANCK
1858 - 1947
40
CELEBRIDADES DE LA CIENCIA

h=6,626·10^-34 Js
E=h·ν
55
Deutschland
1858–1947

UNION DES COMORES
Constante de Planck
225 FC
2008
DECOUVERTES CELEBRES

DEMOKRATISCHE
DEUTSCHE
REPUBLIK
h
MAX PLANCK 10 1858-1947

DEMOKRATISCHE
DEUTSCHE
REPUBLIK
MAX PLANCK 20 1858-1947

30
MAX
PLANCK
DEUTSCHE POST
BERLIN

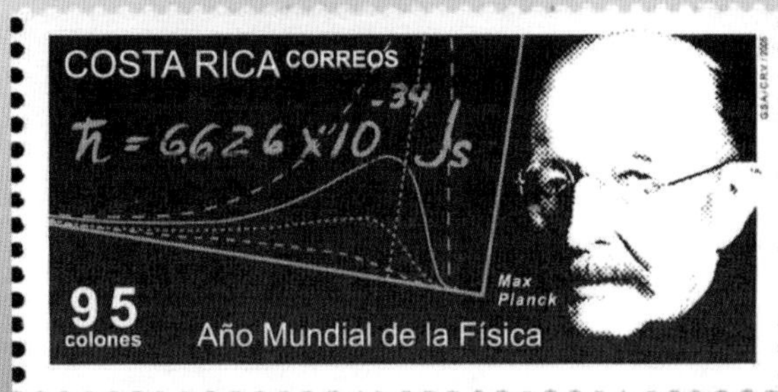
COSTA RICA CORREOS
h = 6.626 x 10^-34 Js
Max
Planck
95
colones
Año Mundial de la Física

N$ 0.60
AEREO
MAX PLANCK
1858-1947
PREMIO NOBEL
DE FISICA 1918
75 AÑOS
PREMIO NOBEL
NAVE ESPACIAL
TERMONUCLEAR
PARA VUELO
TRIPULADO
A MARTE
URUGUAY

GHANA
₵400
GERMANY
MAX PLANCK
(1858-1947) PHYSICS 1918

NOBELPRIS 1918
1.70
SVERIGE
PLANCK
PRIX NOBEL DE PHYSIQUE 1914
LUDWIG ERNST KARL MAX PLANCK
500F
REPUBLIQUE DE CÔTE D'IVOIRE

REPUBLIQUE GABONAISE
500f
Postes
2008
M. PLANCK

Appendix B

Chronologies, ideas and people

In this appendix we list the scientific achievements in the quantum domain over more than a century as well as the names and the dates of the Nobel prizes that were awarded for these. It demonstrates the fact that quantum is everywhere and overtook progress in physics to a large extent.

The tables cover the following topics:

B.1 Foundational concepts and their protagonists

B.2 Turning points in quantum condensed matter theory

B.3 Turning points in elementary particle theory

B.4 Nobel prizes awarded for discovery of fundamental particles

B.5 Nobel prizes for astrophysics and cosmology

B.6 Nobel prizes awarded (from 1944 onwards) for the invention and development of new techniques and devices

Figure B.1: The early quantum giants at the fifth Solvay conference, held in Brussels in 1927. On that occasion quantum mechanics, including the 'Copenhagen interpretation', was presented as a complete and final theory of atomic phenomena.

The person	Year	The concept	The mathematical statement
Planck	1897	Planck's constant	$\hbar = h/2\pi$
	1900	Black-body radiation	$\rho(\nu, T) = \frac{8\pi V\nu^2}{c^3} \frac{h\nu}{(e^{h\nu/kT} - 1)}$
Einstein	1905	Photoelectric effect, the photon	$E = h\nu$
Bohr	1913	Atomic model	$E_n \sim \hbar^2 e^2/2mc^2n^2$
De Broglie	1923	Matter waves	$\lambda = \hbar/m\nu$
Einstein, Podolski, Rosen	1920	EPR paradox, entanglement	$\|\psi(1,2)\rangle = (\|00\rangle \pm \|11\rangle)/\sqrt{2}$
Bose, Einstein	1924	Quantum statistics, Bose condensate	$n_i = g_i/(e^{\beta(\epsilon_i - \mu)} - 1)$
Pauli	1924	Exclusion principle	$\psi(x_1, x_2) = -\psi(x_2, x_1)$
Heisenberg	1925 1927	Matrix mechanics Uncertainty relations	$d\hat{A}/dt = i[\hat{H}, \hat{A}]$ $\Delta x \, \Delta p \geq \hbar/2$
Von Neuman	1925	Density matrix, quantum entropy	$\rho = \Sigma p_a \|\psi_a\rangle\langle\psi_a\|,\ S = \mathrm{tr}(\rho \ln \rho)$
Schrödinger	1926	Wave mechanics	$i\hbar \, d\psi/dt = \hat{H}\,\psi$
Born	1926	Probability interpretation	$\psi = \Sigma \, c_i \, \chi_i \Rightarrow P_{\lambda_i} = \|c_i\|^2$
Fermi	1927	Quantum statistics for fermions	$n_i = g_i/(e^{\beta(\epsilon_i - \mu)} + 1)$
Dirac	1927	Dirac equation	$(i\hbar\partial\!\!\!/ + eA\!\!\!/ + m)\,\psi(\mathbf{x}, t) = 0$
Bell	1964	Bell inequality	$\|P_c(a,b) - P_c(a,c)\| \leq 1 + P_c(b,c)$
Bennett, Brassard, Deutsch, Shor	>1980	Quantum information/computation	key distribution, teleportation, prime factoring algorithm

Table B.1: Foundational quantum concepts and their protagonists.

Kamerling Onnes	Superconductivity (experiment)	1911
Bloch	Conduction band	1920
Uhlenbeck, Goudsmit	Spin	1925
Van Vleck	Theory of magnetism	1935
Kapitza, Allen, Misener	Superfluidity	1938
Pauling	The nature of chemical binding	1939
Rabi	Nuclear magnetic resonance (NMR)	1946
Purcell, Bloch	NMR (implementations)	1952
Bardeen, Houser, Brattain, Shockley	Semiconductors, Transistor	1950
Gabor	Holography	1950
Landau	Fermiliquids, quasiparticles, phase transistions	1952
Bardeen, Cooper, Schrieffer	BCS theory of superconductivity	1957
Townes, Basov, Prokhorov	Laser	1958
Anderson	Localization	1958
Ahoronov, Bohm	Aharonov-Bohm effect	1959
Haldane, Kosterlitz, Thouless	Topological phase transitions	1973
De Gennes	Liquid crystals (mostly classical physics)	1974
Laughlin	Theory of Fractional Quantum Hall effect	1983
Berry	Berry phase	1984
Cornell, Wiegmann	Bose Einstein condensation (experiment)	1995
Kitaev, Wen	Topological order	1997
Lauterbur, Mansfield	Magnetic resonance imaging (MRI)	2003
Geim, Novoselov	Graphene	2004
Aspect, Clauser, Zeilinger	Entangled photons (experiments)	>1980

Table B.2: Turning points in quantum condensed matter (theory) and quantum optics.

Feynman, Swinger, Dyson, Tomonaga	Quantum electrodynamics (QED)	1946
Yang, Mills	Non-Abelian gauge theory	1954
Gellmann, Zweig	SU(3) Quarks	1963
Nambu, Jona Lasinio	Chiral symmetry breaking	1965
Glashow, Weinberg, Salam	Weak and electromagnetic theory	1968
Higgs, Brout, Englert	Higgs mechanism	1969
't Hooft, Veltman	Renormalization of non-Abelian gauge theories	1970
Wilson	Theory of critical phenomena, confinement	1972
Gellmann, Leutwyler, Fritsch	Quantum Chromodynamics (QCD)	1971
Gross, Politzer, Wilczek	Asymptotic freedom	1973
Witten, Schwarz, Green	String theory	1983
Polyakov, Belavin, Zamolodchikov	Conformal Field Theory (CFT)	1983
Witten	Topological Field Theory	1983
Maldacena	Anti de Sitter/CFT correspondence	1995

Table B.3: Turning points in Elementary particle theory.

Röntgen	X-rays	1901
Becquerel, Curie, Curie	Radioactive decay (α and β radiation)	1903
Thomson	Electron	1906
Rutherford	Nucleus	1908
Planck	Quanta of radiation	1918
Einstein	Photon	1921
Compton	Compton effect	1927
Chadwick	Neutron	1935
Anderson	Positron	1936
Powell	Pion	1950
Chamberlain, Segre	Antiproton	1959
Richter, Ting	J/Psi meson	1976
Rubia, Van der Meer	W and Z bosons	1984
Lederman, Schwartz, Steinberger	Muon neutrino	1988
Friedman, Kendall, Taylor	Quarks	1990
Perl	Tau-neutrino	1995
Reines	Neutrino	1995

Table B.4: Nobel prizes awarded for discovery of elementary particles.

Bethe	Energy production in stars	1967
Ryle, Hewish	Pulsars	1974
Penzias, Wilson	Microwave background radiation	1965
Chandrasekhar, Fowler	Theories of star evolution	1983
Hulse, Taylor	Precision tests of gravity	1993
Davis, Koshiba	Cosmic neutrino's	2002
and Giacconi	X-ray sources	
Mather, Smoot	Anisotropy in background radiation	2006
Perlmutter, Schmidt, Riess	Accelerated expansion	2011
Thorn, Weiss, Barish	Gravitational wave detection	2017

Table B-7: Nobel prizes for astrophysics and cosmology.

Rabi	Nuclear magnetic resonance	1944
Bridgman	Apparatus to produce extremely high pressures	1946
Blackett	The Wilson cloud chamber method	1948
Powell	Photographic method of studying nuclear processes	1950
Bloch and Purcell	Nuclear magnetic precision measurements	1952
Zernike	Phase contrast microscope	1953
Glaser	Bubble chamber	1960
Shockley, Bardeen and Brattain	Transistor	1956
Alvarez	Hydrogen bubble chamber and data analysis techniques	1968
Gabor	Holographic method	1971
Ryle and Hewish	Radio astrophysics	1974
Bloembergen and Schawlow	Laser spectroscopy	1981
Siegbahn	High-resolution electron spectroscopy	1981
Ruska	Electron microscope	1986
Binnig and Rohrer	Scanning tunneling microscope	1986
Ramsey	Separated oscillatory fields method and its use in atomic clocks	1989
Dehmelt and Paul	Ion trap technique	1989
Charpak	Multiwire proportional chamber	1990
Brockhouse	Neutron spectroscopy	1994
Shull	Neutron diffraction	1994
Alferov and Kroemer	Semiconductor heterostructures, high-speed- and opto-electronics	2000
Kilby	his part in the invention of the integrated circuit	2000
Hall and Hänsch	Laser-based precision spectroscopy, optical frequency comb technique	2004
Kao	Light transmission in fibers for optical communication	2009
Boyle, Smith	invention of imaging semiconductor circuit - the CCD sensor	2009
Fert and Grünberg	Giant magnetoresistance	2007
Haroche, Wineland	Measuring and manipulation of individual quantum systems	2012
Akasaki, Amano, Nakamura	Bright blue light-emitting diodes	2014
Weiss, Barish, Thorne	Gravitational wave detector LIGO	2017

Table B.6: Nobel prizes awarded (from 1944 onwards) for the invention and development of new techniques and devices.

Indices

Subject index Volume III

Name index Volume III

List of Figures

List of Tables

Acknowledgements

The creation of the book has been an exciting journey and I am indebted to many people who have helped me along the way. These include my colleagues from the Institute for Theoretical Physics in Amsterdam, of whom I like to mention Jan Smit, Chris van Weert, Karel Gaemers, Leendert Suttorp, and Jan Pieter van der Schaar, as well as a number of former students. Indeed: *teaching is the ultimate way of learning*. I am grateful to my former teachers and advisers: Profs Hans van Leeuwen, Michael Nauenberg, Joel Primack, and indirectly Gerard 't Hooft. I am indebted to Erik and Herman Verlinde, Robbert Dijkgraaf, Kareljan Schoutens and Harry Buhrman for thoroughly enriching my quantum perspectives. My views on science in general have been deeply influenced by my collaborators and colleagues at the Santa Fe Institute, in particular with respect to the fundamental notions of computation and evolution.

I thank Dr Manus Visser for a superb job on a thorough and critical proofreading the whole work and suggesting very many ways to improve it. I am indebted to Jan Peter Wissink, director of AUP, for his patience and persistent support during the long journey towards completion of this work. I thank editor Evelien Witte–Van der Veer for coordinating the production at AUP. I have profited from conversations and advice from Peter Ghijsen and Lucy Wenting on matters of style and layout, and last but not least with Doyne Farmer on science in general and the art of writing semi-popular science books.

I lam indebted to the organizations, institutes and individuals that have through their financial support made the publication of this quantum trilogy possible. And I thank Sijbolt Noorda and Joost van Mameren for initiating and coordinating the fundraising effort.

Last but not least, I like to thank my wife Vera, and my beloved children for their continued encouragement and warm support during this mission.

About the Author:

Sander Bais studied applied physics at Delft University in The Netherlands, and obtained a PhD in Theoretical Particle Physics from UCSC and SLAC in the US in 1978. He was a research fellow at the University of Pennsylvania, and scientific associate at CERN, and became full professor of theoretical physics at the University of Amsterdam in 1985. He was associated with the Santa Fe Institute as external professor from 2007 until 2020.

Sander Bais has been director of the Institute for Theoretical Physics of the University of Amsterdam, member of the governing board of the NWO/FOM funding agency, and scientific delegate in the CERN Council.

His active research focussed on topological aspects of gauge and string theory with applications to both particle and condensed matter physics, He also made regular excursions to astrophysics.

He is the author of number of successful semi-popular books on theoretical physics that have been translated in more than 15 languages.